Pictorial Woodwork

J. MATTHEWS

Illustrated by J. D. KERR

Book Three

A Guide to
Practical Work

LONDON: EDWARD ARNOLD (PUBLISHERS) LTD

The Course comprises

BOOK ONE - Background to Wood; Construction; Finishes

BOOK TWO - Tools and Their Correct Use

BOOK THREE - A Guide to Practical Work

SBN: 7131 1305 7

© J. MATTHEWS AND J. D. KERR 1967

First published 1967
Reprinted 1968

Printed in Great Britain by
William Clowes and Sons, Limited, London and Beccles

Preface to the Series

The three books forming the series present in pictorial fashion a guide for the Secondary School Woodwork course.

BOOK ONE deals with three principal topics. The Background to Wood begins with the particulars of growth from the seed to the tree, with various timber trees shown. Then follow the various processes involved in the production of wood suitable for bench work and details of some of the enemies of wood. Secondly there is a large section devoted to Construction: joints, nails, screws, hinges and glues. The book concludes with a substantial section on finishes.

Whenever suitable, points of historical interest are introduced.

BOOK TWO concerns itself with the main tools and their correct use. A wide range of tools is covered, from the Marking Knife to the Multi-Plane. The parts of the tools are illustrated and details are given about hand-positioning, adjustment and setting, grinding and sharpening.

BOOK THREE presents a guide to practical work. Brief introductory exercises with tools come first, followed by a selection of models in progressive constructional order.

Preface to Book Three

This book presents a guide to practical work. An important introduction to Timber and Preparation Methods is given first, followed by Basic Marking Out and Tool Practice Exercises. There follow a number of selected models chosen for the wide range of processes they incorporate. The processes include Basic Marking Out and Shaping, Jointing, Constructing and Designing, and the use of a large range of tools. The aim is to develop a logical inquiring mind and pleasure in producing something of distinction by acquiring skill in design and construction. For each model it is suggested that the teacher leads the pupils stage by stage in preparing the individual practice joints and shapes. After this the pupil should follow the design and construction guide for the particular model, making up his own design from the various alternatives suggested. We wish to express our thanks to my wife Marian and Mr Michael Ward who gave considerable help in compiling this book.

Contents

INTRODUCTION TO TIMBER

❶ FROM THE TIMBER MERCHANTS

CAN BE OBTAINED

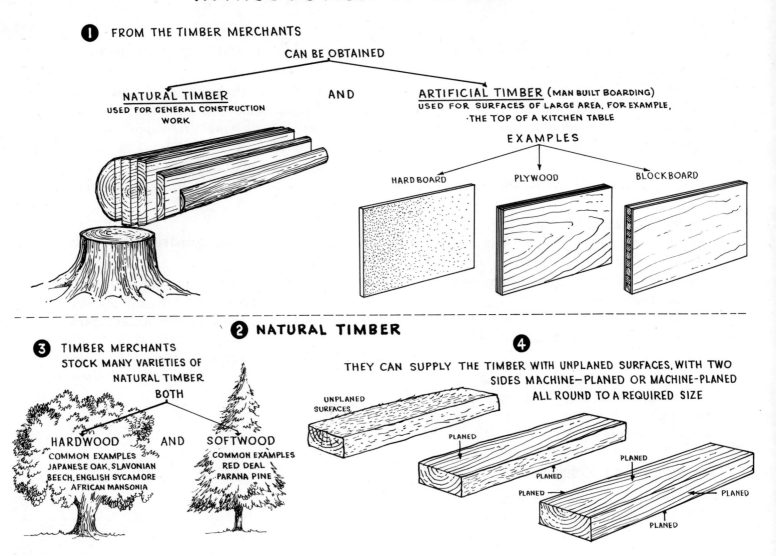

NATURAL TIMBER
USED FOR GENERAL CONSTRUCTION
WORK

AND

ARTIFICIAL TIMBER (MAN BUILT BOARDING)
USED FOR SURFACES OF LARGE AREA, FOR EXAMPLE,
·THE TOP OF A KITCHEN TABLE

EXAMPLES

HARDBOARD   PLYWOOD   BLOCKBOARD

---

❷ NATURAL TIMBER

❸ TIMBER MERCHANTS
STOCK MANY VARIETIES OF
NATURAL TIMBER

BOTH

HARDWOOD   AND   **SOFTWOOD**
COMMON EXAMPLES   COMMON EXAMPLES
JAPANESE OAK, SLAVONIAN   RED DEAL
BEECH, ENGLISH SYCAMORE   PARANA PINE
AFRICAN MANSONIA

❹
THEY CAN SUPPLY THE TIMBER WITH UNPLANED SURFACES, WITH TWO
SIDES MACHINE—PLANED OR MACHINE-PLANED
ALL ROUND TO A REQUIRED SIZE

UNPLANED
SURFACES

PLANED
PLANED

PLANED
PLANED
PLANED
PLANED

8

GAUGING EXERCISE Nº 2

4 SET A GAUGE TO ¼"

5 ON THE PREPARED MEMBER GAUGE, RESET AND GAUGE ¼" LINES
AS BELOW

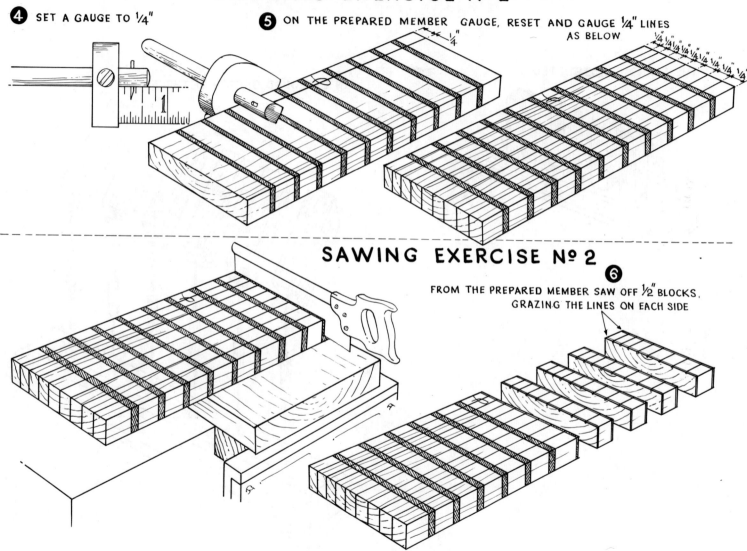

SAWING EXERCISE Nº 2

6 FROM THE PREPARED MEMBER SAW OFF ½" BLOCKS,
GRAZING THE LINES ON EACH SIDE

INTRODUCTION TO TIMBER SAMPLE STAND

THE STAND CONSTRUCTED

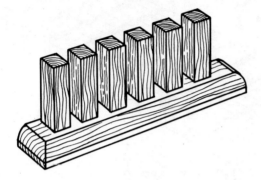

AN EXPLODED SKETCH OF THE STAND

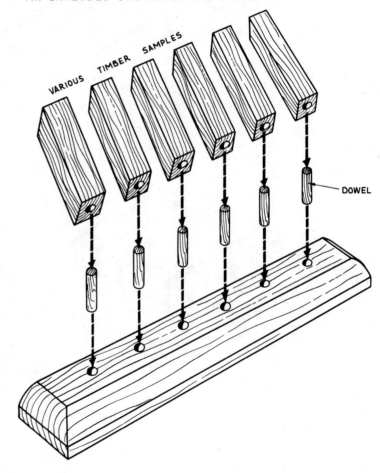

VARIOUS TIMBER SAMPLES

DOWEL

INTRODUCTION TO TIMBER

5 ## ARTIFICIAL TIMBER

TIMBER MERCHANTS STOCK ARTIFICIAL
TIMBER IN LARGE SHEETS AND CAN SUPPLY
IT IN VARIOUS THICKNESSES AND SURFACE
FACINGS

THE TIMBER MERCHANT MAY SUPPLY A
SMALLER PIECE CUT TO REQUESTED SIZE
(EXAMPLE 1'6" x 2'3") BY CUTTING INTO
A LARGE SHEET

6 EXAMPLES OF PLYWOOD SHEETS SIZES

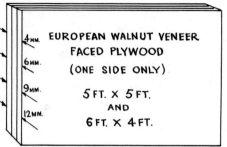

WEST AFRICAN RESIN BONDED
PLYWOOD FACES

(AFRICAN MAHOGANY, SAPELE,
MAKORÉ, GUAREA.)

8 FT. × 4 FT.

4MM. 5MM. 6MM. 9MM. 12MM. 15MM. 18MM.

EUROPEAN WALNUT VENEER
FACED PLYWOOD

(ONE SIDE ONLY)

5 FT. × 5 FT.
AND
6 FT. × 4 FT.

4MM. 6MM. 9MM. 12MM.

7 EXAMPLES OF BLOCKBOARD SHEET SIZES

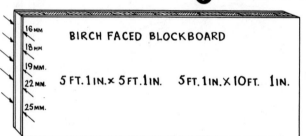

BIRCH FACED BLOCKBOARD

5 FT. 1 IN. × 5 FT. 1 IN.   5 FT. 1 IN. × 10 FT. 1 IN.

16MM 18MM 19MM 22MM 25MM.

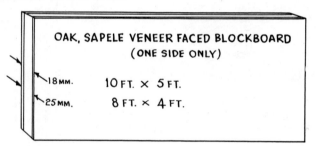

OAK, SAPELE VENEER FACED BLOCKBOARD
(ONE SIDE ONLY)

18MM.   10 FT. × 5 FT.

25MM.   8 FT. × 4 FT.

8 EXAMPLES OF HARDBOARD SHEET SIZES

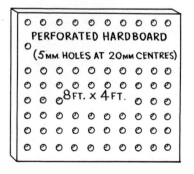

PLAIN FACED HARDBOARD

3 FT. × 4 FT.	6 FT. × 4 FT.	6 FT. 6 IN. × 2 FT. 6 IN.
3 FT. 6 IN. × 4 FT.	7 FT. × 4 FT.	6 FT. 8 IN. × 2 FT. 8 IN.
4 FT. × 4 FT.	8 FT. × 4 FT.	
5 FT. × 4 FT.	10 FT. × 4 FT.	
	12 FT. × 4 FT.	

1/8"

PERFORATED HARDBOARD
(5 MM. HOLES AT 20 MM CENTRES)

8 FT. × 4 FT.

LEATHER GRAIN PATTERN
HARDBOARD

(ONE SIDE ONLY)

8 FT. × 5 FT.

THE FORMS IN WHICH UNPLANED NATURAL TIMBER IS USUALLY OBTAINED FROM THE TIMBER MERCHANT FOR THE SCHOOL STOCKROOM

❶

UNPLANED BOARDING
LONG LENGTHS OF VARIOUS WIDTHS
SAWN TO A REQUESTED THICKNESS

EXAMPLES

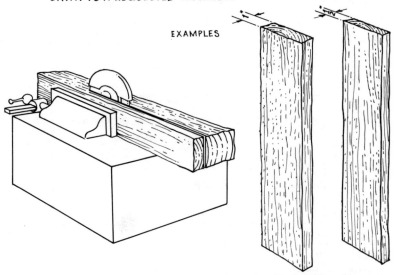

❷

UNPLANED SCANTLINGS (SMALL CROSS-SECTION TIMBER)
LONG LENGTHS SAWN TO A REQUESTED
WIDTH AND THICKNESS

EXAMPLES

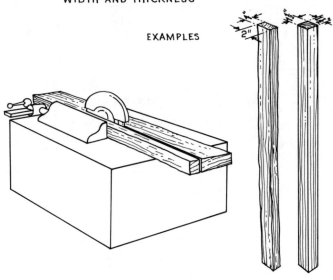

THE FORMS IN WHICH PLANED NATURAL TIMBER IS USUALLY OBTAINED FROM THE TIMBER MERCHANT FOR THE SCHOOL STOCKROOM

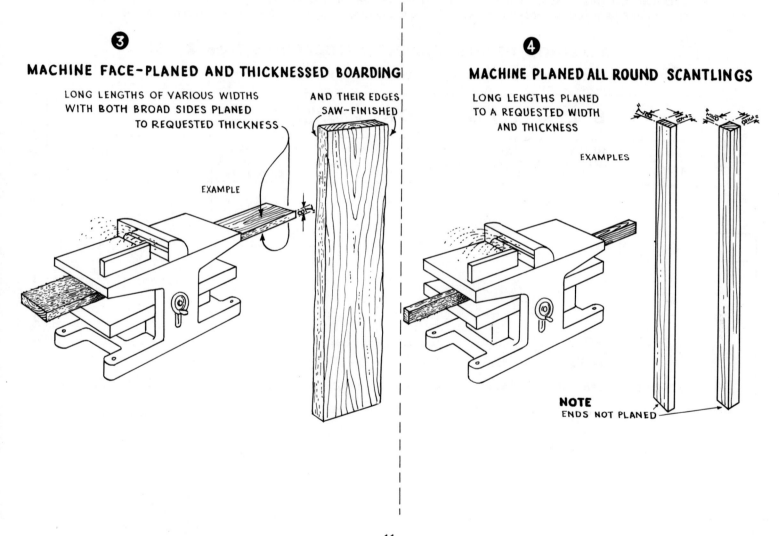

❸

MACHINE FACE-PLANED AND THICKNESSED BOARDING

LONG LENGTHS OF VARIOUS WIDTHS
WITH BOTH BROAD SIDES PLANED
TO REQUESTED THICKNESS

AND THEIR EDGES
SAW-FINISHED

EXAMPLE

❹

MACHINE PLANED ALL ROUND SCANTLINGS

LONG LENGTHS PLANED
TO A REQUESTED WIDTH
AND THICKNESS

EXAMPLES

NOTE
ENDS NOT PLANED

INTRODUCTION TO PREPARING TIMBER

A FEW WORDS

BEFORE OBTAINING ANY TIMBER FROM THE TIMBER MERCHANT OR THE SCHOOL STOCKROOM, MAKE A TIMBER LIST GIVING THE OVERALL SIZES, OF EACH OF THE REQUIRED MEMBERS AND ANY OTHER IMPORTANT DETAILS. THIS SERVES AS A REFERENCE GUIDE

A METHOD OF MARKING OUT A STOCKROOM TIMBER LIST

❶ ON A PIECE OF THICK DRAWING PAPER MARK OUT THE FORM BELOW

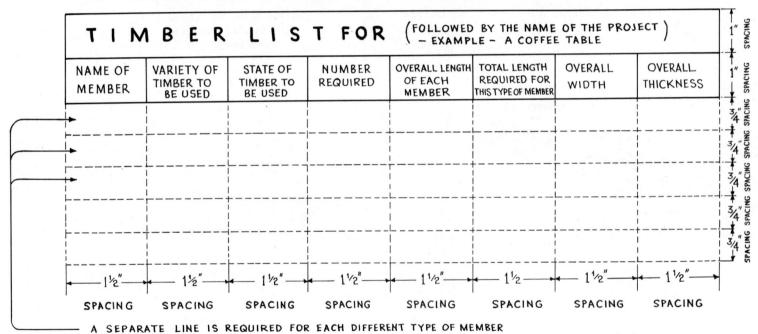

A SEPARATE LINE IS REQUIRED FOR EACH DIFFERENT TYPE OF MEMBER

INTRODUCTION TO PREPARING TIMBER

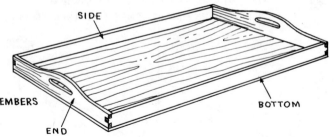

SIDE

END

BOTTOM

**NOTE
THREE
LINES** WOULD BE REQUIRED FOR THIS TEA TRAY WHICH HAS
THREE DIFFERENT TYPES OF MEMBERS

NAME OF MEMBER	VARIETY OF TIMBER TO BE USED	STATE OF TIMBER TO BE USED	NUMBER REQUIRED	OVERALL LENGTH OF EACH MEMBER	TOTAL LENGTH REQUIRED FOR THIS TYPE OF MEMBER	OVERALL WIDTH	OVERALL THICKNESS
SIDE							
END							
BOTTOM							

2 THEN FILL IN REQUIRED INFORMATION
(EXAMPLES GIVEN ON THE NEXT TWO PAGES)

EXAMPLES OF FILLING IN A TIMBER LIST

1 IF FROM UNPLANED NATURAL BOARDING

EXAMPLE, VARIETY PARANA PINE   YOU HAVE TO PREPARE (PLANE ALL ROUND AND SAW TO LENGTH)

THE HULL MEMBER FOR A SMALL BOAT

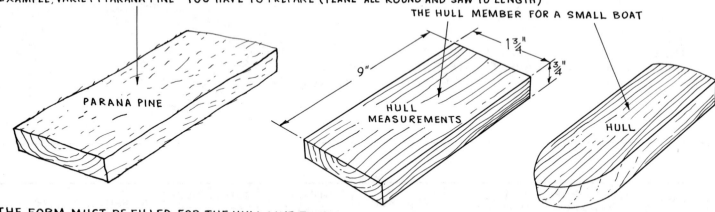

PARANA PINE

9" $1\frac{3}{4}$" $\frac{3}{4}$"

HULL MEASUREMENTS

HULL

2 THE FORM MUST BE FILLED FOR THE HULL LIKE THIS

TIMBER LIST FOR A SMALL MODEL BOAT

NAME OF MEMBER	VARIETY OF TIMBER TO BE USED	STATE OF TIMBER TO BE USED	NUMBER REQUIRED	OVERALL LENGTH OF EACH MEMBER	TOTAL LENGTH REQUIRED FOR THIS TYPE OF MEMBER	OVERALL WIDTH	OVERALL THICKNESS
HULL	PARANA PINE	UNPLANED SCANTLING	1	9" + (1" PREPARATION ALLOWANCE)	SAME	$1\frac{3}{4}$" + ($\frac{1}{4}$" PREPARATION ALLOWANCE)	$\frac{3}{4}$" + ($\frac{1}{4}$" PREPARATION ALLOWANCE)

PREPARATION ALLOWANCE TO ALLOW YOU TO SAW TO LENGTH ACCURATELY AFTER PLANING TO WIDTH AND THICKNESS

PREPARATION ALLOWANCE TO ALLOW FOR PLANING UP

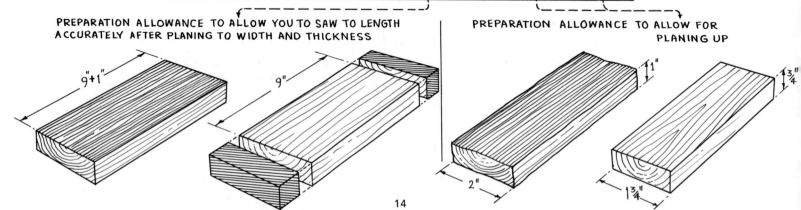

9"+1"   9"   1" $1\frac{3}{4}$"   2" $1\frac{3}{4}$"

14

EXAMPLE OF FILLING IN A TIMBER LIST

1 FROM MACHINE FACE-PLANED AND THICKNESSED
NATURAL BOARDING VARIETY AFRICAN MANSONIA. YOU HAVE TO PREPARE (PLANE TO WIDTH AND THICKNESS) TWO TOP RAILS FOR A COFFEE TABLE
THE MEASUREMENTS ARE GIVEN BELOW

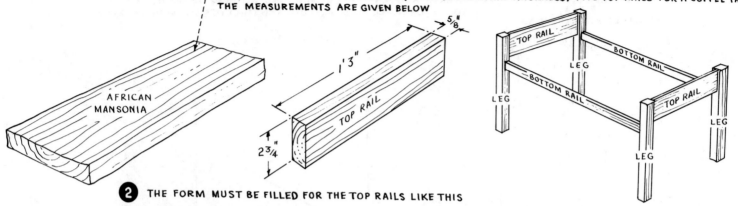

2 THE FORM MUST BE FILLED FOR THE TOP RAILS LIKE THIS

TIMBER LIST FOR A COFFEE TABLE

NAME OF MEMBER	VARIETY OF TIMBER TO BE USED	STATE OF TIMBER TO BE USED	NUMBER REQUIRED	OVERALL LENGTH OF EACH MEMBER	TOTAL LENGTH REQUIRED FOR THIS TYPE OF MEMBER	OVERALL WIDTH	OVERALL THICKNESS
TOP RAILS	AFRICAN MANSONIA	MACHINE FACE-PLANED & THICKNESSED BOARDING	2	1'3"+ (1" PREPARATION ALLOWANCE)	2'8"	2¾"+ (¼" PREPARATION ALLOWANCE)	5/8"

3

NOTE

IT IS OFTEN AN
ADVANTAGE TO INITIALLY PREPARE THE SAME TYPE
OF MEMBER IN ONE LONG LENGTH — — — — — — — — — — → THEN SAW TO LENGTH AFTERWARDS

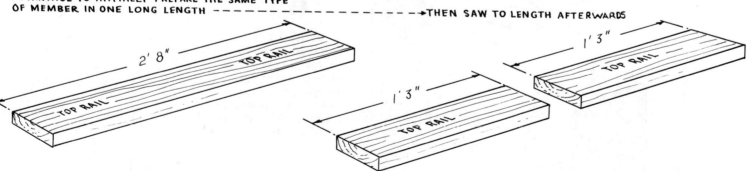

15

INTRODUCTION TO PREPARING NATURAL TIMBER

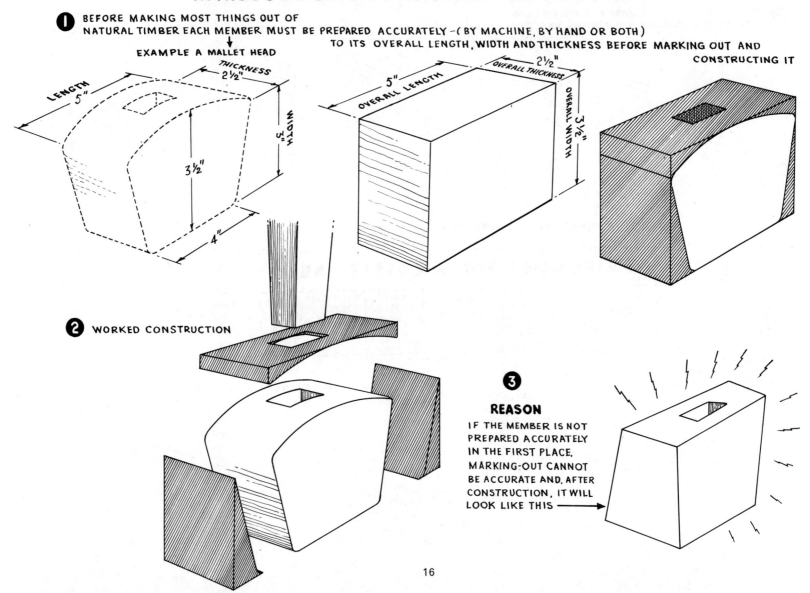

1 BEFORE MAKING MOST THINGS OUT OF NATURAL TIMBER EACH MEMBER MUST BE PREPARED ACCURATELY –(BY MACHINE, BY HAND OR BOTH) TO ITS OVERALL LENGTH, WIDTH AND THICKNESS BEFORE MARKING OUT AND CONSTRUCTING IT

EXAMPLE A MALLET HEAD

THICKNESS 2½"

LENGTH 5"

WIDTH 3"

3½"

4"

OVERALL LENGTH 5"

OVERALL THICKNESS 2½"

OVERALL WIDTH 3½"

2 WORKED CONSTRUCTION

3 REASON

IF THE MEMBER IS NOT PREPARED ACCURATELY IN THE FIRST PLACE, MARKING-OUT CANNOT BE ACCURATE AND, AFTER CONSTRUCTION, IT WILL LOOK LIKE THIS ——►

INTRODUCTION TO PREPARING NATURAL TIMBER

❹

NOTE. A MEMBER, ACCURATELY PREPARED FROM NATURAL TIMBER IS GENERALLY ONE WHOSE EDGES AND SIDES HAVE BEEN PLANED

S T R A I G H T ——— S Q U A R E

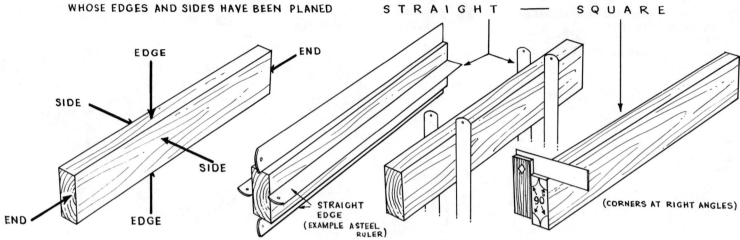

EDGE
END
SIDE
SIDE
END
EDGE

STRAIGHT EDGE (EXAMPLE A STEEL RULER)

90

(CORNERS AT RIGHT ANGLES)

AND UNIFORMLY TO THE REQUIRED
W I D T H   A N D   T H I C K N E S S,

AND THE ENDS HAVE BEEN SAWN SQUARELY
TO THE

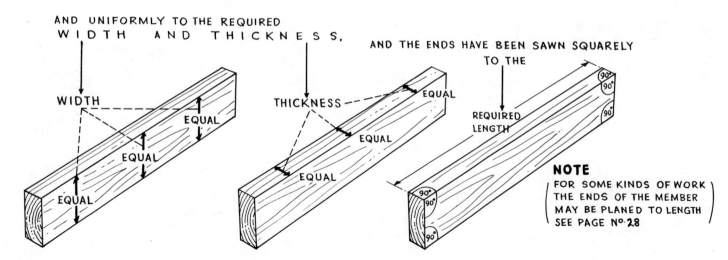

WIDTH
EQUAL
EQUAL
EQUAL

THICKNESS
EQUAL
EQUAL
EQUAL

REQUIRED LENGTH
90°
90°
90°
90°
90°

NOTE
FOR SOME KINDS OF WORK
THE ENDS OF THE MEMBER
MAY BE PLANED TO LENGTH
SEE PAGE Nº 28

A METHOD OF PREPARING MEMBERS FROM UNPLANED NATURAL TIMBER

INITIAL STAGES IN PREPARING UNPLANED NATURAL BOARDING

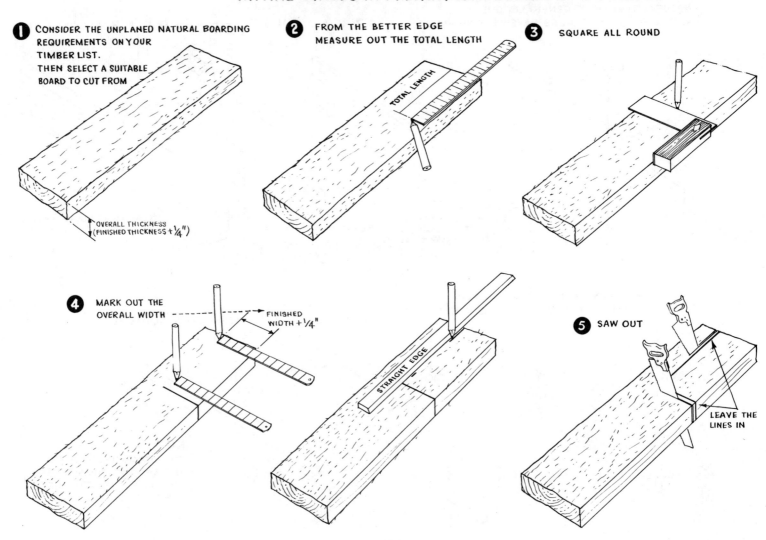

1 CONSIDER THE UNPLANED NATURAL BOARDING REQUIREMENTS ON YOUR TIMBER LIST.
THEN SELECT A SUITABLE BOARD TO CUT FROM

OVERALL THICKNESS (FINISHED THICKNESS + ¼")

2 FROM THE BETTER EDGE MEASURE OUT THE TOTAL LENGTH

TOTAL LENGTH

3 SQUARE ALL ROUND

4 MARK OUT THE OVERALL WIDTH

FINISHED WIDTH + ¼"

STRAIGHT EDGE

5 SAW OUT

LEAVE THE LINES IN

A METHOD OF PREPARING MEMBERS FROM UNPLANED NATURAL TIMBER

INITIAL STAGES FOR PREPARING UNPLANED SCANTLING

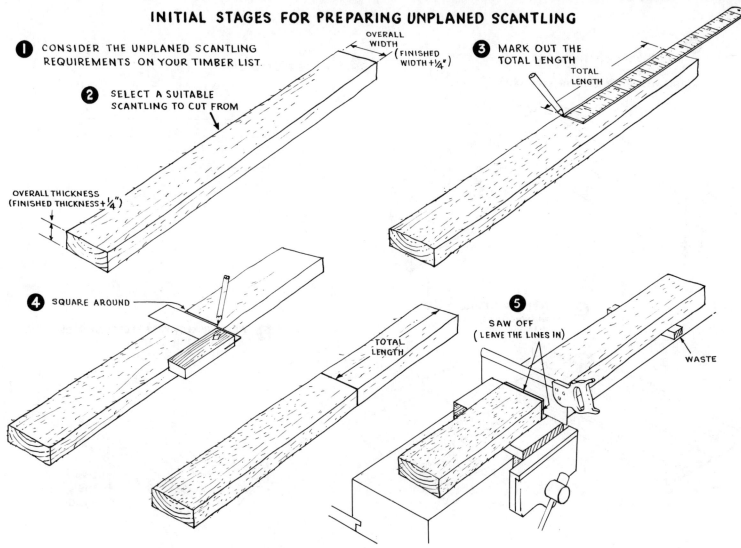

① CONSIDER THE UNPLANED SCANTLING REQUIREMENTS ON YOUR TIMBER LIST.

OVERALL WIDTH (FINISHED WIDTH + ¼")

② SELECT A SUITABLE SCANTLING TO CUT FROM

OVERALL THICKNESS (FINISHED THICKNESS + ¼")

③ MARK OUT THE TOTAL LENGTH

TOTAL LENGTH

④ SQUARE AROUND

TOTAL LENGTH

⑤ SAW OFF (LEAVE THE LINES IN)

WASTE

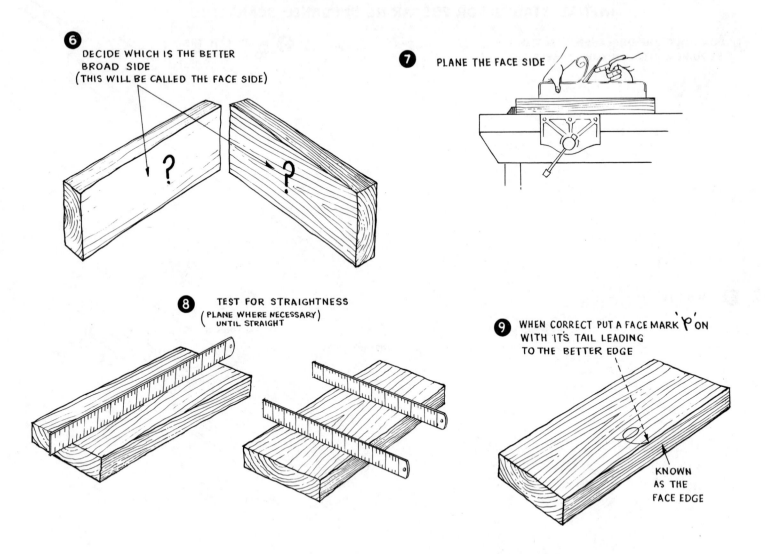

6 DECIDE WHICH IS THE BETTER BROAD SIDE (THIS WILL BE CALLED THE FACE SIDE)

?

?

7 PLANE THE FACE SIDE

8 TEST FOR STRAIGHTNESS (PLANE WHERE NECESSARY) UNTIL STRAIGHT

9 WHEN CORRECT PUT A FACE MARK 'Φ' ON WITH ITS TAIL LEADING TO THE BETTER EDGE

KNOWN AS THE FACE EDGE

METHOD OF PREPARING MEMBERS FROM UNPLANED NATURAL TIMBER

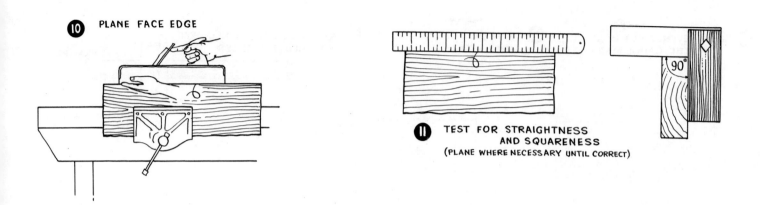

10 PLANE FACE EDGE

11 TEST FOR STRAIGHTNESS
AND SQUARENESS
(PLANE WHERE NECESSARY UNTIL CORRECT)

90°

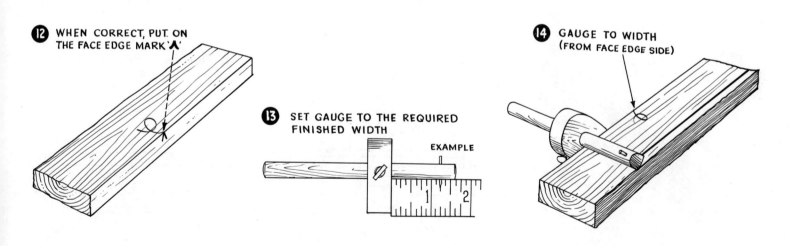

12 WHEN CORRECT, PUT ON
THE FACE EDGE MARK 'Λ'

13 SET GAUGE TO THE REQUIRED
FINISHED WIDTH

EXAMPLE

1   2

14 GAUGE TO WIDTH
(FROM FACE EDGE SIDE)

METHOD OF PREPARING MEMBERS FROM UNPLANED NATURAL TIMBER

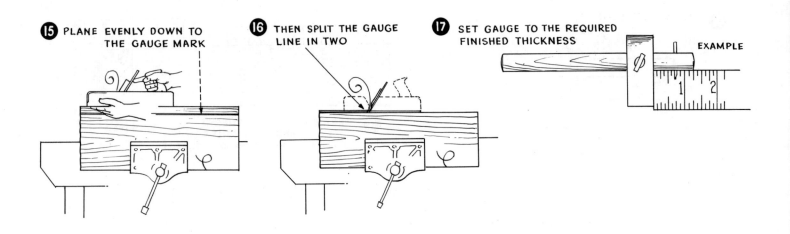

15 PLANE EVENLY DOWN TO THE GAUGE MARK

16 THEN SPLIT THE GAUGE LINE IN TWO

17 SET GAUGE TO THE REQUIRED FINISHED THICKNESS

EXAMPLE

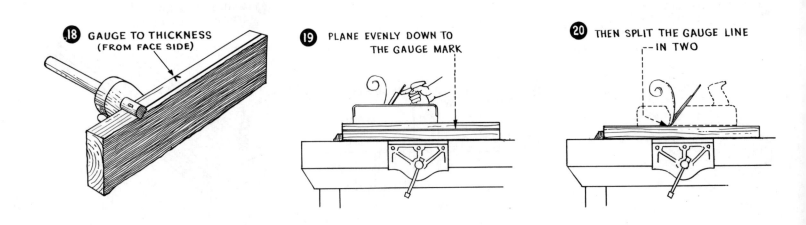

18 GAUGE TO THICKNESS (FROM FACE SIDE)

19 PLANE EVENLY DOWN TO THE GAUGE MARK

20 THEN SPLIT THE GAUGE LINE IN TWO

A METHOD OF PREPARING MEMBERS FROM UNPLANED NATURAL TIMBER

21 MEASURE AND SQUARE ALL ROUND AT ONE END ½" LINE

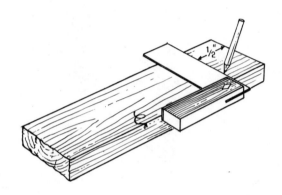

22 FROM THE SQUARED LINE MEASURE AND MARK A MEMBERS FINISHING LENGTH

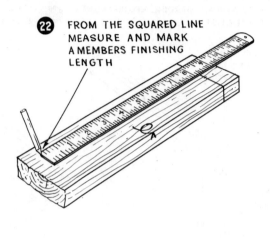

23 SQUARE AROUND

COLOUR IN THE WASTE

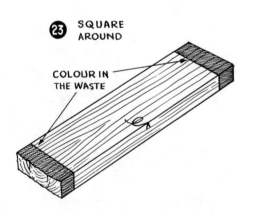

24 SAW TO LENGTH (GRAZING THE LINES)

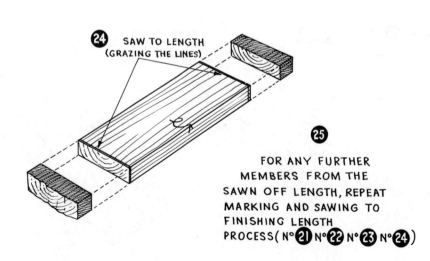

25

FOR ANY FURTHER MEMBERS FROM THE SAWN OFF LENGTH, REPEAT MARKING AND SAWING TO FINISHING LENGTH PROCESS(N° **21** N° **22** N° **23** N° **24**)

A METHOD OF PREPARING MEMBERS FROM MACHINE FACE-PLANED AND THICKNESSED BOARDING

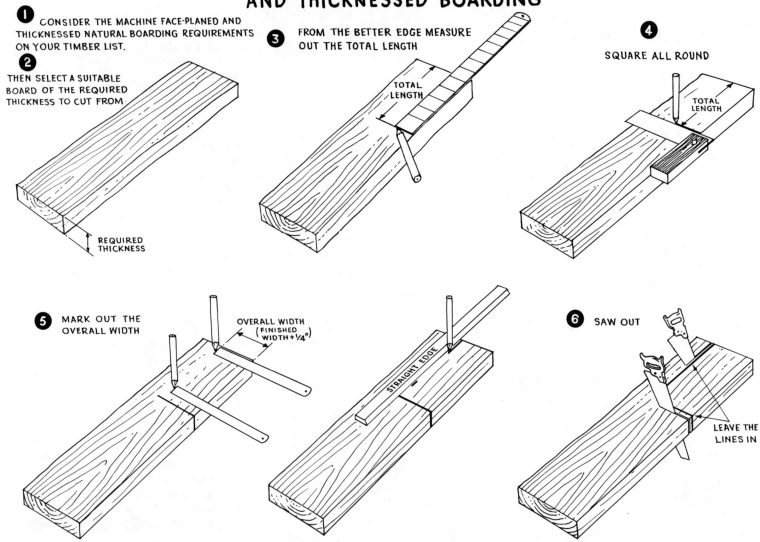

1 CONSIDER THE MACHINE FACE-PLANED AND THICKNESSED NATURAL BOARDING REQUIREMENTS ON YOUR TIMBER LIST.

2 THEN SELECT A SUITABLE BOARD OF THE REQUIRED THICKNESS TO CUT FROM.

REQUIRED THICKNESS

3 FROM THE BETTER EDGE MEASURE OUT THE TOTAL LENGTH

TOTAL LENGTH

4 SQUARE ALL ROUND

TOTAL LENGTH

5 MARK OUT THE OVERALL WIDTH

OVERALL WIDTH (FINISHED WIDTH + ¼")

STRAIGHT EDGE

6 SAW OUT

LEAVE THE LINES IN

A METHOD OF PREPARING MEMBERS FROM MACHINE FACE-PLANED AND THICKNESSED BOARDING

7 DECIDE WHICH IS THE BETTER BROAD SIDE (THIS WILL BE CALLED THE FACE SIDE)

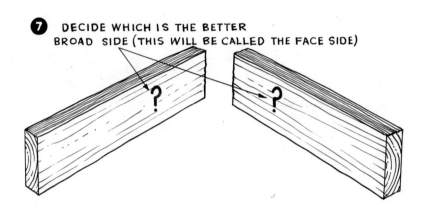

8 ON THE FACE SIDE PUT ON A FACE MARK WITH ITS TAIL LEADING TO THE BETTER EDGE

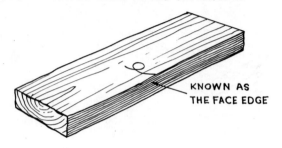

KNOWN AS THE FACE EDGE

9 PLANE THE FACE EDGE

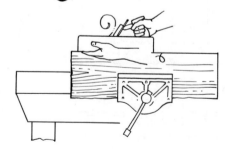

10 TEST FOR STRAIGHTNESS AND SQUARENESS (PLANE WHERE NECESSARY UNTIL CORRECT)

STRAIGHT EDGE

90°

A METHOD OF PREPARING MEMBERS FROM MACHINE FACE-PLANED AND THICKNESSED BOARDING

11 WHEN CORRECT PUT ON THE FACE EDGE MARK

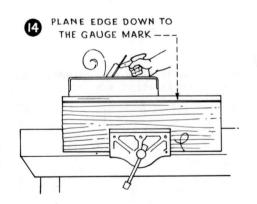

12 SET GAUGE TO REQUIRED FINISHED WIDTH
EXAMPLE

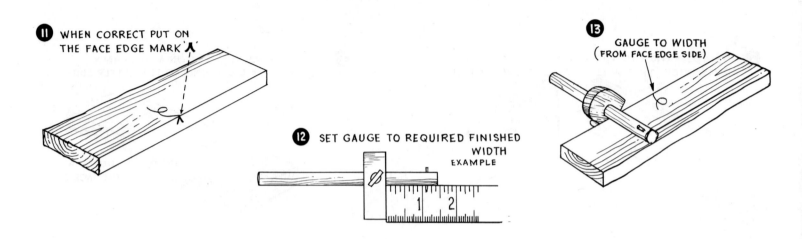

13 GAUGE TO WIDTH
(FROM FACE EDGE SIDE)

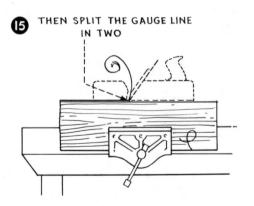

14 PLANE EDGE DOWN TO THE GAUGE MARK - - -

15 THEN SPLIT THE GAUGE LINE IN TWO

A METHOD OF PREPARING MEMBERS FROM MACHINE FACE-PLANED AND THICKNESSED BOARDING

16 MEASURE ½" FROM ONE END MARK AND SQUARE ROUND

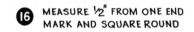
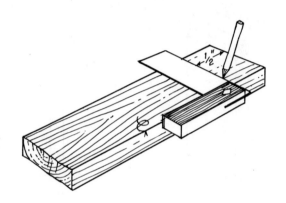

17 FROM THE SQUARED LINE MARK THE FINISHED LENGTH

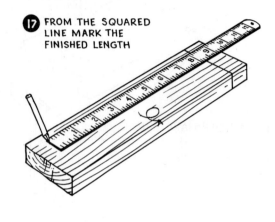

18 SQUARE AROUND

COLOUR IN THE WASTE

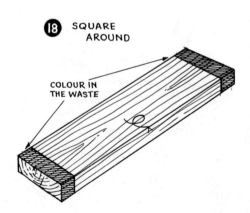

19 SAW TO LENGTH (GRAZING THE LINES)

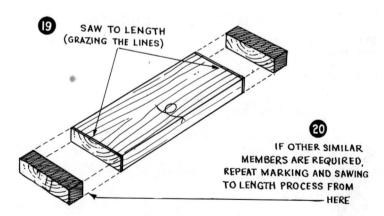

20 IF OTHER SIMILAR MEMBERS ARE REQUIRED, REPEAT MARKING AND SAWING TO LENGTH PROCESS FROM —— HERE

INTRODUCTION TO SHOOTING MEMBERS TO LENGTH

AN EXAMPLE OF WHEN MEMBERS WOULD REQUIRE SHOOTING TO LENGTH

IF MEMBERS ARE TO BE JOINED TOGETHER WITH DOVETAIL JOINTS, EXTREMELY ACCURATE LENGTHS WITH CLEAN ENDS TO RECEIVE FINE MARKS ARE REQUIRED. SHOOTING TO LENGTH IS THE BEST WAY TO ACHIEVE THIS

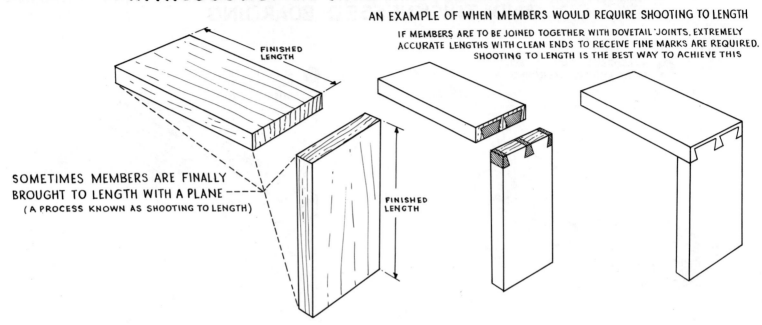

FINISHED LENGTH

FINISHED LENGTH

SOMETIMES MEMBERS ARE FINALLY BROUGHT TO LENGTH WITH A PLANE — (A PROCESS KNOWN AS SHOOTING TO LENGTH)

A METHOD OF SHOOTING MEMBERS TO LENGTH

AFTER MEMBERS HAVE BEEN PLANED TO WIDTH AND THICKNESS, MARK OUT AND SAW THEM TO LENGTH. LEAVING LENGTH LINES WELL IN

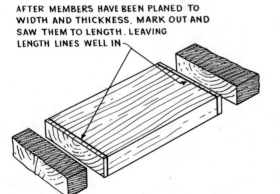

THEN PLANE THE ENDS DOWN TO THEIR LENGTH LINES ON A SHOOTING BOARD

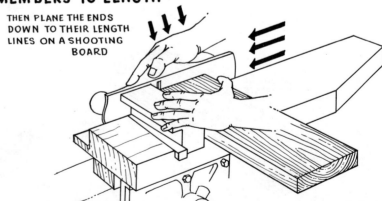

A METHOD OF PREPARING MEMBERS FROM SCANTLINGS MACHINE-PLANED ALL ROUND

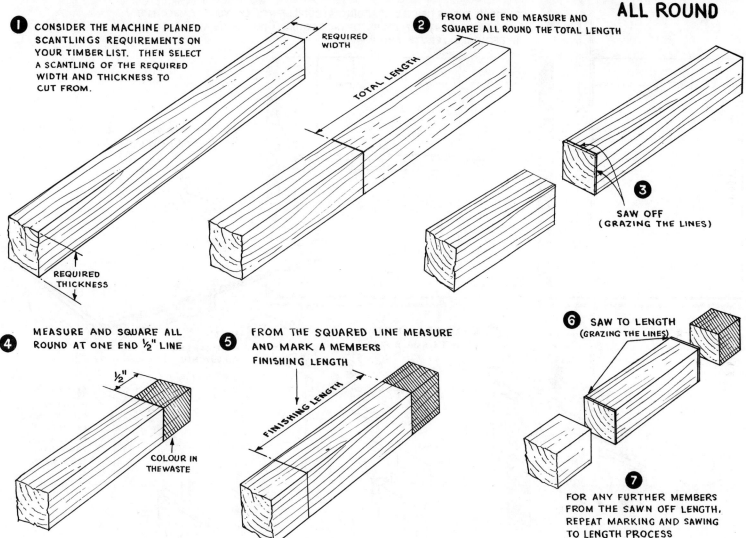

1 CONSIDER THE MACHINE PLANED SCANTLINGS REQUIREMENTS ON YOUR TIMBER LIST. THEN SELECT A SCANTLING OF THE REQUIRED WIDTH AND THICKNESS TO CUT FROM.

REQUIRED WIDTH

REQUIRED THICKNESS

2 FROM ONE END MEASURE AND SQUARE ALL ROUND THE TOTAL LENGTH

TOTAL LENGTH

3 SAW OFF (GRAZING THE LINES)

4 MEASURE AND SQUARE ALL ROUND AT ONE END ½" LINE

½"

COLOUR IN THE WASTE

5 FROM THE SQUARED LINE MEASURE AND MARK A MEMBERS FINISHING LENGTH

FINISHING LENGTH

6 SAW TO LENGTH (GRAZING THE LINES)

7 FOR ANY FURTHER MEMBERS FROM THE SAWN OFF LENGTH, REPEAT MARKING AND SAWING TO LENGTH PROCESS

29

A METHOD OF PREPARING MEMBERS FROM ARTIFICIAL BOARDING
(PLYWOOD, BLOCKBOARD ETC.)

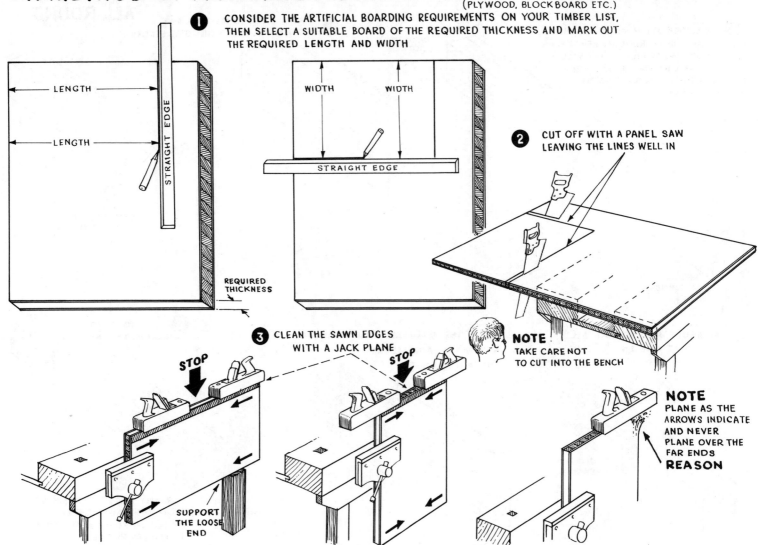

1 CONSIDER THE ARTIFICIAL BOARDING REQUIREMENTS ON YOUR TIMBER LIST, THEN SELECT A SUITABLE BOARD OF THE REQUIRED THICKNESS AND MARK OUT THE REQUIRED LENGTH AND WIDTH

LENGTH

LENGTH

STRAIGHT EDGE

REQUIRED THICKNESS

WIDTH   WIDTH

STRAIGHT EDGE

2 CUT OFF WITH A PANEL SAW LEAVING THE LINES WELL IN

NOTE TAKE CARE NOT TO CUT INTO THE BENCH

3 CLEAN THE SAWN EDGES WITH A JACK PLANE

STOP

STOP

SUPPORT THE LOOSE END

NOTE PLANE AS THE ARROWS INDICATE AND NEVER PLANE OVER THE FAR ENDS **REASON**

A METHOD OF PREPARING MEMBERS FROM ARTIFICIAL BOARDING
(PLYWOOD, BLOCKBOARD, ETC.)

4 SHOOT THE TOP EDGES SQUARE AND STRAIGHT

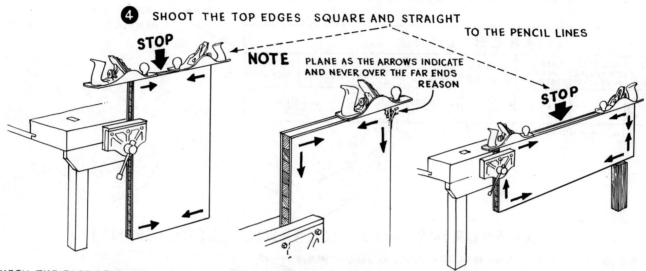

STOP

NOTE PLANE AS THE ARROWS INDICATE
AND NEVER OVER THE FAR ENDS
REASON

TO THE PENCIL LINES

STOP

5 CHECK THE FACE AREA AND EDGES FOR SQUARENESS AND ADJUST WHERE NECESSARY

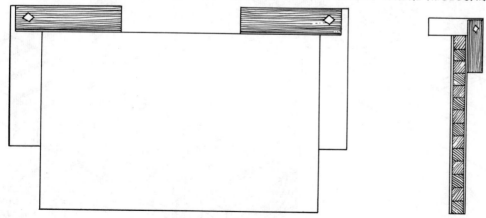

NATURAL TIMBER PREPARATION EXERCISE Nº1

1 MARK OUT A TIMBER LIST, FILL IN THE NECESSARY INFORMATION. FOR PREPARING, FROM
UNPLANED SOFTWOOD BOARDING OR SCANTLING,
A MEMBER TO THE MEASUREMENTS GIVEN BELOW

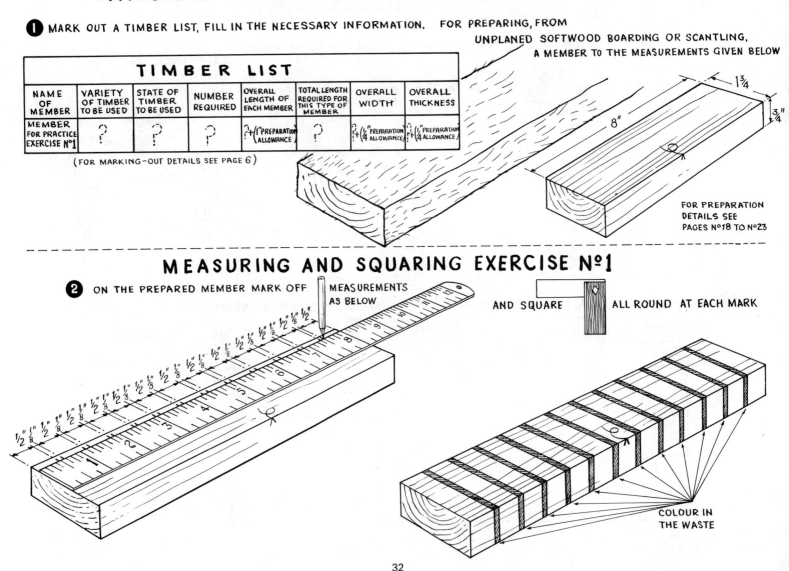

TIMBER LIST

NAME OF MEMBER	VARIETY OF TIMBER TO BE USED	STATE OF TIMBER TO BE USED	NUMBER REQUIRED	OVERALL LENGTH OF EACH MEMBER	TOTAL LENGTH REQUIRED FOR THIS TYPE OF MEMBER	OVERALL WIDTH	OVERALL THICKNESS
MEMBER FOR PRACTICE EXERCISE Nº1	?	?	?	?+(1"PREPARATION ALLOWANCE)	?	?+(¼"PREPARATION ALLOWANCE)	?+(¼"PREPARATION ALLOWANCE)

(FOR MARKING-OUT DETAILS SEE PAGE 6)

FOR PREPARATION
DETAILS SEE
PAGES Nº18 TO Nº23

MEASURING AND SQUARING EXERCISE Nº1

2 ON THE PREPARED MEMBER MARK OFF MEASUREMENTS AS BELOW

AND SQUARE ALL ROUND AT EACH MARK

COLOUR IN
THE WASTE

GAUGING EXERCISE Nº 1

3 SET A GAUGE TO ¼"

4 ON THE PREPARED MEMBER GAUGE, RESET AND GAUGE ¼" LINES AS BELOW

¼" ¼" ¼" ¼" ¼" ¼" ¼" ¼"

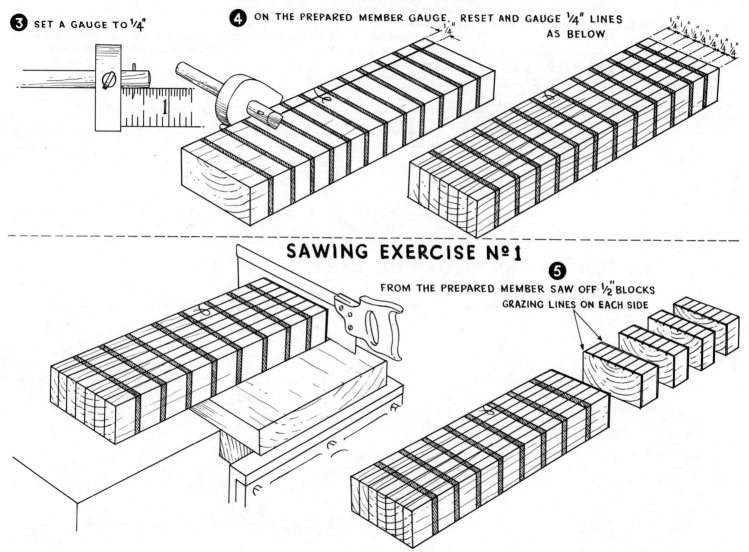

SAWING EXERCISE Nº 1

5 FROM THE PREPARED MEMBER SAW OFF ½" BLOCKS GRAZING LINES ON EACH SIDE

NATURAL TIMBER PREPARATION EXERCISE №2

① MARK OUT A TIMBER LIST AND FILL IN THE REQUIRED INFORMATION

FOR PREPARING, FROM MACHINE FACE-PLANED AND THICKNESSED HARDWOOD BOARDING, A MEMBER TO THE MEASUREMENTS GIVEN BELOW.

TIMBER LIST

NAME OF MEMBER	VARIETY OF TIMBER TO BE USED	STATE OF TIMBER TO BE USED	NUMBER REQUIRED	OVERALL LENGTH OF EACH MEMBER	TOTAL LENGTH REQUIRED FOR THIS TYPE OF MEMBER	OVERALL WIDTH	OVERALL THICKNESS
MEMBER FOR PRACTICE EXERCISE №2	?	?	? +P.A.	+1" PREPARATION ALLOWANCE	?	?+ 1/4" PREPARATION ALLOWANCE	?

(FOR MARKING OUT DETAILS SEE PAGE №12)

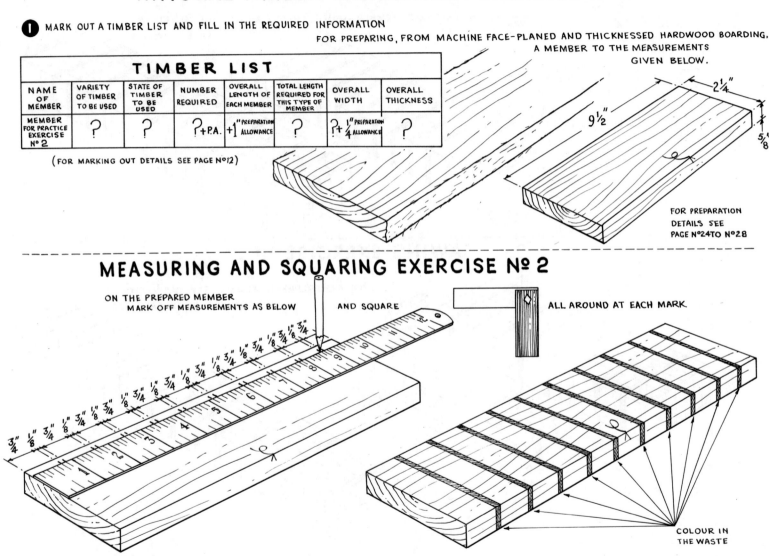

2¼"

9½"

⅝"

FOR PREPARATION DETAILS SEE PAGE №24 TO №28

MEASURING AND SQUARING EXERCISE №2

ON THE PREPARED MEMBER MARK OFF MEASUREMENTS AS BELOW   AND SQUARE   ALL AROUND AT EACH MARK

3/4" 1/8" 3/4" 1/8" 3/4" 1/8" 3/4" 1/8" 3/4" 1/8" 3/4" 1/8" 3/4" 1/8" 3/4"

COLOUR IN THE WASTE

TIMBER SAMPLE STAND

1 ON A SHEET OF DRAWING PAPER SKETCH
OR TRACE THE DETAILS GIVEN BELOW

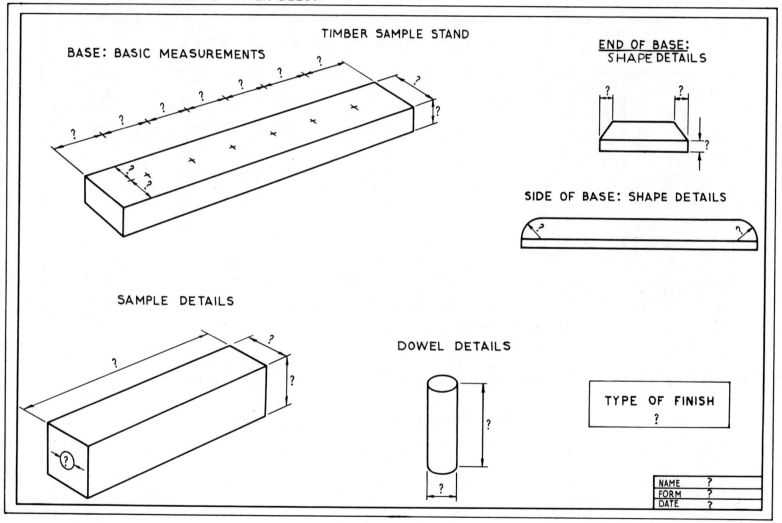

TIMBER SAMPLE STAND

BASE: BASIC MEASUREMENTS

END OF BASE:
SHAPE DETAILS

SIDE OF BASE: SHAPE DETAILS

SAMPLE DETAILS

DOWEL DETAILS

TYPE OF FINISH
?

NAME	?
FORM	?
DATE	?

CONSTRUCTION GUIDE FOR TIMBER SAMPLE STAND

2

MAKE OUT A TIMBER LIST FOR THE TIMBER SAMPLE STAND
(GUIDE BELOW)

TIMBER LIST FOR THE TIMBER SAMPLE STAND

NAMES OF MEMBERS	VARIETY OF TIMBER TO BE USED	STATE OF TIMBER TO BE USED	NUMBER REQUIRED	OVERALL LENGTH OF EACH MEMBER	TOTAL LENGTH REQUIRED FOR THIS TYPE OF MEMBER	OVERALL WIDTH	OVERALL THICKNESS
BASE	?	?	?	? + P.A.	———	? + ¼" P.A.	?
SAMPLE N°1	?	?	?	?	———	?	?
SAMPLE N°2	?	?	?	?	———	?	?
SAMPLE N°3	?	?	?	?	———	?	?
SAMPLE N°4	?	?	?	?	———	?	?
SAMPLE N°5	?	?	?	?	———	?	?
SAMPLE N°6	?	?	?	?	———	?	?
DOWEL DETAILS							

3 NOW FOLLOW THE INSTRUCTIONS AND ANSWER
EACH OF THE QUESTIONS IN TURN

AS YOU PROGRESS, FILL IN THE REQUIRED INFORMATION
ON YOUR TIMBER LIST AND YOUR SKETCH OR TRACING

EVENTUALLY BUILD UP AN ORTHOGRAPHIC DRAWING
OF YOUR TIMBER STAND

CONSTRUCTION GUIDE FOR TIMBER SAMPLE STAND

4 WHAT TYPE OF FINISH WILL YOU
APPLY TO THE SURFACE OF
THE SAMPLE STAND

PAINT   OR

A CLEAR FINISH
EXAMPLES
CELLULOSE
LAQUER
FRENCH POLISH
ETC.

5 WHAT VARIETIES OF

HARDWOOD OR SOFTWOOD

WILL YOU USE FOR YOUR

TIMBER SAMPLES AND THE STAND

6 PREPARE THE TIMBER SAMPLE STAND MEMBERS
TO THEIR MARKING OUT SIZES

(FOR PREPARATION GUIDES SEE PAGES 24-29)

BASE MARKING OUT SIZES

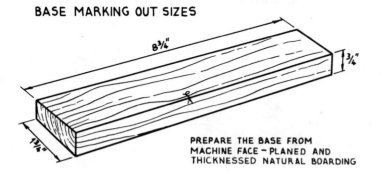

8¾"

¾"

1¾"

PREPARE THE BASE FROM
MACHINE FACE — PLANED AND
THICKNESSED NATURAL BOARDING

TIMBER SAMPLE MARKING
OUT SIZES

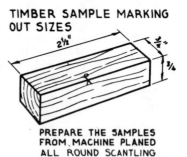

2½"

¾"

¾

PREPARE THE SAMPLES
FROM MACHINE PLANED
ALL ROUND SCANTLING

DOWEL MARKING OUT SIZES

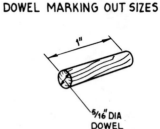

1"

5/16" DIA
DOWEL

CONSTRUCTION GUIDE FOR MAKING TIMBER SAMPLE STAND

7 MARK OUT ON THE BASE THE CENTRES FOR THE DOWELS

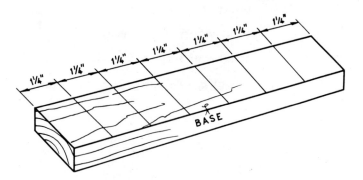

1¼" 1¼" 1¼" 1¼" 1¼" 1¼" 1¼"

BASE

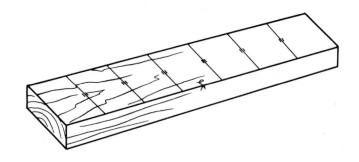

8 BORE TEST HOLES FOR RECEIVING THE DOWEL WITH VARIOUS BITS ON A PIECE OF WASTE WOOD

9 NOTE THE BIT WHICH BORES HOLES OF THE MOST SUITABLE SIZE FOR A PUSH-IN FIT

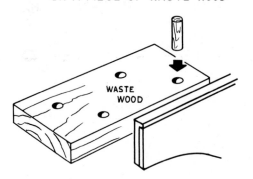

WASTE WOOD

10 BORE THE DOWEL HOLES IN THE BASE
(DEPTH OF DOWEL HOLE ½")

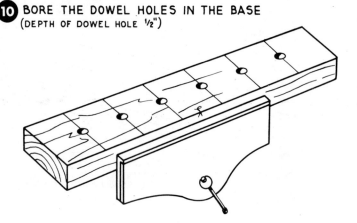

CONSTRUCTION GUIDE FOR TIMBER SAMPLE STAND

11 MARK DIAGONALS AT THE BOTTOM END OF THE TIMBER SAMPLES TO OBTAIN THE CENTRE

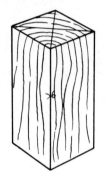

12 BORE THE DOWEL HOLES IN THE TIMBER SAMPLES

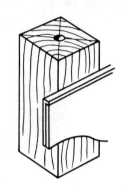

13 PUSH HOME THE DOWELS

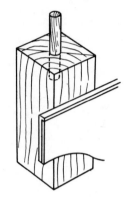

14 NUMBER OFF THE JOINTS THEN FIT EACH ONE SEPARATELY

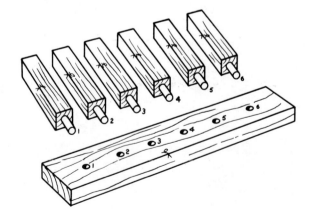

15 REMOVE THE DOWELS THEN APPLY GLUE ONLY TO THE DOWEL HOLES IN THE SAMPLES

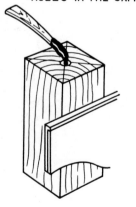

16 PUSH HOME THE DOWELS

17 WIPE OFF ANY SURPLUS GLUE

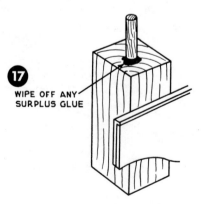

CONSTRUCTION GUIDE FOR TIMBER SAMPLE STAND

18 MARK OUT THE HALF ROUNDS
AT THE CORNERS OF THE BASE

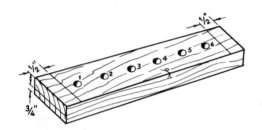

20 ROUND OFF THE BULK
OF THE WASTE WITH
A MEDIUM CUTTING
RASP THEN FINISH
OFF WITH A FINE
CUTTING WOOD FILE
(LEAVE THE LINES JUST IN)

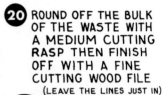

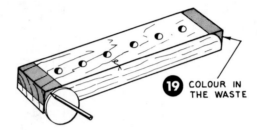

19 COLOUR IN
THE WASTE

21 MARK OUT THE CHAMFERS
ON THE SIDE OF THE BASE

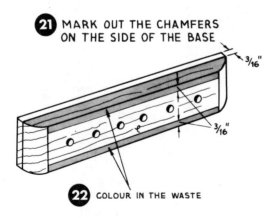

3/16"

3/16"

22 COLOUR IN THE WASTE

23

REMOVE THE WASTE
WITH A JACK PLANE

(LEAVE THE LINES JUST IN)

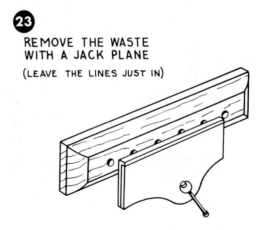

CONSTRUCTION GUIDE FOR TIMBER SAMPLE STAND

24 PREPARE FOR RECEIVING A FINISH
(METHOD GIVEN BELOW FOR A CLEAR FINISH)

25 FROM THE BASE AND TIMBER SAMPLES REMOVE ANY SERIOUS MARKS WITH A SMOOTH PLANE

26 SCRAPE

27 RUB DOWN THEN DUST

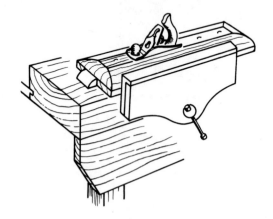

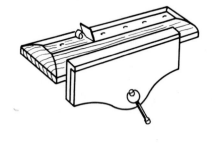

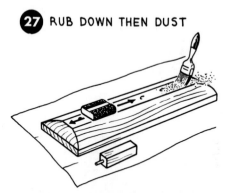

NOTE: PLACE A PIECE OF CLEAN THICK CLOTH UNDERNEATH FOR A PROTECTION AGAINST SCRATCHING

28 DAMP DOWN, THEN LEAVE TO DRY

29 RUB DOWN AGAIN THEN DUST
(GLASS PAPER GRADE Nº 1 OR)
(GARNET PAPER GRADE Nº 4/0)

30

APPLY THE FINISH
(FOR A GUIDE SEE BOOK Nº 1)

WATER

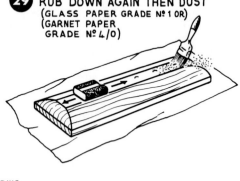

NOTE: PLACE BOARDING UNDERNEATH TO PROTECT THE BENCH TOP

31

SCRIBE CLEARLY ON ONE SIDE OF EACH SAMPLE THE NAME OF EACH VARIETY

MODEL AIRCRAFT CARRIER

AN EXPLODED SKETCH

A CONSTRUCTED SKETCH

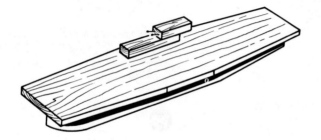

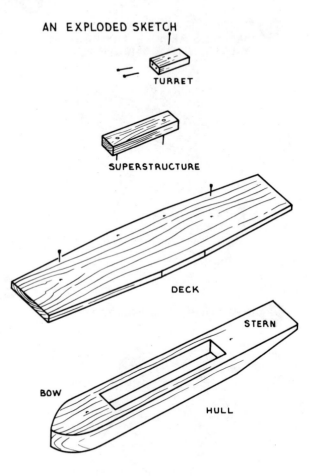

TURRET

SUPERSTRUCTURE

DECK

STERN

BOW

HULL

CONSTRUCTION GUIDE FOR MAKING MODEL AIRCRAFT CARRIER

1 ON A SHEET OF DRAWING PAPER FAINTLY SKETCH OR
TRACE THE DETAILS GIVEN BELOW

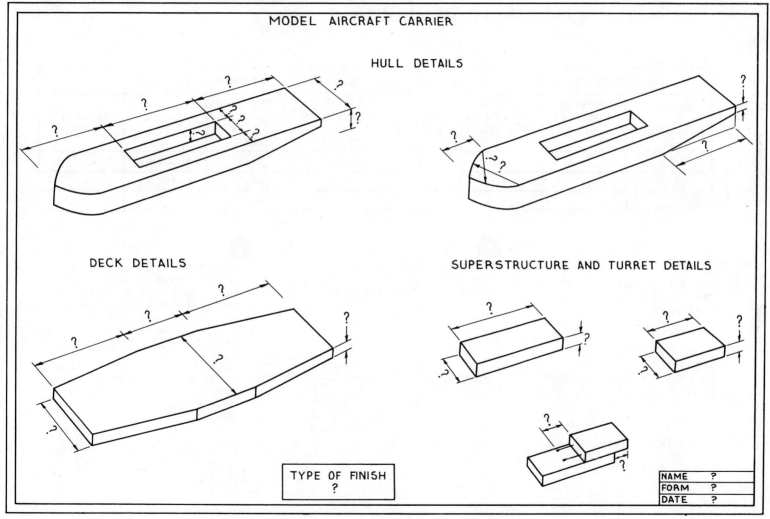

MODEL AIRCRAFT CARRIER

HULL DETAILS

DECK DETAILS

SUPERSTRUCTURE AND TURRET DETAILS

TYPE OF FINISH
?

NAME	?
FORM	?
DATE	?

CONSTRUCTION GUIDE FOR MAKING MODEL AIRCRAFT CARRIER

2

MAKE OUT A TIMBER LIST FOR THE MODEL AIRCRAFT CARRIER
(GUIDE BELOW)

TIMBER LIST FOR THE MODEL AIRCRAFT CARRIER							
NAMES OF MEMBERS	VARIETY OF TIMBER TO BE USED	STATE OF TIMBER TO BE USED	NUMBER REQUIRED	OVERALL LENGTH OF EACH MEMBER	TOTAL LENGTH REQUIRED FOR THIS TYPE OF MEMBER	OVERALL WIDTH	OVERALL THICKNESS
HULL	?	?	?	?	/	? + ¼" P.A.	? + ¼" P.A.
DECK	?	?	?	?	/	? + ¼" P.A.	?
SUPERSTRUCTURE AND TURRET	?	?	?	?	/	? + ¼" P.A.	?

3

NOW FOLLOW THE INSTRUCTIONS AND ANSWER EACH OF THE QUESTIONS IN TURN

AS YOU PROGRESS FILL IN THE REQUIRED INFORMATION ON YOUR TIMBER LIST AND SKETCH OR TRACING

EVENTUALLY DEVELOP AN ORTHOGRAPHIC DRAWING OF YOUR AIRCRAFT CARRIER

4

WHAT TYPE OF FINISH WILL YOU APPLY TO YOUR MODEL AIRCRAFT CARRIER

PAINT OR A CLEAR FINISH EXAMPLE CELLULOSE LAQUER FRENCH POLISH ETC.

5

WHAT VARIETY OR VARIETIES OF HARDWOOD OR SOFTWOOD WILL YOU USE FOR YOUR MODEL AIRCRAFT CARRIER ?
(CONSIDER THE TYPE OF FINISH YOU HAVE CHOSEN)

FOR A CLEAR FINISH USE A HARDWOOD

FOR A PAINT FINISH USE A SOFTWOOD

CONSTRUCTION GUIDE FOR MAKING MODEL AIRCRAFT CARRIER

6 PREPARE THE TIMBER FOR THE HULL, DECK, SUPERSTRUCTURE, AND TURRET TO THEIR MARKING OUT SIZES

HULL MARKING OUT SIZES

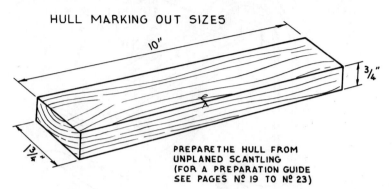

10"

3/4"

3/4"

PREPARE THE HULL FROM UNPLANED SCANTLING (FOR A PREPARATION GUIDE SEE PAGES Nº 19 TO Nº 23)

SUPERSTRUCTURE AND TURRET MARKING OUT SIZES

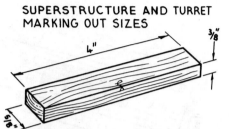

4"

3/8"

3/8"

PREPARE THE SUPERSTRUCTURE AND TURRET FROM MACHINE FACE-PLANED AND THICKNESSED NATURAL BOARDING (FOR A PREPARATION GUIDE SEE PAGES Nº 24 TO Nº 28)

DECK MARKING OUT SIZES

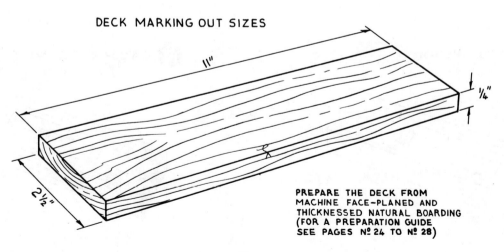

11"

1/4"

2½"

PREPARE THE DECK FROM MACHINE FACE-PLANED AND THICKNESSED NATURAL BOARDING (FOR A PREPARATION GUIDE SEE PAGES Nº 24 TO Nº 28)

CONSTRUCTION GUIDE FOR MAKING MODEL AIRCRAFT CARRIER

7 MARK OUT THE HOLD

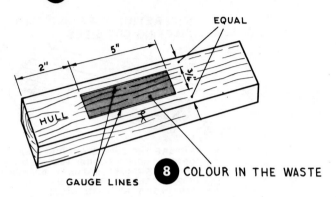

EQUAL

5"

2"

3/4"

HULL

GAUGE LINES

8 COLOUR IN THE WASTE

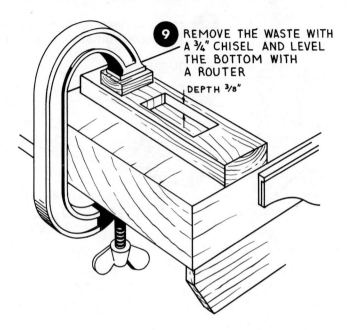

9 REMOVE THE WASTE WITH A ¾" CHISEL AND LEVEL THE BOTTOM WITH A ROUTER

DEPTH ⅜"

10 MARK OUT THE BOW

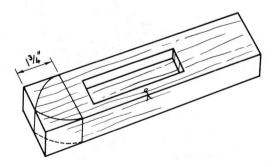

1¾"

11 COLOUR IN THE WASTE

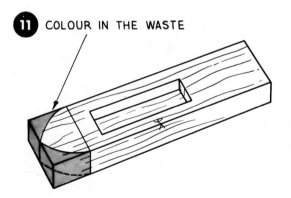

CONSTRUCTION GUIDE FOR MAKING MODEL AIRCRAFT CARRIER

12 REMOVE THE WASTE WITH
A COPING SAW
(SAW IN THE WASTE LEAVING THE LINES WELL IN)

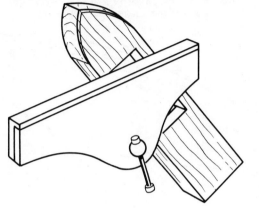

13 CLEAN FIRST WITH A MEDIUM CUTTING RASP
THEN FINISH OFF WITH A FINE CUTTING
WOOD FILE (LEAVE THE LINES JUST IN)

14 MARK OUT THE STERN RAKE

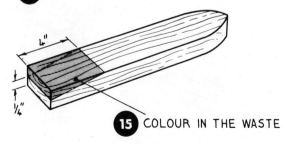

4"

1/4"

15 COLOUR IN THE WASTE

16 REMOVE THE WASTE
WITH A JACK PLANE
(LEAVE THE LINES JUST IN)

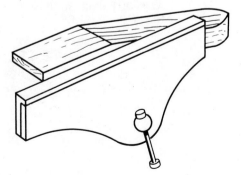

4

CONSTRUCTION GUIDE FOR MAKING MODEL AIRCRAFT CARRIER

17 MARK OUT THE DECK

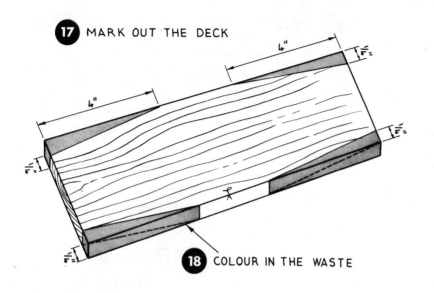

4"

4"

18 COLOUR IN THE WASTE

19 REMOVE THE WASTE
WITH A JACK PLANE
(LEAVE THE LINES JUST IN)

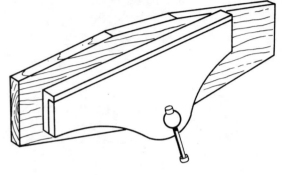

20 MARK OUT THE SUPERSTRUCTURE
AND THE TURRET

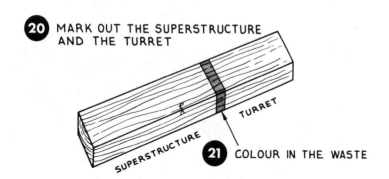

TURRET

SUPERSTRUCTURE

21 COLOUR IN THE WASTE

22 SAW IN TWO THEN SMOOTH THE
SAWN ENDS
(LEAVE THE LINES JUST IN)

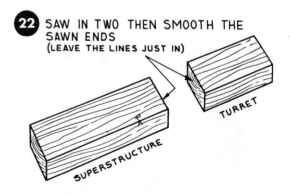

TURRET

SUPERSTRUCTURE

CONSTRUCTION GUIDE FOR MAKING MODEL AIRCRAFT CARRIER

23 | PREPARE AND ASSEMBLE THE AIRCRAFT CARRIER FOR RECEIVING A FINISH
(A METHOD GIVEN BELOW)

24 ON EACH MEMBER
REMOVE ANY SERIOUS
MARKS WITH A SMOOTH
PLANE. THEN SCRAPE IF
USING HARDWOOD. THEN
RUB DOWN WITH GLASS
PAPER OR GARNET
PAPER (GRADE ?)

25 DRIVE TWO ½" PANEL PINS
JUST THROUGH THE
SUPERSTRUCTURE

½"
½"

SUPERSTRUCTURE

26 PLACE THE
SUPERSTRUCTURE
ON THE DECK NEAR
ONE EDGE THEN
DRIVE HOME
THE PANEL
PINS

⅛"

27

AT ONE END OF THE
TURRET DRIVE IN
TWO ¾" PANEL PINS
TO REPRESENT GUNS

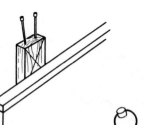

29 PLACE THE TURRET ON THE
SUPERSTRUCTURE AND DRIVE
HOME THE PANEL PIN

28

MARK THE CENTRE OF
THE TURRET TOP, THEN
DRIVE A ¾" PANEL PIN JUST THROUGH

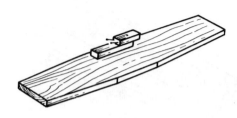

CONSTRUCTION GUIDE FOR MAKING MODEL AIRCRAFT CARRIER

30 POSITION THEN DRIVE TWO
¾" PANEL PINS JUST THROUGH
THE DECK

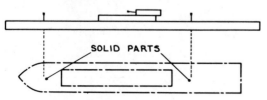

SOLID PARTS

NOTE: MAKE SURE THAT THE PINS ARE
POSITIONED IN LINE WITH THE SOLID
PART OF THE HULL

31 POSITION THE HULL ON THE UNDERSIDE
OF THE DECK NEAR THE SIDE WHERE
THE SUPERSTRUCTURE IS

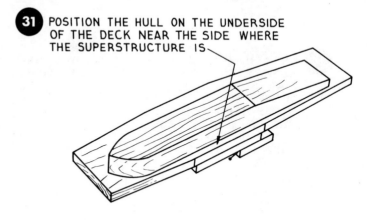

32

NOTE: POSITIONING THE HULL NEAR THE
SUPERSTRUCTURE SIDE ALLOWS
MORE DECK OVERHANG ON THE
OTHER SIDE EVENING THE WEIGHT
FOR BALANCING

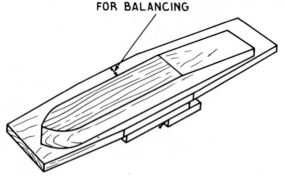

33 TURN OVER CAREFULLY AND
DRIVE IN THE PANEL PINS
(LEAVE PANEL PINS ¼" ABOVE
THE DECK FOR FURTHER ADJUSTMENT)

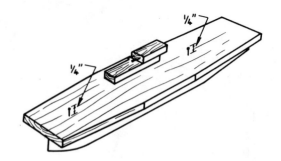

¼"

¼"

CONSTRUCTION GUIDE FOR MAKING MODEL AIRCRAFT CARRIER

34 TEST FOR BALANCE IN A BOWL OF WATER
(ADJUST DECK POSITION UNTIL CORRECT)

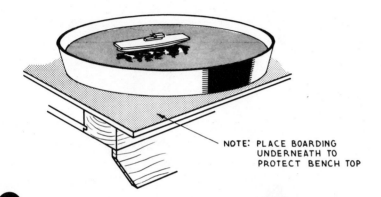

NOTE: PLACE BOARDING
UNDERNEATH TO
PROTECT BENCH TOP

35 WHEN THE CARRIER BALANCES
TAKE IT OUT AND DRIVE HOME
THE PANEL PINS

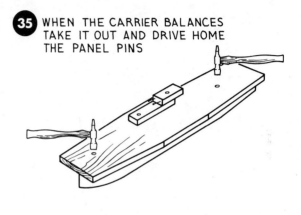

36

PUNCH THE PANEL PIN HEADS BELOW
THE SURFACE AND LEAVE TO DRY

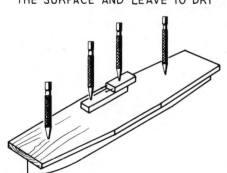

37 RUB DOWN AGAIN THEN DUST
(GARNET OR GLASS PAPER GRADE ?)

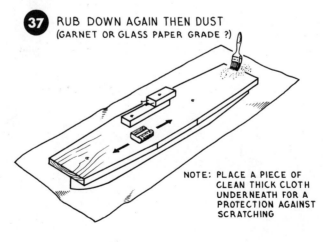

38 APPLY THE FINISH
(FOR A GUIDE SEE BOOK 1)

NOTE: PLACE A PIECE OF
CLEAN THICK CLOTH
UNDERNEATH FOR A
PROTECTION AGAINST
SCRATCHING

INTRODUCTION TO CHEESE BOARDS

1 <u>THE MAIN FUNCTION</u>
A BOARD FOR CUTTING
AND SERVING CHEESE ON

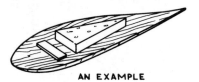

AN EXAMPLE

2 THE UNDER EDGE IS OFTEN
BEVELLED BACK SO THAT THE   OR
CHEESE BOARD CAN EASILY
BE PICKED UP

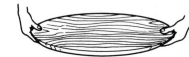

A LARGE BEVEL CAN BE USED
AT ONE CORNER TO FORM
A TAIL-LIKE HANDLE

3 CHEESE BOARDS MUST BE MADE
OF A HARD SURFACED TIMBER TO
RESIST THE CUT OF THE KNIFE

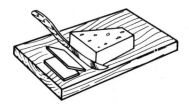

4 NO FINISH (POLISH ETC.) IS GENERALLY
APPLIED BECAUSE THE KNIFE EDGE
WOULD CUT PIECES OF POLISH AWAY
LEAVING A PATCHY UNEVEN SURFACE

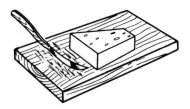

INTRODUCTION TO CHEESE BOARDS

5 AS NO FINISH IS ADDED
THE TIMBER USED MUST
BE ONE WHOSE NATURAL
SURFACE IS AND LOOKS
HYGENIC

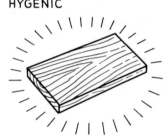

6 NOTE: CHEESE BOARDS MUST
BE THOROUGHLY WASHED
DOWN AFTER USE

7 THEREFORE AN OPEN GRAIN
TIMBER IS UNSUITABLE AS THE
WATER WOULD TEND TO LIFT
THE COARSE FIBRES LEAVING
A ROUGH SURFACE. ALSO SMALL
PARTICLES OF CHEESE WOULD
BE DIFFICULT TO WASH OUT OF
THE OPEN GRAIN

8 SUITABLE VARIETIES FOR A CHEESE BOARD

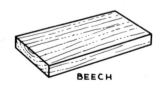

BEECH

CHILEAN RAULI

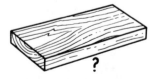

?

9 TO GAIN EXPERIENCE

MAKE THE CHEESE BOARD

PRACTICE BASE SHAPE

CHEESE BOARD PRACTICE BASE SHAPE

1 MAKE OUT A TIMBER LIST FOR THE PRACTICE BASE SHAPE
(GUIDE BELOW)

TIMBER LIST FOR CHEESE BOARD PRACTICE BASE							
NAMES OF MEMBERS	VARIETY OF TIMBER TO BE USED	STATE OF TIMBER TO BE USED	NUMBER REQUIRED	OVERALL LENGTH OF EACH MEMBER	TOTAL LENGTH REQUIRED FOR THIS TYPE OF MEMBER	OVERALL WIDTH	OVERALL THICKNESS
BASE	?	?	?	? + 1"	/	? + ¼"	?

2 FILL IN THE REQUIRED INFORMATION

3 CHEESE BOARD PRACTICE SHAPE
MARKING OUT SIZES

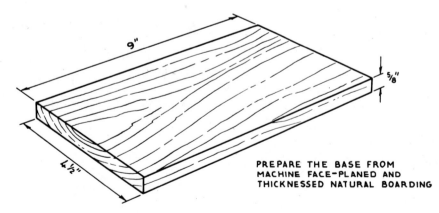

9"

5/8"

4½"

PREPARE THE BASE FROM
MACHINE FACE-PLANED AND
THICKNESSED NATURAL BOARDING

4 PREPARE THE BASE SHAPE'S

TIMBER TO ITS

MARKING OUT SIZE
(FOR A PREPARATION GUIDE
SEE PAGES Nº 24 TO 27)

CHEESE BOARD PRACTICE BASE SHAPE

5 ON A SHEET OF TRACING PAPER
TRACE THE FULL SIZE OUTLINE
OF THE PRACTICE BASE
(SHAPE BELOW)

CHEESE BOARD PRACTICE BASE SHAPE

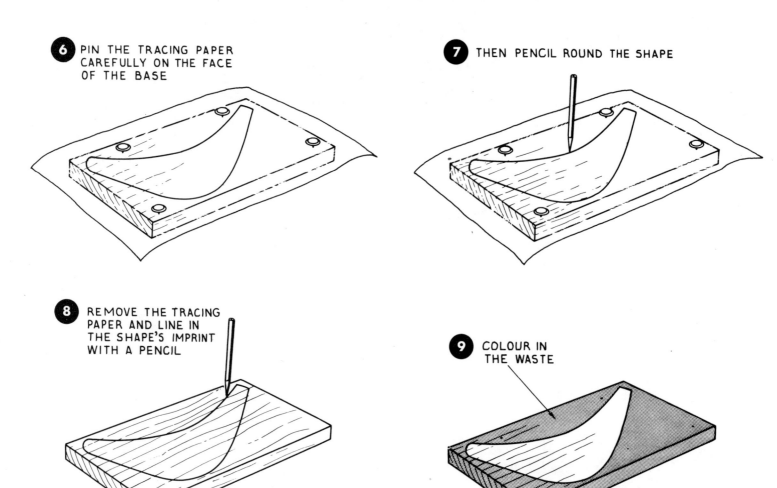

6 PIN THE TRACING PAPER CAREFULLY ON THE FACE OF THE BASE

7 THEN PENCIL ROUND THE SHAPE

8 REMOVE THE TRACING PAPER AND LINE IN THE SHAPE'S IMPRINT WITH A PENCIL

9 COLOUR IN THE WASTE

CHEESE BOARD PRACTICE BASE SHAPE

10 REMOVE THE WASTE WITH
A COPING SAW
(SAW IN THE WASTE
LEAVE THE LINES WELL IN)

SQUARE ACROSS
A GUIDE STARTING LINE

11

TRUE THE STRAIGHT
SIDE WITH A JACK PLANE
(LEAVE THE LINES JUST IN)

12 REMOVE ANY LUMPS OR MARKS LEFT BY THE SAW
WITH A MEDIUM CUTTING RASP
FINISH OFF WITH A FINE CUTTING WOOD FILE

CHEESE BOARD PRACTICE BASE SHAPE

13 FINISH OFF THE LONG CURVES
WITH SUITABLE SPOKESHAVES
(LEAVE THE LINES JUST IN)

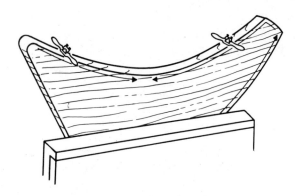

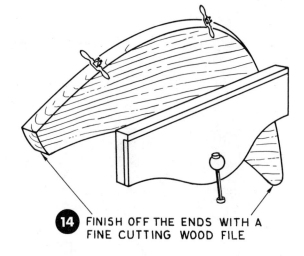

14 FINISH OFF THE ENDS WITH A
FINE CUTTING WOOD FILE

15 MARK OUT THE EDGE BEVEL
USE THE END OF YOUR
FOREFINGER AS A GAUGE STOCK

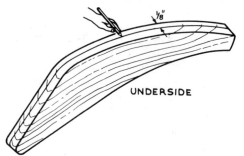

⅛"

UNDERSIDE

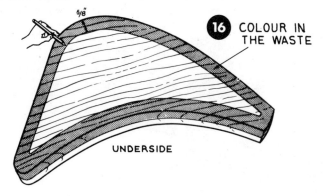

⅝"

16 COLOUR IN
THE WASTE

UNDERSIDE

CHEESE BOARD PRACTICE BASE SHAPE

17 DIAGONALLY REMOVE THE STRAIGHT SIDE
BEVEL WITH A JACK PLANE
(LEAVE THE LINES JUST IN)

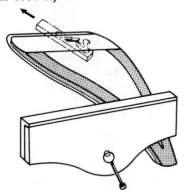

18 REMOVE THE CONCAVE SIDE
BEVEL WASTE WITH A
SUITABLE SPOKESHAVE
(LEAVE THE LINES JUST IN)

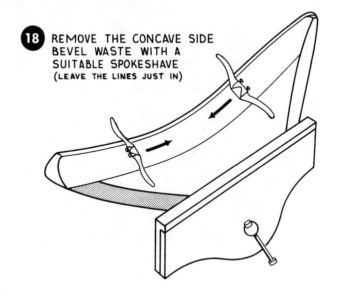

19 REMOVE THE CONVEX SIDE BEVEL
WASTE WITH A SUITABLE SPOKESHAVE
(LEAVE THE LINES JUST IN)

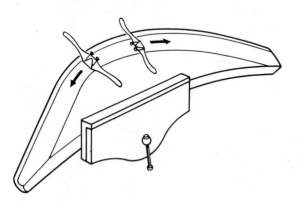

20 MARK OUT AND MAKE THE
CORNER BEVELS

COLOUR IN
THE WASTE

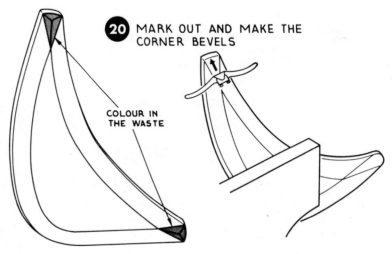

DESIGN AND CONSTRUCTION GUIDE FOR MAKING A CHEESE BOARD

1

MAKE OUT A TIMBER LIST FOR YOUR CHEESE BOARD
(GUIDE BELOW)

TIMBER LIST FOR A CHEESE BOARD							
NAMES OF MEMBERS	VARIETY OF TIMBER TO BE USED	STATE OF TIMBER TO BE USED	NUMBER REQUIRED	OVERALL LENGTH OF EACH MEMBER	TOTAL LENGTH REQUIRED FOR THIS TYPE OF MEMBER	OVERALL WIDTH	OVERALL THICKNESS
BASE	?	?	?	? + 1" P.A.	/	? + ¼" P.A.	?

3 WHAT VARIETY OF HARDWOOD OR SOFTWOOD WILL YOU USE FOR YOUR CHEESE BOARD

2 NOW FOLLOW THE INSTRUCTIONS AND ANSWER EACH OF THE QUESTIONS IN TURN

AS YOU PROGRESS FILL IN THE REQUIRED INFORMATION ON YOUR TIMBER LIST

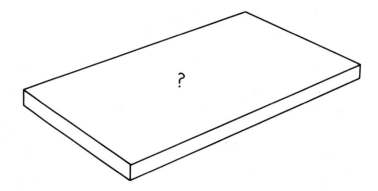

DESIGN AND CONSTRUCTION GUIDE FOR MAKING A CHEESE BOARD

4

CONSIDER THE SIZE OF CHEESE
YOUR MOTHER GENERALLY BUYS
ADD TO THIS THE NECESSARY
OVERHANG FOR CUTTING UP ETC.
THEN NOTE THE OVERALL AREA

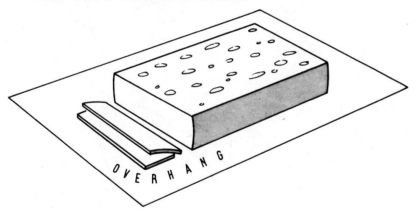

5 DESIGN   YOUR

CHEESE   BOARD

(TWO METHODS ARE
GIVEN ON THE FOLLOWING PAGES)

DESIGN AND CONSTRUCTION GUIDE FOR MAKING A CHEESE BOARD

6 ON A LARGE SHEET OF TRACING PAPER
SCRIBE CONTINUOUS LOOPS IN FIGURE EIGHT PATTERNS
(AN EXAMPLE BELOW)

NOTE: MAKE THE AREA OF EACH
COMPLETE LOOP ROUGHLY EQUAL
TO THAT OF YOUR CHEESE BOARD
OVERALL AREA

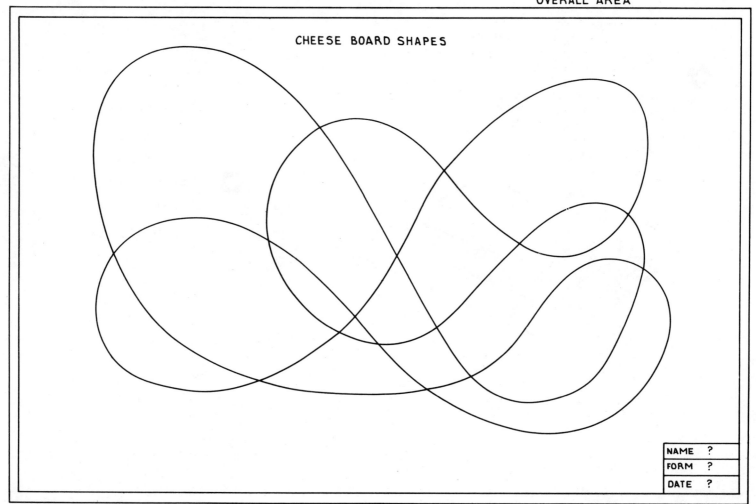

CHEESE BOARD SHAPES

NAME	?
FORM	?
DATE	?

DESIGN AND CONSTRUCTION GUIDE FOR MAKING A CHEESE BOARD

 7 LOOK AT THE VARIOUS SHAPES FORMED ON YOUR PAPER
AND SHADE IN THE MOST PLEASING ONES
(THREE EXAMPLES BELOW)

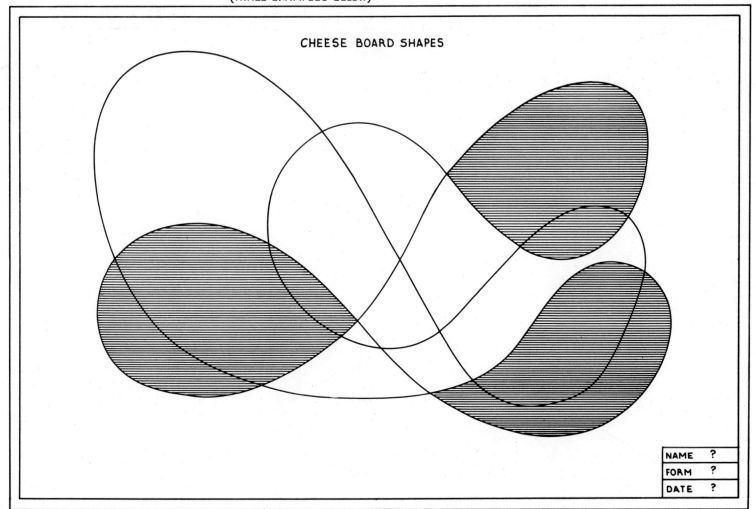

CHEESE BOARD SHAPES

NAME	?
FORM	?
DATE	?

DESIGN AND CONSTRUCTION GUIDE FOR MAKING A CHEESE BOARD

8 ON A LARGE SHEET OF TRACING PAPER
DRAW A NUMBER OF SQUARES,
CIRCLES AND TRIANGLES
(AN EXAMPLE BELOW)

NOTE: MAKE THE AREA OF THESE
SHAPES ROUGHLY EQUAL TO THAT
OF YOUR CHEESE BOARD AREA

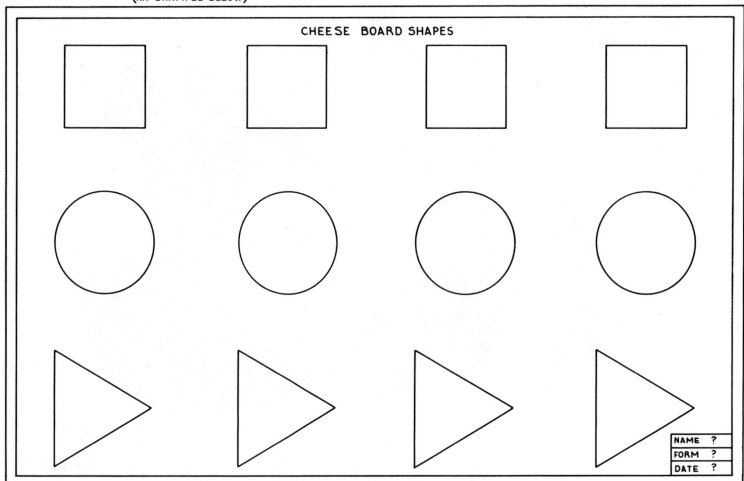

CHEESE BOARD SHAPES

NAME	?
FORM	?
DATE	?

DESIGN AND CONSTRUCTION GUIDE FOR MAKING A CHEESE BOARD

9 NOW CONSIDER AND BUILD UP SHAPES AROUND THE OUTLINES
(THREE EXAMPLES BELOW)

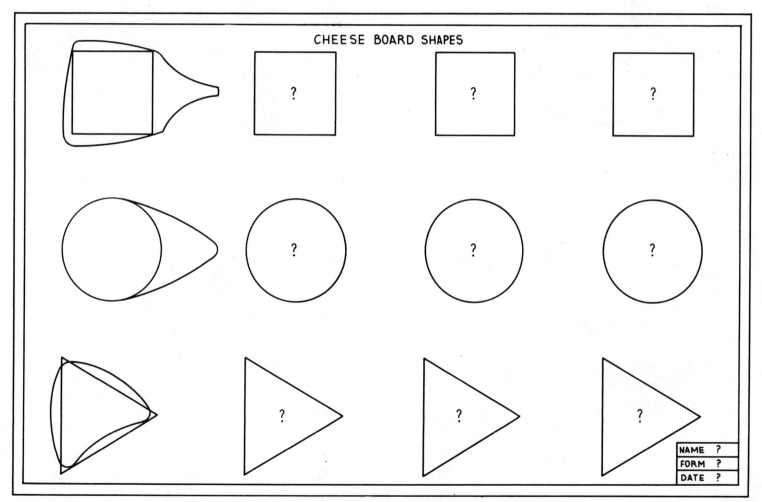

CHEESE BOARD SHAPES

NAME	?
FORM	?
DATE	?

DESIGN AND CONSTRUCTION GUIDE FOR MAKING A CHEESE BOARD

10 CONSIDER YOUR VARIOUS
CHEESE BOARD SHAPES THEN
CUT OUT THE ONE YOU LIKE BEST

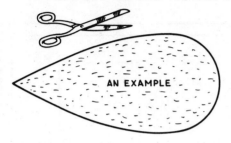

AN EXAMPLE

MARKING OUT SIZES

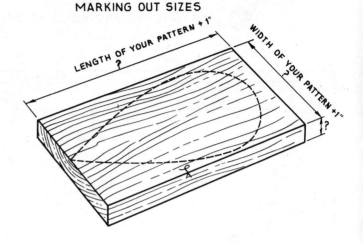

LENGTH OF YOUR PATTERN + 1"
?

WIDTH OF YOUR PATTERN + 1"
?

12 TAPE YOUR CUT-OUT PATTERN ON
THE PREPARED TIMBER AND MARK
AROUND THE OUTLINE

11

PREPARE THE TIMBER
FOR THE CHEESE BOARD
TO ITS MARKING OUT SIZES

(PREPARE FROM MACHINE FACE
PLANED AND THICKNESSED
NATURAL BOARDING)

(FOR A PREPARATION GUIDE
SEE PAGES № 24 TO 27)

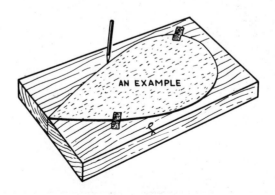

AN EXAMPLE

13

COLOUR IN THE WASTE

THEN SHAPE YOUR

CHEESE BOARD

DESIGN AND CONSTRUCTION GUIDE FOR MAKING A CHEESE BOARD

14 CLEAN UP THE CHEESE BOARD
(A METHOD GIVEN BELOW)

15 REMOVE ANY SERIOUS MARKS WITH A SMOOTH PLANE

16 SCRAPE

17 RUB DOWN THEN DUST
(GLASSPAPER GRADE Nº M2)
(OR GARNET PAPER GRADE Nº 2/0)

NOTE: PLACE A PIECE OF CLEAN THICK CLOTH UNDERNEATH FOR PROTECTION AGAINST SCRATCHING

18 DAMP DOWN THEN LEAVE TO DRY

WATER

NOTE: PLACE BOARDING UNDERNEATH TO PROTECT THE BENCH TOP

19 RUB DOWN AGAIN THEN DUST
(GLASSPAPER GRADE Nº 1)
(OR GARNET PAPER GRADE Nº 4/0)

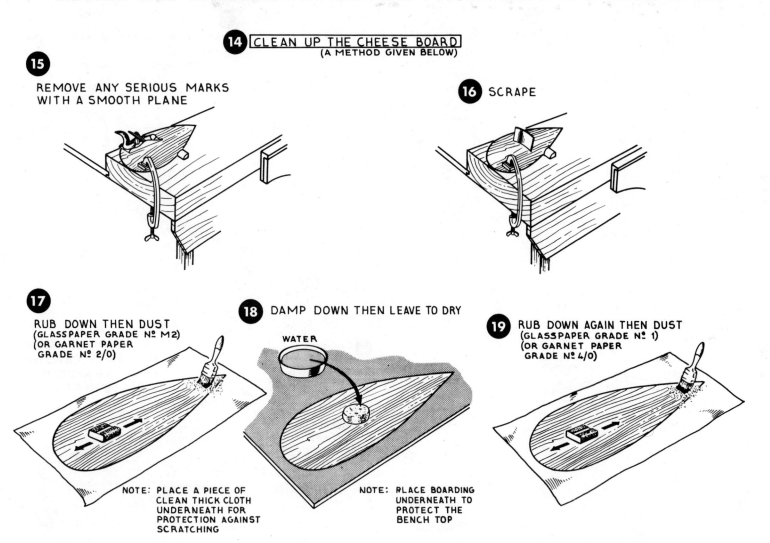

5*

INTRODUCTION TO TOAST RACKS

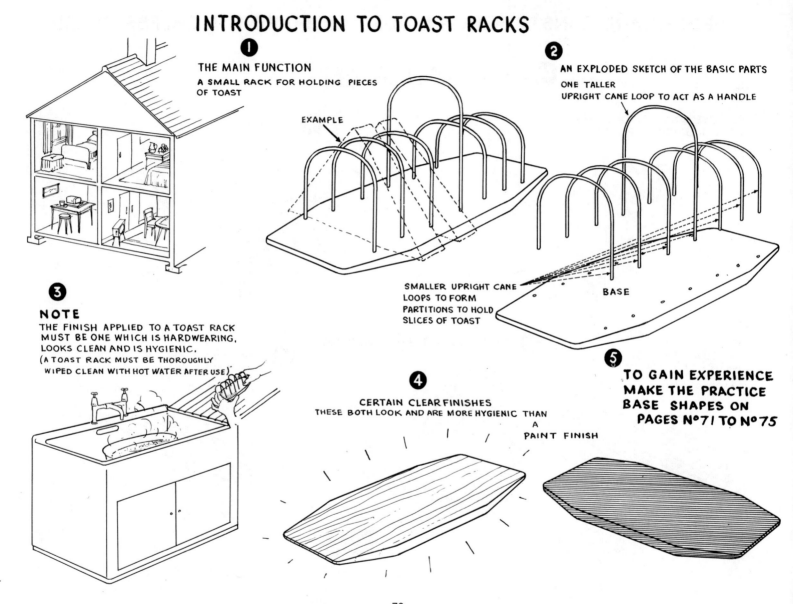

1

THE MAIN FUNCTION
A SMALL RACK FOR HOLDING PIECES OF TOAST

EXAMPLE

2

AN EXPLODED SKETCH OF THE BASIC PARTS
ONE TALLER
UPRIGHT CANE LOOP TO ACT AS A HANDLE

SMALLER UPRIGHT CANE LOOPS TO FORM PARTITIONS TO HOLD SLICES OF TOAST

BASE

3

NOTE
THE FINISH APPLIED TO A TOAST RACK MUST BE ONE WHICH IS HARDWEARING, LOOKS CLEAN AND IS HYGIENIC.
(A TOAST RACK MUST BE THOROUGHLY WIPED CLEAN WITH HOT WATER AFTER USE)

4

CERTAIN CLEAR FINISHES
THESE BOTH LOOK AND ARE MORE HYGIENIC THAN
A
PAINT FINISH

5

TO GAIN EXPERIENCE MAKE THE PRACTICE BASE SHAPES ON PAGES Nº71 TO Nº75

70

TOAST RACK BASE SHAPES

DIMENSIONAL SKETCHES OF THE DIFFERENT SHAPES

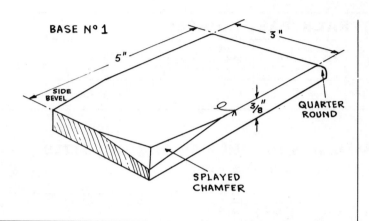

BASE Nº 1

5"

3"

SIDE BEVEL

3/8"

QUARTER ROUND

SPLAYED CHAMFER

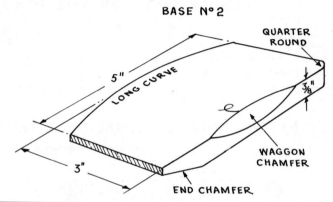

BASE Nº 2

QUARTER ROUND

5"

LONG CURVE

3/8"

WAGGON CHAMFER

END CHAMFER

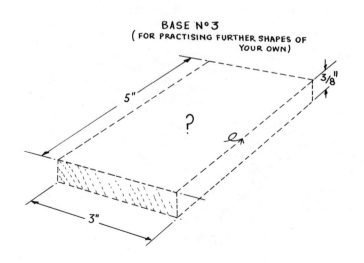

BASE Nº 3
(FOR PRACTISING FURTHER SHAPES OF YOUR OWN)

5"

3/8"

?

3"

NOTE

PREPARE THE BASES
FROM MACHINE FACE-
PLANED AND THICKNESSED
NATURAL BOARDING 3/8" THICK

(FOR A PREPARATION GUIDE SEE PAGES Nº 24 TO 29)

TOAST RACK PRACTICE BASE SHAPES

① MARK OUT A TIMBER LIST AND FILL IN THE REQUIRED INFORMATION FOR THE BASE SHAPES

TIMBER LIST FOR THE TOAST RACK BASE SHAPES							
NAMES OF MEMBERS	VARIETY OF TIMBER TO BE USED	STATE OF TIMBER TO BE USED	REQUIRED NUMBER	OVERALL LENGTH OF EACH MEMBER	TOTAL LENGTH OF TIMBER REQUIRED	OVERALL WIDTH	OVERALL THICKNESS
BASE SHAPES	?	?	?	? + 1" P.A.	?	? + 1/4" P.A.	?

② PREPARE THE TIMBER FOR THE MEMBERS TO THEIR MARKING OUT SIZES

(FOR PREPARATION DETAILS SEE PAGE Nº 24 TO PAGE Nº 28)

③ MARK OUT AND SHAPE PRACTICE BASE Nº 1

(A METHOD IS GIVEN BELOW AND CONTINUED ON THE NEXT PAGE)

④ MARK OUT THE QUARTER ROUND ON THE END

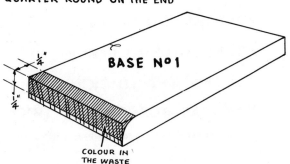

BASE Nº 1

1/4"

1/4"

COLOUR IN THE WASTE

⑤ ROUND OFF THE BULK OF THE WASTE WITH A MEDIUM CUTTING RASP. THEN FINISH OFF WITH A FINE CUTTING WOOD FILE.
(LEAVE THE LINES)
JUST IN

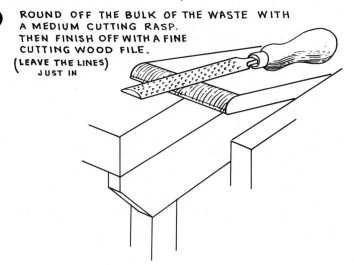

TOAST RACK PRACTICE BASE SHAPES

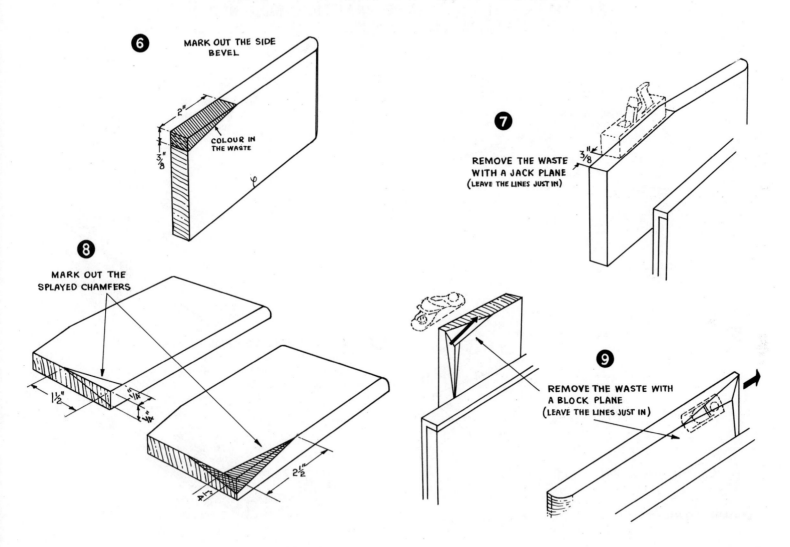

6 MARK OUT THE SIDE BEVEL

2"

3/8"

COLOUR IN THE WASTE

7 REMOVE THE WASTE WITH A JACK PLANE (LEAVE THE LINES JUST IN)

3/8"

8 MARK OUT THE SPLAYED CHAMFERS

1½"

1¼"

¼"

2½"

4"

9 REMOVE THE WASTE WITH A BLOCK PLANE (LEAVE THE LINES JUST IN)

TOAST RACK PRACTICE BASE SHAPES

⑩ MARK OUT AND SHAPE PRACTICE BASE Nº 2
A METHOD IS GIVEN BELOW AND CONTINUED ON THE NEXT PAGE

⑪ MARK OUT THE END CHAMFER

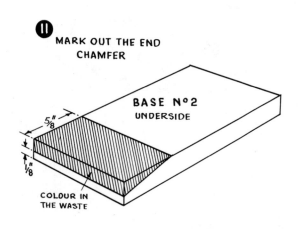

BASE Nº 2
UNDERSIDE

$\frac{5}{8}$"

$\frac{1}{8}$"

COLOUR IN
THE WASTE

⑫ REMOVE THE BULK OF THE WASTE WITH A JACK PLANE AND FINISH WITH A SMOOTH PLANE
(LEAVE THE LINES JUST IN)

⑬ MARK $\frac{3}{8}$" DOTS AT EACH END

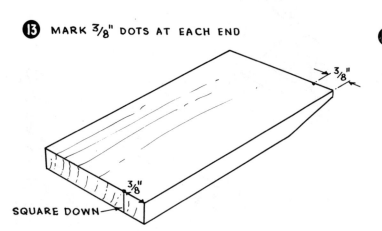

$\frac{3}{8}$"

$\frac{3}{8}$"

SQUARE DOWN

⑭ GET SOMEONE TO BEND A LATH TOUCHING THE DOTS AND THE EDGE AS BELOW – THEN MARK IN A CURVE

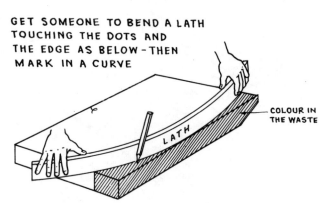

LATH

COLOUR IN
THE WASTE

74

TOAST RACK PRACTICE BASE SHAPES

15 REMOVE THE WASTE
WITH A FLAT FACED
SPOKESHAVE
(LEAVE THE LINES JUST IN)

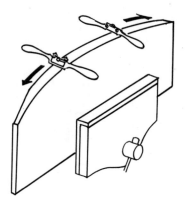

16 MARK OUT THE
QUADRANT

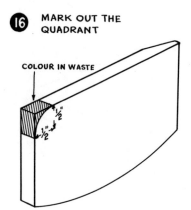

COLOUR IN WASTE

$\frac{1}{2}"$ $\frac{1}{2}"$ $\frac{1}{2}"$

17 ROUND OFF THE BULK OF THE WASTE
WITH A MEDIUM CUTTING RASP. THEN
FINISH OFF WITH A FINE
CUTTING WOOD FILE

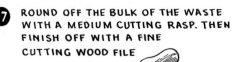

18 MAKE OR FIND A BRASS OR TIN PLATE
PATTERN OF A SUITABLE SIZE TO MARK
OUT THE WAGGON CHAMFER

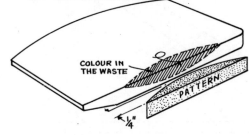

COLOUR IN
THE WASTE

PATTERN

$\frac{1}{4}"$

19 REMOVE THE WASTE WITH
A ROUND FACED SPOKESHAVE
(LEAVE THE LINES JUST IN)

20

PRACTISE MARKING

OUT AND SHAPING

FURTHER SHAPES OF

YOUR OWN ON BASE Nº 3

DESIGN AND CONSTRUCTION GUIDE FOR MAKING A TOAST RACK

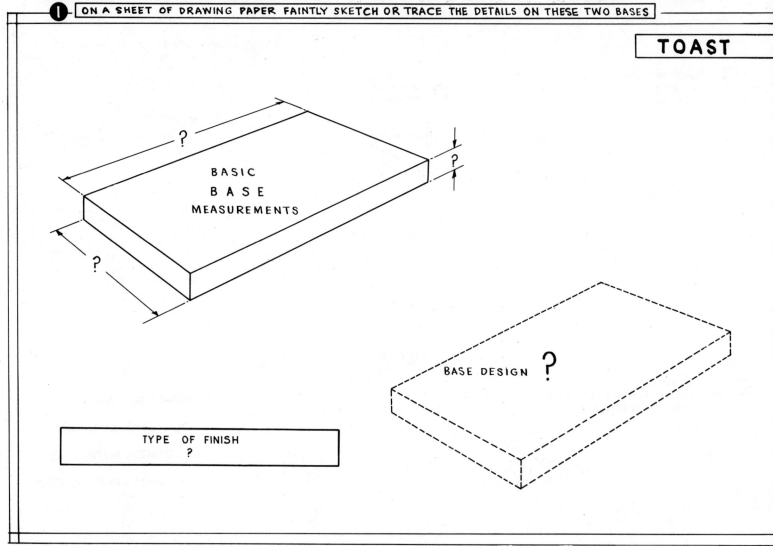

TOAST

BASIC
B A S E
MEASUREMENTS

?

?

?

BASE DESIGN ?

TYPE OF FINISH
?

DESIGN AND CONSTRUCTION GUIDE FOR MAKING A TOAST RACK

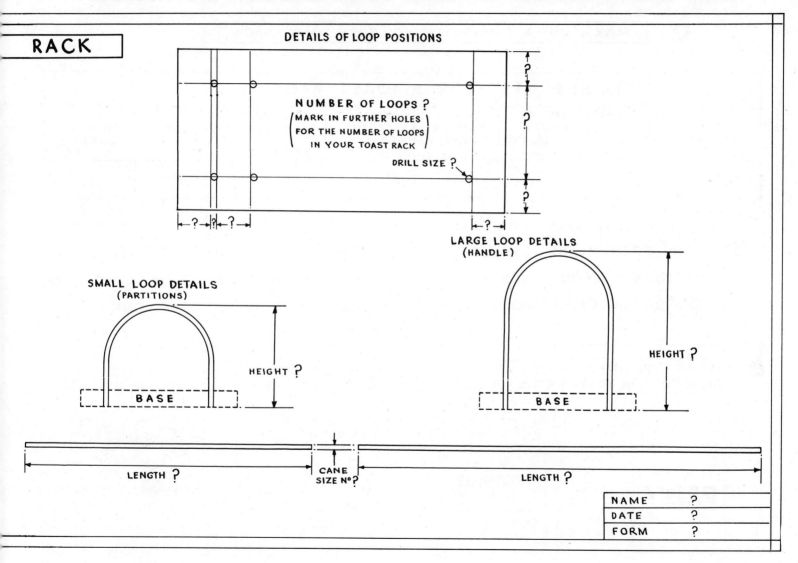

RACK

DETAILS OF LOOP POSITIONS

NUMBER OF LOOPS ?
(MARK IN FURTHER HOLES
FOR THE NUMBER OF LOOPS
IN YOUR TOAST RACK)

DRILL SIZE ?

LARGE LOOP DETAILS
(HANDLE)

HEIGHT ?

SMALL LOOP DETAILS
(PARTITIONS)

HEIGHT ?

BASE

BASE

LENGTH ?

CANE
SIZE Nº?

LENGTH ?

NAME	?
DATE	?
FORM	?

DESIGN AND CONSTRUCTION GUIDE FOR MAKING A TOAST RACK

❷ MARK OUT A TIMBER LIST FOR YOUR TOAST RACK

TIMBER LIST FOR A TOAST RACK

NAME OF MEMBERS	VARIETY OF TIMBER TO BE USED	STATE OF TIMBER TO BE USED	NUMBER REQUIRED	OVERALL LENGTH OF EACH MEMBER	TOTAL LENGTH OF DIFFERENT TYPES OF MEMBER	OVERALL WIDTH	OVERALL THICKNESS
BASE	?	?	?	? + 1 P.A.	?	? + ¼" P.A.	?

❸ NOW FOLLOW THE INSTRUCTIONS AND ANSWER EACH OF THE QUESTIONS IN TURN. AS YOU PROGRESS FILL IN THE REQUIRED INFORMATION ON YOUR SKETCH OR TRACING. EVENTUALLY DEVELOP AN ORTHOGRAPHIC DRAWING OF YOUR TOAST RACK

❹ WHAT TYPE OF FINISH WILL YOU APPLY TO YOUR TOAST RACK'S SURFACE ?

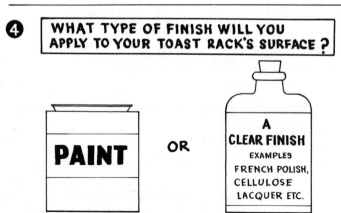

PAINT OR

A CLEAR FINISH
EXAMPLES
FRENCH POLISH,
CELLULOSE
LACQUER ETC.

❺ WHAT VARIETY OF HARDWOOD OR SOFTWOOD WILL YOU USE FOR THE BASE ?

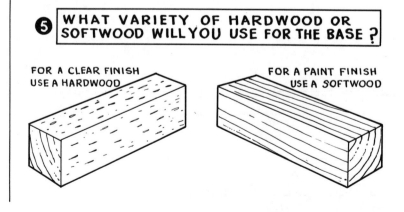

FOR A CLEAR FINISH USE A HARDWOOD

FOR A PAINT FINISH USE A SOFTWOOD

DESIGN AND CONSTRUCTION GUIDE FOR MAKING A TOAST RACK

6 | **WHAT WILL BE THE LENGTH OF YOUR TOAST RACK ?**
(A METHOD OF FINDING GIVEN BELOW)

7 CONSIDER AND THEN NOTE THE NUMBER OF PIECES OF TOAST YOU WISH YOUR RACK TO HOLD

NOTE
MAKE THE NUMBER OF PIECES OF TOAST AN EVEN ONE SO THAT THE HANDLE WILL BE CENTRAL

8 BRING TO SCHOOL A PIECE OF TOAST AND MEASURE AND NOTE THE THICKNESS

9 LAY OUT ENOUGH LENGTHS OF Nº 11 CANE TO HOLD THE REQUIRED NUMBER OF PIECES OF TOAST. LEAVE SUFFICIENT ROOM FOR THE TOAST BETWEEN EACH CANE

TOAST THICKNESS

EXAMPLE FOR 6 PIECES OF TOAST

10 AT EACH END ADD ON 3/4" FOR THE OVERHANG THEN MEASURE THE LENGTH

OVERHANG 3/4"

LENGTH OF THE TOAST RACK

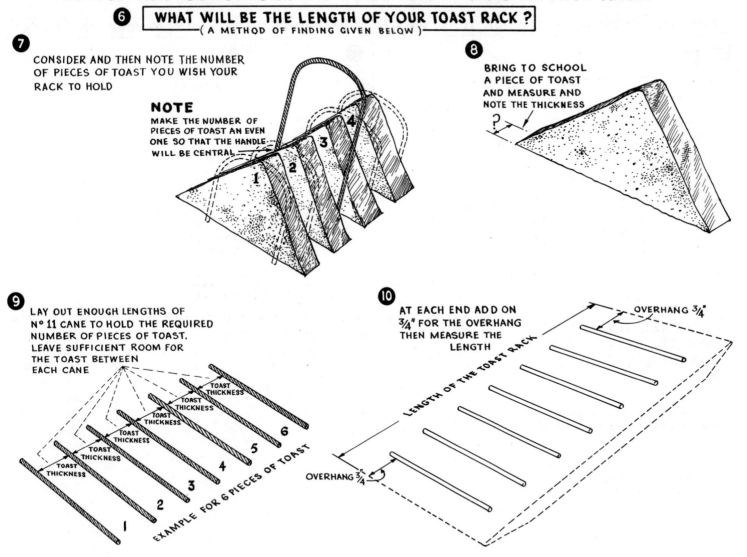

79

DESIGN AND CONSTRUCTION GUIDE FOR MAKING A TOAST RACK

WHAT WILL BE THE WIDTH OF YOUR TOAST RACK?

11 **NOTE**
THE RACK MUST BE WIDE ENOUGH
FOR THE TOAST TO BALANCE ON FIRMLY

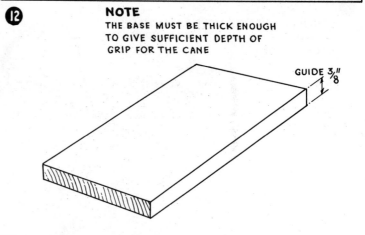

GUIDE TO THE WIDTH

3"

WHAT WILL BE THE THICKNESS OF YOUR TOAST RACK?

12 **NOTE**
THE BASE MUST BE THICK ENOUGH
TO GIVE SUFFICIENT DEPTH OF
GRIP FOR THE CANE

GUIDE $\frac{3}{8}$"

13

PREPARE THE TIMBER FOR THE BASE TO ITS MARKING OUT SIZES

PREPARE FROM MACHINE FACE-PLANED
AND THICKNESSED NATURAL BOARDING.

FOR PREPARATION DETAILS SEE
PAGES Nº 24 TO 29

14 INTRODUCTION TO CANE

CANE IS PURCHASED BY WEIGHT, CANE IS NUMBERED ACCORDING TO THE SIZE OF ITS DIAMETER

COMMON RANGE

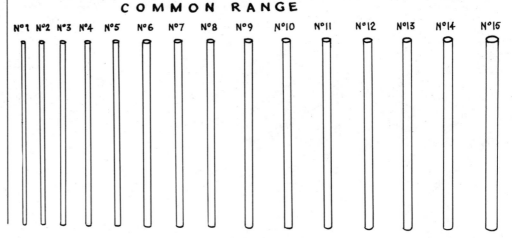

Nº1 Nº2 Nº3 Nº4 Nº5 Nº6 Nº7 Nº8 Nº9 Nº10 Nº11 Nº12 Nº13 Nº14 Nº15

DESIGN AND CONSTRUCTION GUIDE FOR MAKING A TOAST RACK

(15)

NOTE

THE SIZE OF CANE USED MUST BE STRONG
ENOUGH TO SUPPORT BOTH THE TOAST AND
THE BASE WHEN THE TOAST
RACK IS BEING CARRIED

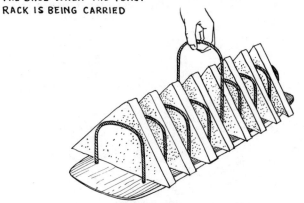

(16)

NOTE
ALSO THE SIZE OF CANE
USED MUST BE EASY

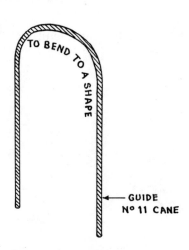

TO BEND TO A SHAPE

← GUIDE
N° 11 CANE

---

(17)
WHAT WILL BE THE CANE SIZE YOU WILL USE?
(A METHOD FOR FINDING GIVEN BELOW)

JUDGE THE CANE SIZE MOST
SUITABLE BY BENDING VARIOUS
SIZES TO SUITABLE SHAPES
ON THE END OF THE BASE
WITH A PIECE OF TOAST
BEHIND AS A GUIDE

½"   ½"

NOTE
ALLOW AT LEAST ½"
OVERHANG ON EACH
SIDE FOR BASE SHAPING

← GUIDE N°11 CANE

(17)
WHAT WILL BE THE WIDTH OF YOUR CANE HOOPS AT THE BASE?
A METHOD FOR FINDING GIVEN BELOW

PLACE THE MOST SUITABLE
SHAPED CANE ONTO THE
END OF THE BASE.
THEN MEASURE THE WIDTH

? WIDTH

DESIGN AND CONSTRUCTION GUIDE FOR MAKING A TOAST RACK

19 ON THE BASE MARK OUT AND BORE THE HOLES FOR THE CANE LOOPS

(A METHOD IS GIVEN BELOW)

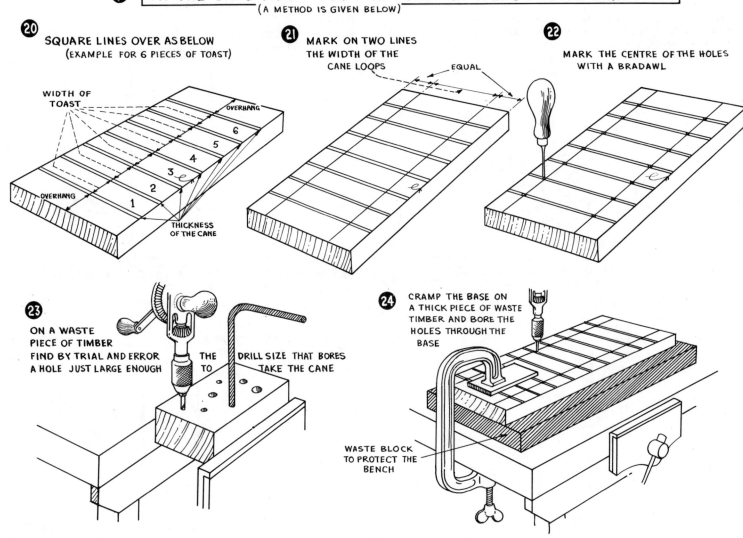

20 SQUARE LINES OVER AS BELOW
(EXAMPLE FOR 6 PIECES OF TOAST)

WIDTH OF TOAST

OVERHANG

OVERHANG

THICKNESS OF THE CANE

21 MARK ON TWO LINES THE WIDTH OF THE CANE LOOPS

EQUAL

22 MARK THE CENTRE OF THE HOLES WITH A BRADAWL

23 ON A WASTE PIECE OF TIMBER FIND BY TRIAL AND ERROR A HOLE JUST LARGE ENOUGH TO THE DRILL SIZE THAT BORES TO TAKE THE CANE

24 CRAMP THE BASE ON A THICK PIECE OF WASTE TIMBER AND BORE THE HOLES THROUGH THE BASE

WASTE BLOCK TO PROTECT THE BENCH

DESIGN AND CONSTRUCTION GUIDE FOR MAKING A TOAST RACK

㉕ WHAT WILL BE THE HEIGHT OF YOUR SMALL CANE LOOPS ?

(A METHOD FOR FINDING THEM IS GIVEN BELOW)
FORM A SUITABLY SIZED LOOP WITH A PIECE OF CANE POSITIONED IN THE BASE, THEN MEASURE THE HEIGHT

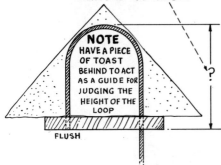

NOTE
HAVE A PIECE OF TOAST BEHIND TO ACT AS A GUIDE FOR JUDGING THE HEIGHT OF THE LOOP

?

FLUSH

㉖ WHAT WILL BE THE LENGTH OF YOUR SMALL CANE LOOPS ?

(A METHOD FOR FINDING THEM IS GIVEN BELOW)
WITH THE LOOP STILL IN THE BASE CUT IT TO LENGTH AT THE BOTTOM, TAKE OUT AND THEN MEASURE

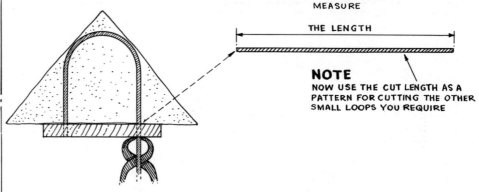

THE LENGTH

NOTE
NOW USE THE CUT LENGTH AS A PATTERN FOR CUTTING THE OTHER SMALL LOOPS YOU REQUIRE

㉗ WHAT WILL BE THE HEIGHT OF YOUR LARGE CANE LOOP ?

(A METHOD FOR FINDING IT IS GIVEN BELOW)
FORM A SUITABLY SIZED LOOP WITH A PIECE OF CANE POSITIONED IN THE BASE, THEN MEASURE THE HEIGHT

NOTE
HAVE A PIECE OF TOAST BEHIND TO ACT AS A GUIDE FOR JUDGING THE HEIGHT OF THE LOOP

?

FLUSH

㉘ WHAT WILL BE THE LENGTH OF YOUR LARGE CANE LOOP ?

(A METHOD FOR FINDING IT IS GIVEN BELOW)
WITH THE LOOP STILL IN THE BASE CUT IT TO LENGTH AT THE BOTTOM, TAKE OUT AND THEN MEASURE.

THE LENGTH

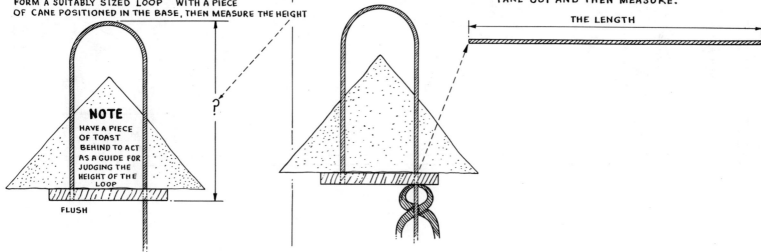

DESIGN AND CONSTRUCTION GUIDE FOR MAKING A TOAST RACK

29 ON A LARGE SHEET OF DRAWING PAPER
SKETCH OR TRACE A NUMBER OF TOAST RACK BASES
(AN EXAMPLE BELOW)

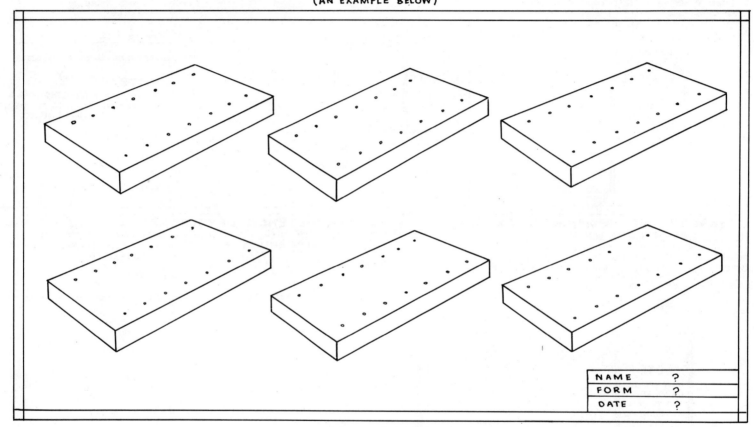

NAME	?
FORM	?
DATE	?

DESIGN AND CONSTRUCTION GUIDE FOR MAKING A TOAST RACK

30 THEN BUILD UP DESIGNS FROM
THE SHAPES USED WHEN PRACTISING
(SOME EXAMPLES BELOW)

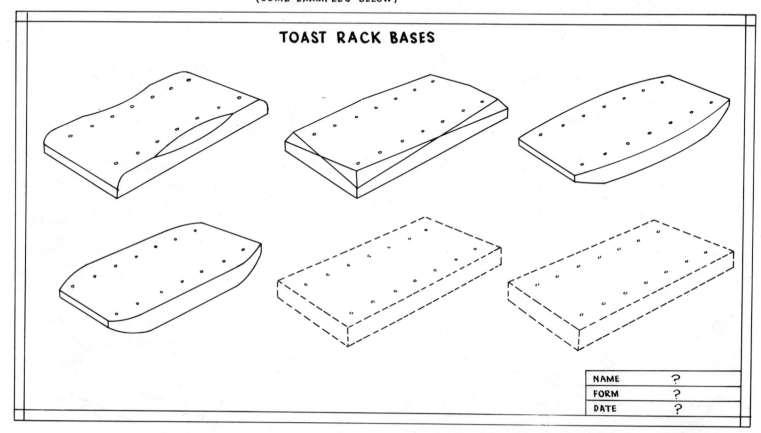

TOAST RACK BASES

NAME	?
FORM	?
DATE	?

31 CONSIDER THEN BUILD UP DESIGNS, THEN
MARK OUT AND SHAPE THE ONE YOU LIKE
THE BEST

6*

DESIGN AND CONSTRUCTION GUIDE FOR MAKING A TOAST RACK

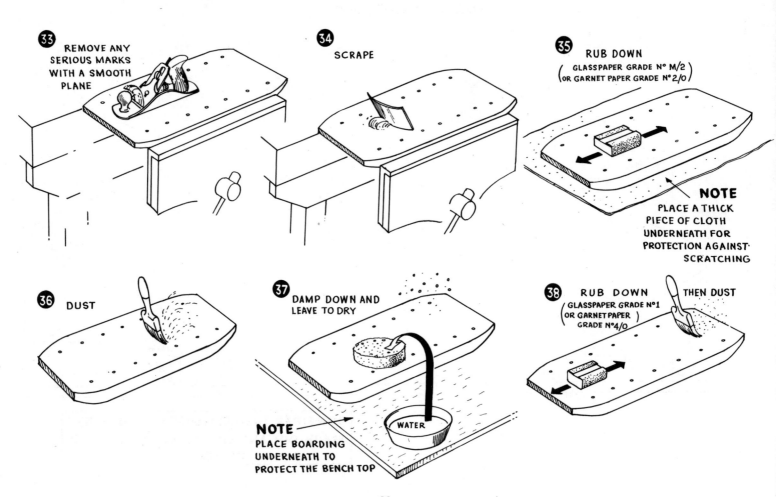

32 **PREPARE THE TOAST RACK FOR RECEIVING A FINISH**
(A METHOD IS GIVEN BELOW)

33 REMOVE ANY SERIOUS MARKS WITH A SMOOTH PLANE

34 SCRAPE

35 RUB DOWN
(GLASSPAPER GRADE N° M/2)
(OR GARNET PAPER GRADE N° 2/0)

NOTE
PLACE A THICK PIECE OF CLOTH UNDERNEATH FOR PROTECTION AGAINST SCRATCHING

36 DUST

37 DAMP DOWN AND LEAVE TO DRY

WATER

NOTE
PLACE BOARDING UNDERNEATH TO PROTECT THE BENCH TOP

38 RUB DOWN
(GLASSPAPER GRADE N°1)
(OR GARNET PAPER GRADE N°4/0)
THEN DUST

DESIGN AND CONSTRUCTION GUIDE FOR MAKING A TOAST RACK

㊴ APPLY THE FINISH AND THE CANE LOOPS
(A METHOD IS GIVEN BELOW)

㊵ BEFORE APPLYING THE FINISH PLUG THE HOLES WITH SMALL PIECES OF CANE TO PREVENT THE POLISH FROM RUNNING INTO THEM, AS THIS WILL LINE THE SIDES AND PREVENT THE GLUE FROM GRIPPING THE TIMBER

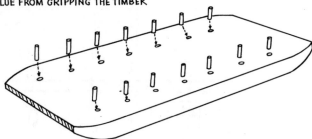

㊶

APPLY THE FINISH
(FOR PROCESS SEE BOOK 1)

㊷ REMOVE THE CANE PLUGS, THEN CAREFULLY APPLY GLUE TO THE HOLES WITH A LONG SPLINTER

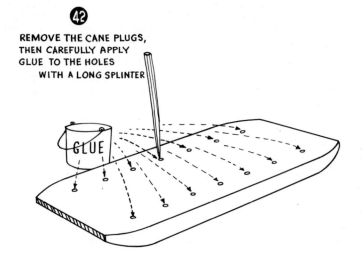

GLUE

㊸

FIT IN CANE LOOPS AND LEAVE UNTIL THE GLUE SETS

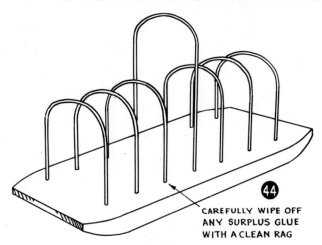

㊹ CAREFULLY WIPE OFF ANY SURPLUS GLUE WITH A CLEAN RAG

INTRODUCTION TO COLUMN BASED TABLE LAMPS

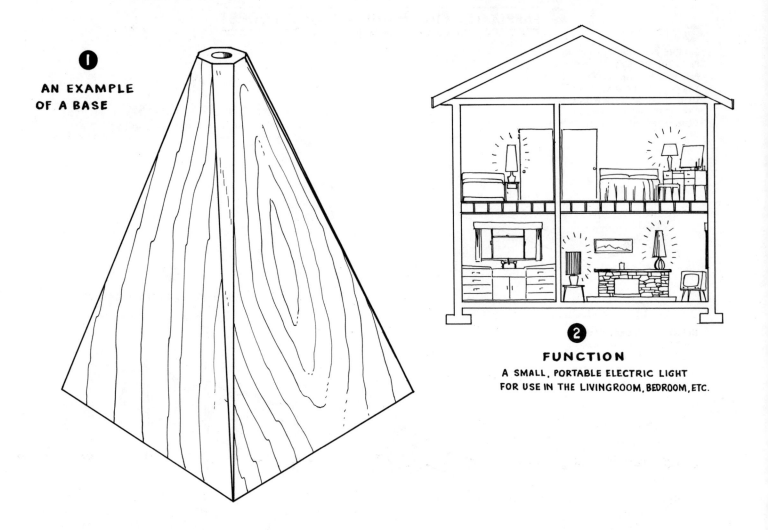

❶

AN EXAMPLE
OF A BASE

❷

FUNCTION

A SMALL, PORTABLE ELECTRIC LIGHT
FOR USE IN THE LIVINGROOM, BEDROOM, ETC.

INTRODUCTION TO COLUMN-BASED TABLE LAMP

3 **EXPLODED SKETCH OF A BASE WITH FITTINGS**

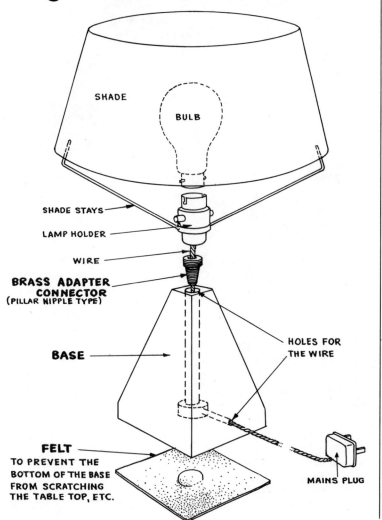

SHADE

BULB

SHADE STAYS

LAMP HOLDER

WIRE

**BRASS ADAPTER
CONNECTOR**
(PILLAR NIPPLE TYPE)

BASE

HOLES FOR
THE WIRE

FELT
TO PREVENT THE
BOTTOM OF THE BASE
FROM SCRATCHING
THE TABLE TOP, ETC.

MAINS PLUG

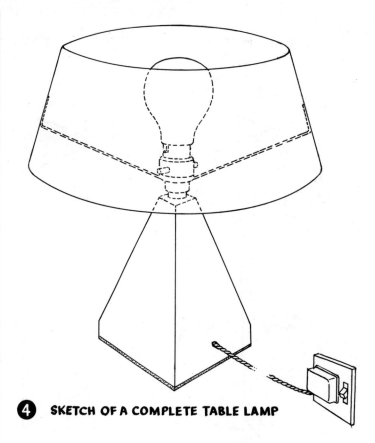

4 **SKETCH OF A COMPLETE TABLE LAMP**

5 **TO GAIN EXPERIENCE, MAKE
THE PRACTICE BASE SHAPES**
PAGE Nº90 TO PAGE Nº99

TABLE LAMP PRACTICE BASE SHAPES
SKETCHES OF PRACTICE SHAPES WITH DIMENSIONS

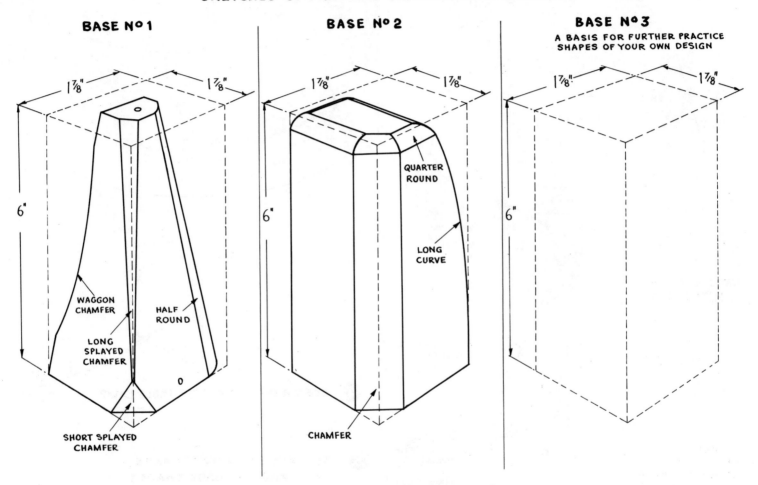

BASE Nº 1

BASE Nº 2

BASE Nº 3
A BASIS FOR FURTHER PRACTICE
SHAPES OF YOUR OWN DESIGN

1⅞" 1⅞" 1⅞" 1⅞" 1⅞" 1⅞"

6" 6" 6"

WAGGON
CHAMFER

HALF
ROUND

LONG
SPLAYED
CHAMFER

0

SHORT SPLAYED
CHAMFER

QUARTER
ROUND

LONG
CURVE

CHAMFER

PREPARE THE BASES FROM MACHINE PLANED ALL ROUND SCANTLING

TABLE LAMP PRACTICE BASE SHAPES

1 MAKE OUT A TIMBER LIST FOR THE PRACTICE BASE SHAPES
(GUIDE BELOW)

TIMBER LIST FOR TABLE LAMP PRACTICE BASE SHAPES

NAMES OF MEMBERS	VARIETY OF TIMBER TO BE USED	STATE OF TIMBER TO BE USED	NUMBER REQUIRED	OVERALL LENGTH OF EACH MEMBER	TOTAL LENGTH REQUIRED FOR THIS TYPE OF MEMBER	OVERALL WIDTH	OVERALL THICKNESS
PRACTICE BASE SHAPES	?	?	?	?	?	?	?

2 THEN FILL IN THE REQUIRED INFORMATION

3 PREPARE THE TIMBER FOR THE PRACTICE BASE SHAPES TO THEIR MARKING OUT SIZES

FOR A PREPARATION GUIDE SEE PAGE Nº 29

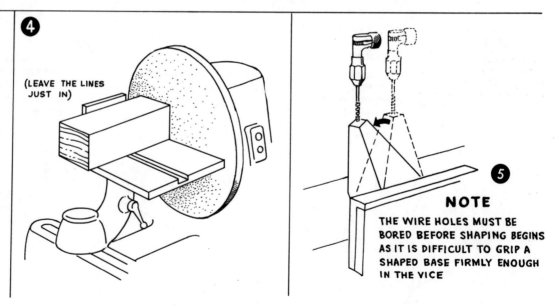

4 (LEAVE THE LINES JUST IN)

5 NOTE
THE WIRE HOLES MUST BE BORED BEFORE SHAPING BEGINS AS IT IS DIFFICULT TO GRIP A SHAPED BASE FIRMLY ENOUGH IN THE VICE

TABLE LAMP PRACTICE BASE SHAPES

6 A METHOD FOR BORING THE WIRE HOLES IN THE PRACTICE BASE
(BELOW AND CONTINUED ON THE NEXT PAGE)

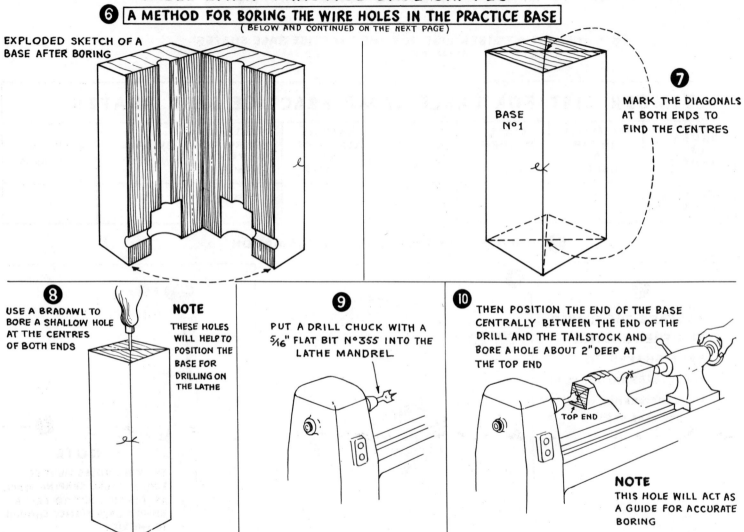

EXPLODED SKETCH OF A BASE AFTER BORING

7 MARK THE DIAGONALS AT BOTH ENDS TO FIND THE CENTRES

BASE Nº1

8 USE A BRADAWL TO BORE A SHALLOW HOLE AT THE CENTRES OF BOTH ENDS

NOTE
THESE HOLES WILL HELP TO POSITION THE BASE FOR DRILLING ON THE LATHE

9 PUT A DRILL CHUCK WITH A 5/16" FLAT BIT Nº355 INTO THE LATHE MANDREL

10 THEN POSITION THE END OF THE BASE CENTRALLY BETWEEN THE END OF THE DRILL AND THE TAILSTOCK AND BORE A HOLE ABOUT 2" DEEP AT THE TOP END

TOP END

NOTE
THIS HOLE WILL ACT AS A GUIDE FOR ACCURATE BORING

TABLE LAMP PRACTICE BASE SHAPES

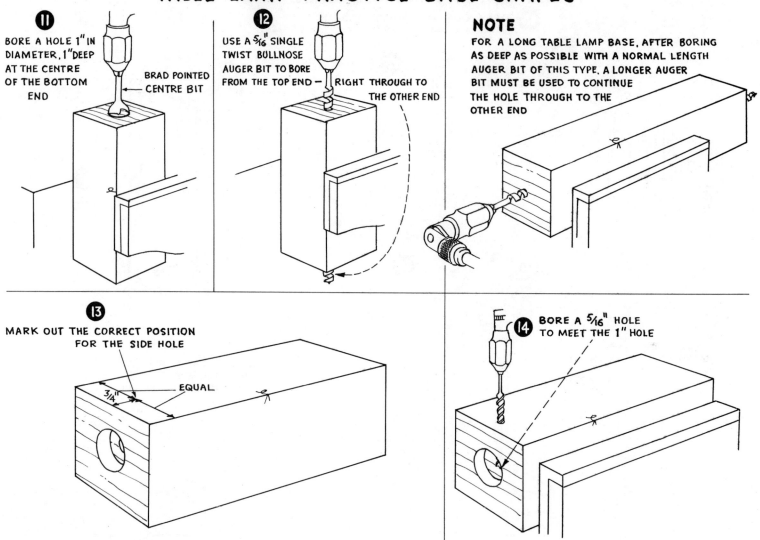

11 BORE A HOLE 1" IN DIAMETER, 1" DEEP AT THE CENTRE OF THE BOTTOM END

BRAD POINTED CENTRE BIT

12 USE A 5/16" SINGLE TWIST BULLNOSE AUGER BIT TO BORE FROM THE TOP END — RIGHT THROUGH TO THE OTHER END

NOTE

FOR A LONG TABLE LAMP BASE, AFTER BORING AS DEEP AS POSSIBLE WITH A NORMAL LENGTH AUGER BIT OF THIS TYPE, A LONGER AUGER BIT MUST BE USED TO CONTINUE THE HOLE THROUGH TO THE OTHER END

13 MARK OUT THE CORRECT POSITION FOR THE SIDE HOLE

EQUAL

3/4"

14 BORE A 5/16" HOLE TO MEET THE 1" HOLE

TABLE LAMP PRACTICE BASE SHAPES

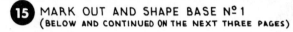

15 MARK OUT AND SHAPE BASE Nº 1
(BELOW AND CONTINUED ON THE NEXT THREE PAGES)

16 MARK OUT THE RAKES
ON TWO OPPOSITE SIDES

WIDTH HERE AT LEAST 1"
TO LEAVE ENOUGH TIMBER
FOR THE ELECTRIC CONNECTOR
TO BE FITTED

17 SQUARE THE LINES
ACROSS

18 COLOUR IN
THE WASTE

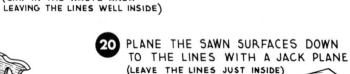

19 REMOVE THE WASTE
WITH A RIP SAW
(SAW IN THE WASTE AREA
LEAVING THE LINES WELL INSIDE)

WASTE WOOD TO
PROTECT THE BENCH TOP

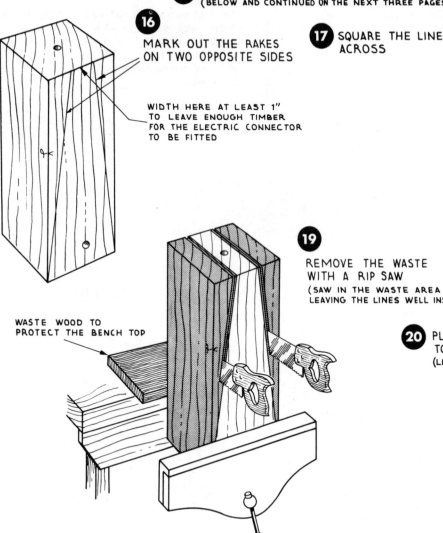

20 PLANE THE SAWN SURFACES DOWN
TO THE LINES WITH A JACK PLANE
(LEAVE THE LINES JUST INSIDE)

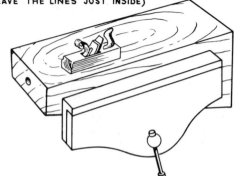

TABLE LAMP PRACTICE BASE SHAPES

BASE Nº 1

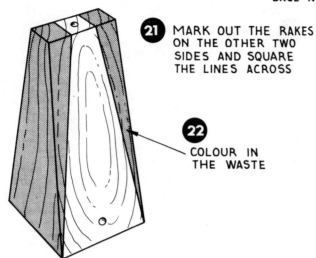

21 MARK OUT THE RAKES ON THE OTHER TWO SIDES AND SQUARE THE LINES ACROSS

22 COLOUR IN THE WASTE

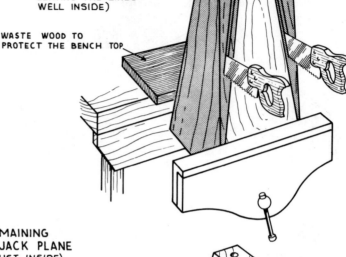

23 REMOVE THE WASTE WITH A RIP SAW (SAW IN THE WASTE AREA LEAVING THE LINES WELL INSIDE)

WASTE WOOD TO PROTECT THE BENCH TOP

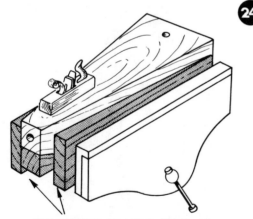

24 REMOVE THE REMAINING WASTE WITH A JACK PLANE (LEAVE THE LINES JUST INSIDE)

THE WEDGES OF WASTE WOOD ARE USED TO PACK THE FRONT END SO THAT THE BASE CAN BE GRIPPED IN THE VICE

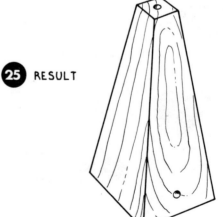

25 RESULT

TABLE LAMP PRACTICE BASE SHAPES

BASE Nº 1

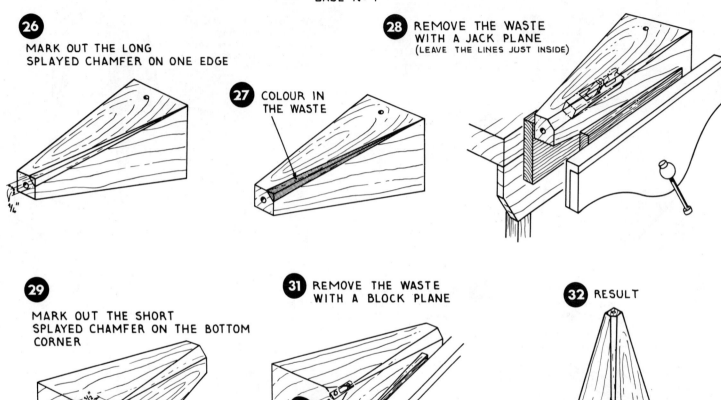

26 MARK OUT THE LONG
SPLAYED CHAMFER ON ONE EDGE

¼"

27 COLOUR IN
THE WASTE

28 REMOVE THE WASTE
WITH A JACK PLANE
(LEAVE THE LINES JUST INSIDE)

29 MARK OUT THE SHORT
SPLAYED CHAMFER ON THE BOTTOM
CORNER

½"   ½"

30 COLOUR IN
THE WASTE

31 REMOVE THE WASTE
WITH A BLOCK PLANE

32 RESULT

TABLE LAMP PRACTICE BASE SHAPES
BASE Nº 1

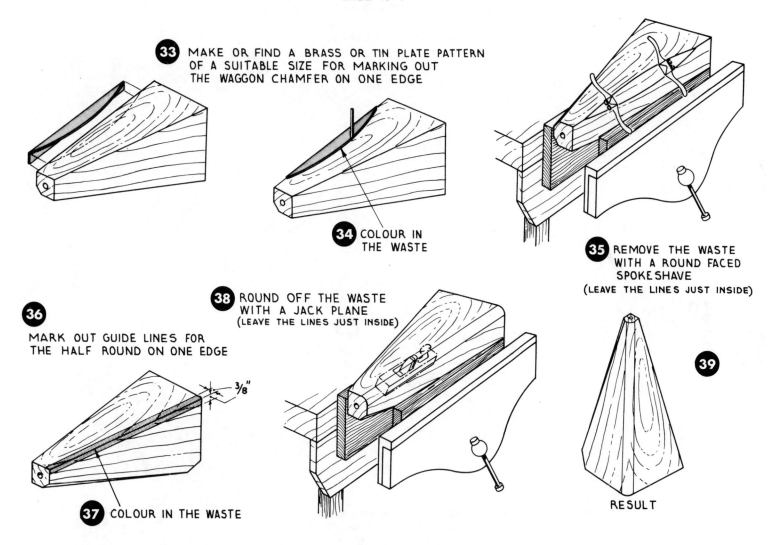

33 MAKE OR FIND A BRASS OR TIN PLATE PATTERN OF A SUITABLE SIZE FOR MARKING OUT THE WAGGON CHAMFER ON ONE EDGE

34 COLOUR IN THE WASTE

35 REMOVE THE WASTE WITH A ROUND FACED SPOKESHAVE
(LEAVE THE LINES JUST INSIDE)

36 MARK OUT GUIDE LINES FOR THE HALF ROUND ON ONE EDGE

3/8"

37 COLOUR IN THE WASTE

38 ROUND OFF THE WASTE WITH A JACK PLANE
(LEAVE THE LINES JUST INSIDE)

39

RESULT

97

7

TABLE LAMP PRACTICE BASE SHAPES

40 MARK OUT AND SHAPE BASE Nº2
(BELOW AND CONTINUED ON THE NEXT PAGE)

41 MARK OUT THE CHAMFER ON ONE CORNER

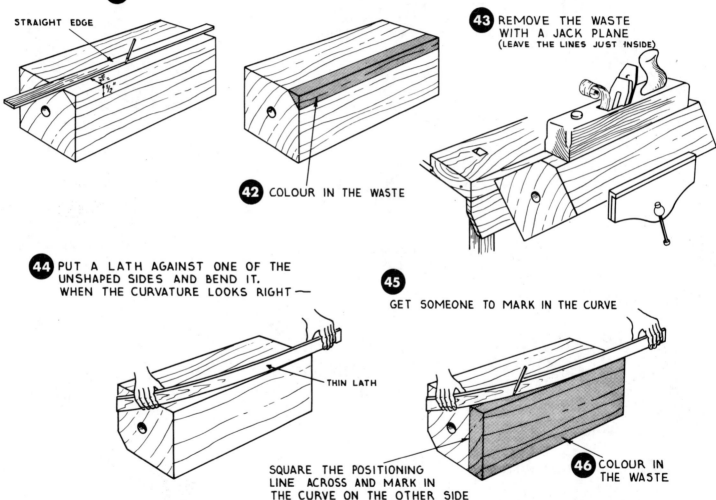

STRAIGHT EDGE

43 REMOVE THE WASTE
WITH A JACK PLANE
(LEAVE THE LINES JUST INSIDE)

42 COLOUR IN THE WASTE

44 PUT A LATH AGAINST ONE OF THE
UNSHAPED SIDES AND BEND IT.
WHEN THE CURVATURE LOOKS RIGHT —

45

GET SOMEONE TO MARK IN THE CURVE

THIN LATH

SQUARE THE POSITIONING
LINE ACROSS AND MARK IN
THE CURVE ON THE OTHER SIDE

46 COLOUR IN
THE WASTE

98

TABLE LAMP PRACTICE BASE SHAPES

BASE Nº 2

47 REMOVE THE WASTE
WITH A BOW SAW
(SAW IN THE WASTE AREA
LEAVING THE LINES WELL IN)

48 REMOVE ANY LARGE LUMPS LEFT
BY THE SAW WITH A JACK PLANE
THEN FINISH SHAPING WITH A FLAT
FACED SPOKESHAVE
(LEAVE THE LINES JUST INSIDE)

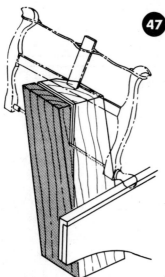

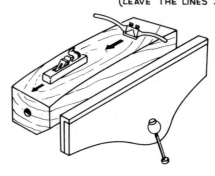

49 MARK OUT ¼" LINES
RIGHT ROUND THE TOP AND SIDES
FOR THE HALF ROUND

51 REMOVE THE BULK OF THE WASTE
WITH A MEDIUM CUTTING RASP
AND FINISH OFF WITH A FINE CUTTING
WOOD FILE
(LEAVE THE LINES JUST INSIDE)

¼"

50 COLOUR IN
THE WASTE

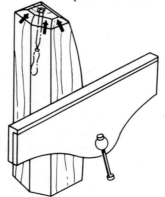

52 NOW MARK OUT AND SHAPE
FURTHER PRACTICE SHAPES
OF YOUR OWN ON BASE Nº 3

DESIGN AND CONSTRUCTION GUIDE FOR MAKING A COLUMN-BASED TABLE LAMP

1 ON A SHEET OF DRAWING PAPER
FAINTLY SKETCH OR TRACE THE DETAILS BELOW

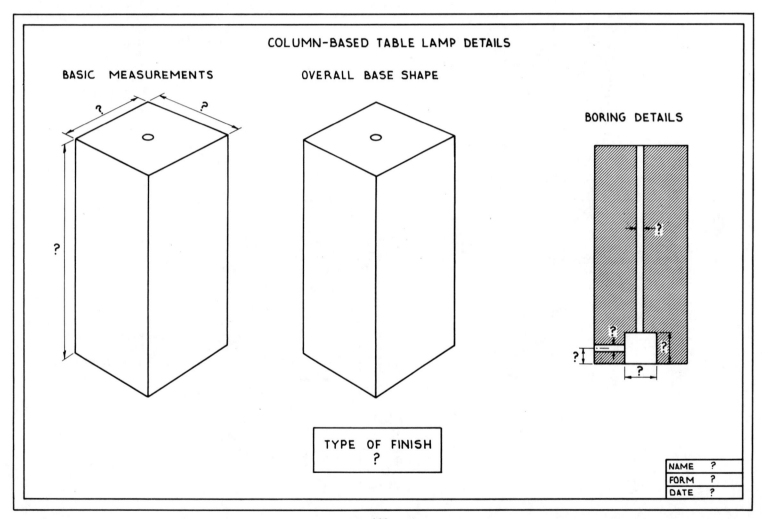

COLUMN-BASED TABLE LAMP DETAILS

BASIC MEASUREMENTS

OVERALL BASE SHAPE

BORING DETAILS

TYPE OF FINISH
?

NAME	?
FORM	?
DATE	?

DESIGN AND CONSTRUCTION GUIDE FOR MAKING A COLUMN-BASED TABLE LAMP

2 MAKE OUT A TIMBER LIST FOR YOUR COLUMN-BASED TABLE LAMP
(GUIDE BELOW)

TIMBER LIST FOR A COLUMN-BASED TABLE LAMP

NAMES OF MEMBERS	VARIETY OF TIMBER TO BE USED	STATE OF TIMBER TO BE USED	NUMBER REQUIRED	OVERALL LENGTH OF EACH MEMBER	TOTAL LENGTH REQUIRED FOR THIS TYPE OF MEMBER	OVERALL WIDTH	OVERALL THICKNESS
BASE	?	?	?	?	SAME	?	?

3 NOW FOLLOW THE INSTRUCTIONS AND ANSWER EACH OF THE QUESTIONS IN TURN

AS YOU PROGRESS FILL IN THE NECESSARY INFORMATION ON YOUR TIMBER LIST AND YOUR SKETCH OR TRACING

EVENTUALLY YOU WILL BUILD UP AN ORTHOGRAPHIC DRAWING OF YOUR COLUMN-BASED TABLE LAMP

4 WHAT TYPE OF FINISH WILL YOU APPLY TO THE SURFACE OF YOUR COLUMN-BASED TABLE LAMP?

PAINT

OR

A CLEAR FINISH
(EXAMPLES)
FRENCH POLISH
CELLULOSE LAQUER
LINSEED OIL
ETC.

FOR A CLEAR FINISH USE A VARIETY OF HARDWOOD

FOR A PAINT FINISH USE A VARIETY OF SOFTWOOD

7*

DESIGN AND CONSTRUCTION GUIDE FOR MAKING A COLUMN-BASED TABLE LAMP

5 EXAMPLES OF SHADE SHAPES
(MOST OF THESE SHAPES MAY BE
PURCHASED EITHER ROUND OR SQUARE IN PLAN)

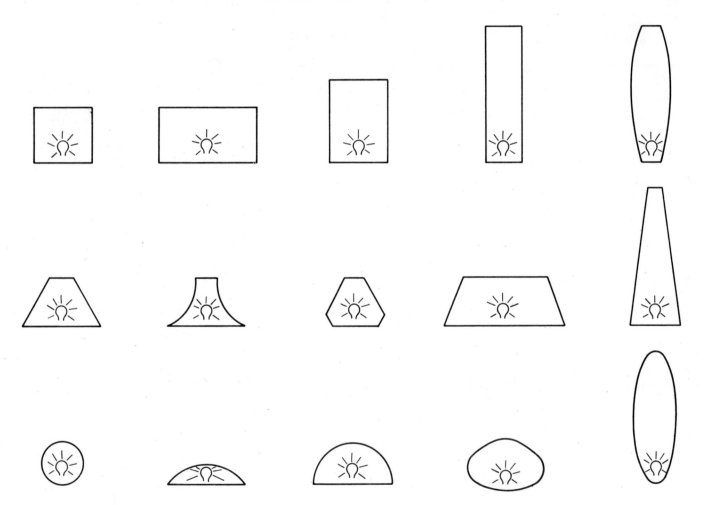

DESIGN AND CONSTRUCTION GUIDE FOR MAKING A COLUMN-BASED TABLE LAMP

6 ON A SHEET OF DRAWING PAPER BUILD UP DESIGNS OF TABLE LAMPS USING SHADES WHICH ARE AVAILABLE AND BASES WHICH INCORPORATE PAST SHAPING EXPERIENCE
(SOME SAMPLES BELOW)

7 NOTE: REMEMBER THAT THE TABLE LAMP MUST BE STABLE, SENSIBLE AND GOOD-LOOKING NOT TOP-HEAVY OR UNSIGHTLY

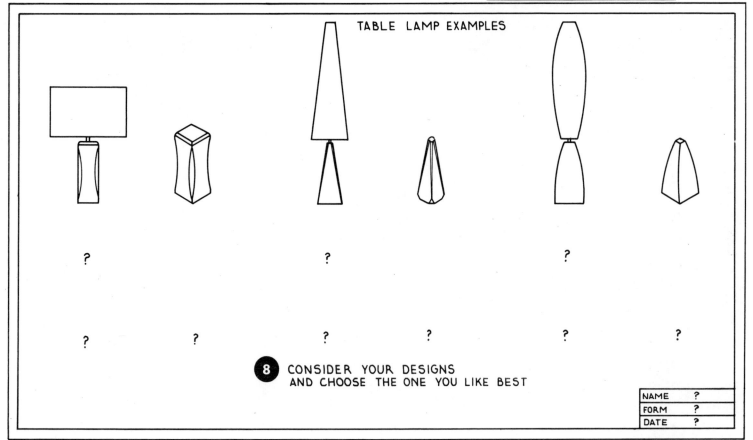

TABLE LAMP EXAMPLES

?   ?   ?

?   ?   ?   ?   ?   ?

8 CONSIDER YOUR DESIGNS AND CHOOSE THE ONE YOU LIKE BEST

NAME	?
FORM	?
DATE	?

9

MAKE A FULL-SIZE SKETCH OF THE SHADE
YOU HAVE CHOSEN AND CUT IT OUT AS A
PAPER PATTERN — OR, BETTER STILL, PURCHASE
AND BRING TO SCHOOL THE SHADE ITSELF

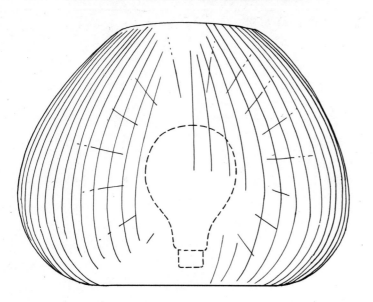

10

WHAT WILL BE THE WIDTH
AND THICKNESS OF YOUR
COLUMN—BASE ?

(GUIDE BELOW)

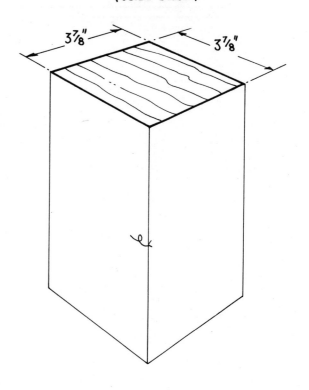

$3\frac{7}{8}"$ $3\frac{7}{8}"$

DESIGN AND CONSTRUCTION GUIDE FOR MAKING A COLUMN-BASED TABLE LAMP

⑪ WHAT WILL BE THE HEIGHT OF YOUR COLUMN-BASE
(A METHOD FOR WORKING IT OUT IS GIVEN BELOW)

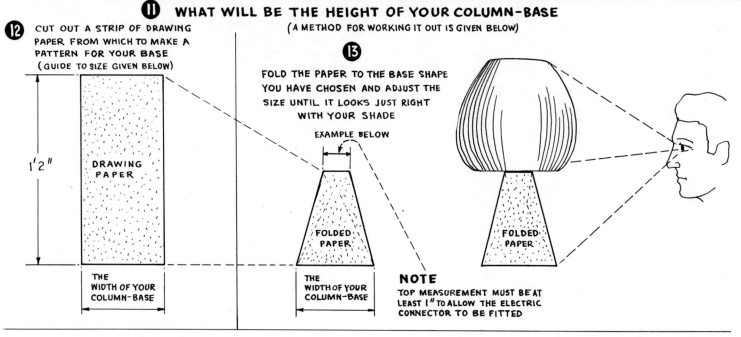

⑫ CUT OUT A STRIP OF DRAWING PAPER FROM WHICH TO MAKE A PATTERN FOR YOUR BASE
(GUIDE TO SIZE GIVEN BELOW)

DRAWING PAPER

1' 2"

THE WIDTH OF YOUR COLUMN-BASE

⑬ FOLD THE PAPER TO THE BASE SHAPE YOU HAVE CHOSEN AND ADJUST THE SIZE UNTIL IT LOOKS JUST RIGHT WITH YOUR SHADE

EXAMPLE BELOW

FOLDED PAPER

THE WIDTH OF YOUR COLUMN-BASE

FOLDED PAPER

NOTE
TOP MEASUREMENT MUST BE AT LEAST 1" TO ALLOW THE ELECTRIC CONNECTOR TO BE FITTED

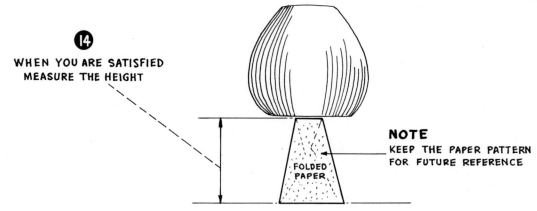

⑭

WHEN YOU ARE SATISFIED MEASURE THE HEIGHT

FOLDED PAPER

NOTE
KEEP THE PAPER PATTERN FOR FUTURE REFERENCE

DESIGN AND CONSTRUCTION GUIDE FOR MAKING A COLUMN-BASED TABLE LAMP

⑮

PREPARE THE TIMBER FOR THE BASE TO THE RIGHT SIZE FOR MARKING OUT

PREPARE FROM MACHINE PLANED
ALL ROUND SCANTLING
(FOR A PREPARATION GUIDE
SEE PAGE N° 29)

⑯ CLEAN THE ENDS OF THE BASE ON A
SANDING DISC ON
THE FACE PLATE OF
A LATHE
(LEAVE THE LINES JUST INSIDE)

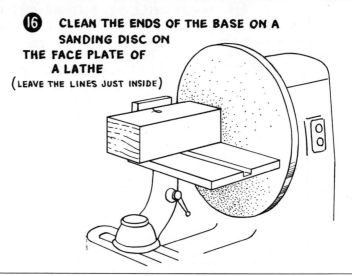

⑰

BORE THE WIRE HOLES

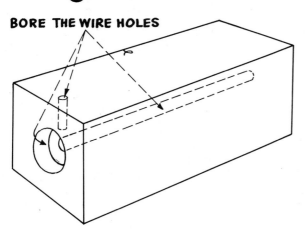

⑱

CONSIDER, MARK OUT AND SHAPE THE BASE

DESIGN AND CONSTRUCTION GUIDE FOR MAKING A COLUMN-BASED TABLE LAMP

19 FIX THE BRASS CONNECTOR FITTING
(A METHOD IS GIVEN BELOW FOR FITTING A TAPERED PILLAR NIPPLE TYPE)

PILLAR
NIPPLE TYPE

A 19 IF THE BASE IS TAPERED SHARPLY AT THE TOP
PACK AND CRAMP TIGHT WITH THE WASTE WEDGES TO PREVENT SPLITTING

B 19

WITH A REAMER BIT REMOVE ENOUGH WOOD AT THE TOP
TO ALLOW THE SHANK OF THE FITTING TO BE DRIVEN TIGHTLY INTO THE BASE

C 19

THEN DRIVE THE
FITTING HOME

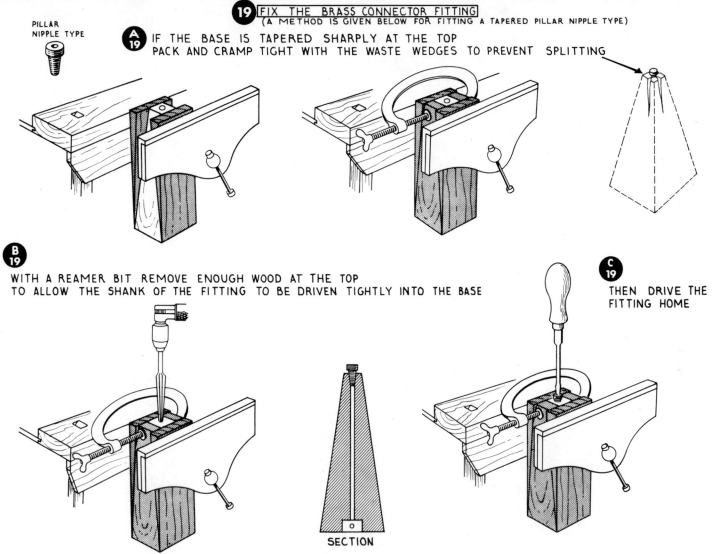

SECTION

DESIGN AND CONSTRUCTION GUIDE FOR MAKING A COLUMN-BASED TABLE LAMP

(21) REMOVE ANY SERIOUS BLEMISHES WITH A SMOOTHING PLANE

(20) PREPARE THE BASE FOR RECEIVING A FINISH
(A METHOD GIVEN BELOW FOR A CLEAR FINISH)

(22) SCRAPE

(23) RUB DOWN
(GLASSPAPER GRADE Nº M2)
(OR GARNET PAPER GRADE Nº 2/0)

NOTE: PUT A PIECE OF THICK CLEAN CLOTH UNDERNEATH FOR PROTECTION AGAINST SCRATCHING

(24) DUST

(25) DAMP DOWN THEN LEAVE TO DRY

WATER

NOTE: PLACE BOARDING UNDERNEATH TO PROTECT THE BENCH

(26) RUB DOWN AGAIN, THEN DUST
(GLASSPAPER GRADE Nº 1)
(OR GARNET PAPER GRADE Nº 4/0)

DESIGN AND CONSTRUCTION GUIDE FOR MAKING A COLUMN-BASED TABLE LAMP

27 COVER THE BOTTOM WITH FELT
(A METHOD GIVEN BELOW)

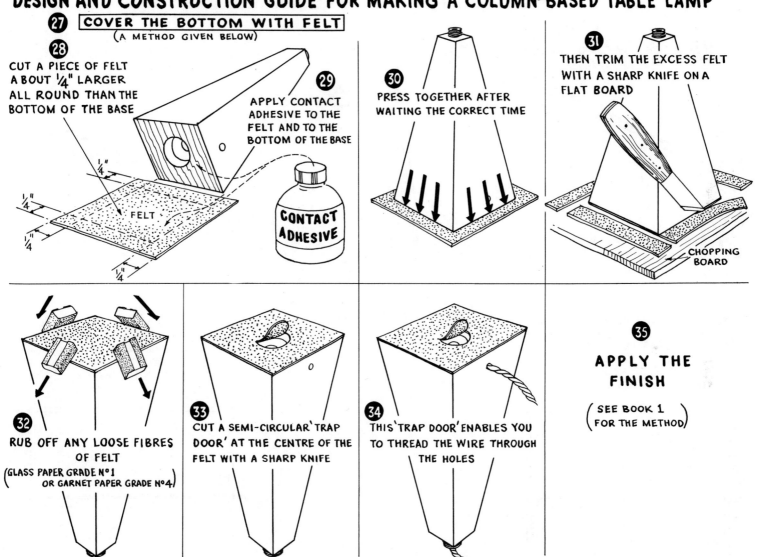

28 CUT A PIECE OF FELT ABOUT ¼" LARGER ALL ROUND THAN THE BOTTOM OF THE BASE

29 APPLY CONTACT ADHESIVE TO THE FELT AND TO THE BOTTOM OF THE BASE

CONTACT ADHESIVE

FELT

¼" ¼" ¼" ¼"

30 PRESS TOGETHER AFTER WAITING THE CORRECT TIME

31 THEN TRIM THE EXCESS FELT WITH A SHARP KNIFE ON A FLAT BOARD

CHOPPING BOARD

32 RUB OFF ANY LOOSE FIBRES OF FELT
(GLASS PAPER GRADE Nº1 OR GARNET PAPER GRADE Nº4)

33 CUT A SEMI-CIRCULAR 'TRAP DOOR' AT THE CENTRE OF THE FELT WITH A SHARP KNIFE

34 THIS 'TRAP DOOR' ENABLES YOU TO THREAD THE WIRE THROUGH THE HOLES

35 APPLY THE FINISH
(SEE BOOK 1 FOR THE METHOD)

INTRODUCTION TO T-SQUARES

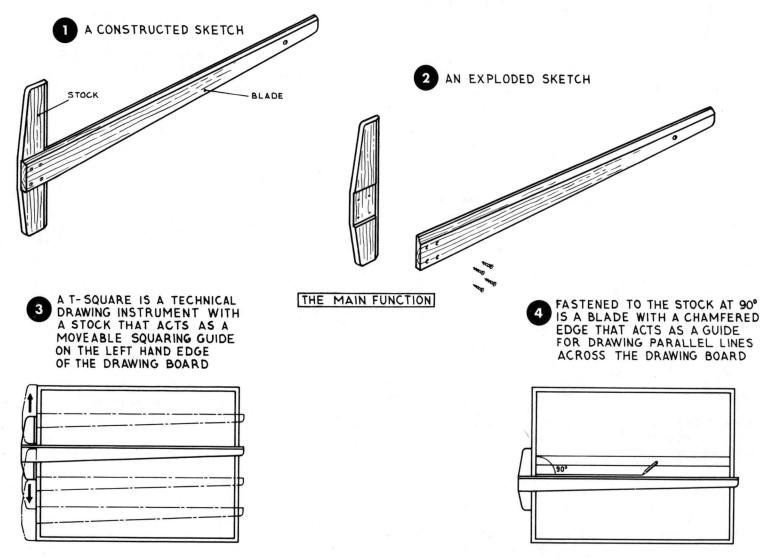

1 A CONSTRUCTED SKETCH

STOCK

BLADE

2 AN EXPLODED SKETCH

THE MAIN FUNCTION

3 A T-SQUARE IS A TECHNICAL DRAWING INSTRUMENT WITH A STOCK THAT ACTS AS A MOVEABLE SQUARING GUIDE ON THE LEFT HAND EDGE OF THE DRAWING BOARD

4 FASTENED TO THE STOCK AT 90° IS A BLADE WITH A CHAMFERED EDGE THAT ACTS AS A GUIDE FOR DRAWING PARALLEL LINES ACROSS THE DRAWING BOARD

90°

INTRODUCTION TO T-SQUARES

5 A T-SQUARE ALSO ACTS AS A
PARALLEL REST FOR SET SQUARES
WHEN DRAWING VERTICAL LINES AND INCLINED LINES

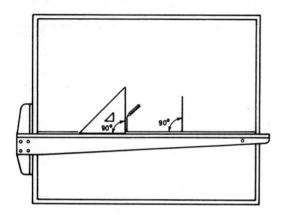

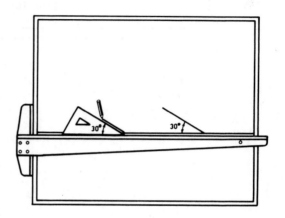

6 NOTE: TO PRODUCE GOOD TECHNICAL DRAWINGS
IT IS VERY IMPORTANT THAT THE CHAMFERED
EDGE IS TRUE AND THAT THE BLADE IS FIRMLY
ANCHORED TO THE STOCK

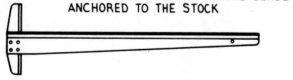

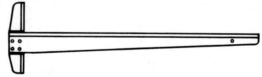

REASON: INACCURATE TECHNICAL DRAWINGS WILL BE PRODUCED WITH T-SQUARES
WHOSE CHAMFERED EDGE IS NOT TRUE AND BLADE
NOT FIRMLY ANCHORED TO THE STOCK

DESIGN AND CONSTRUCTION GUIDE FOR MAKING A T-SQUARE

1 ON A SHEET OF DRAWING PAPER FAINTLY SKETCH OR TRACE
THE DETAILS FROM THESE TWO PAGES

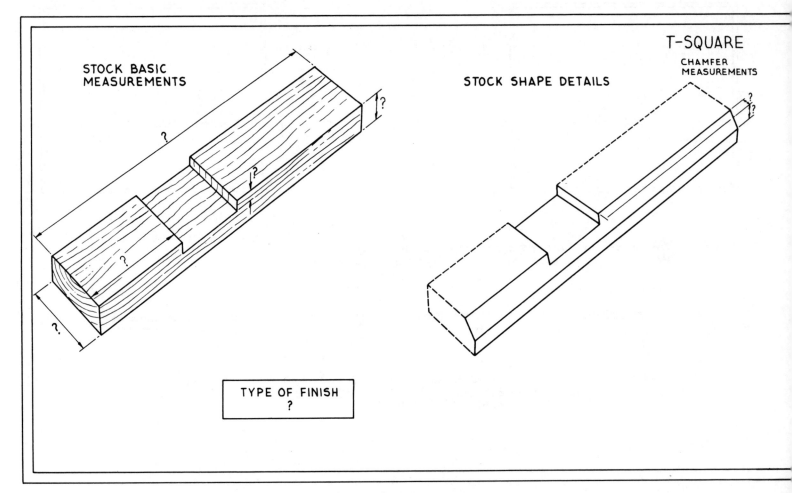

STOCK BASIC
MEASUREMENTS

STOCK SHAPE DETAILS

T-SQUARE

CHAMFER
MEASUREMENTS

TYPE OF FINISH
?

DESIGN AND CONSTRUCTION GUIDE FOR MAKING A T-SQUARE

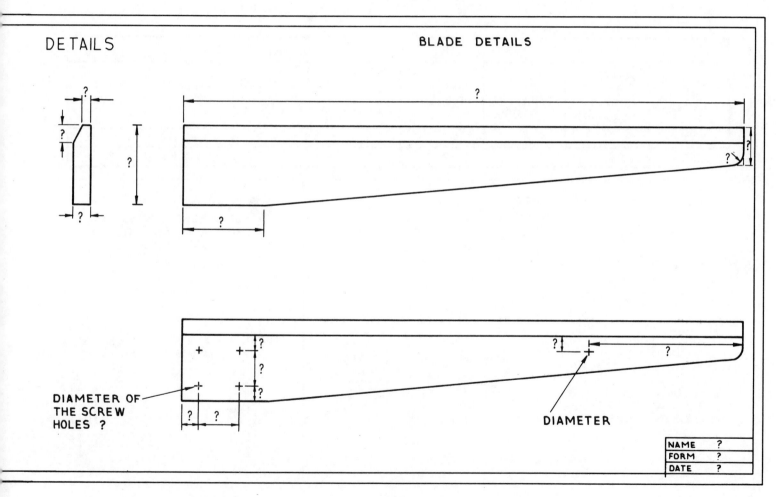

DETAILS

BLADE DETAILS

DIAMETER OF
THE SCREW
HOLES ?

DIAMETER

NAME	?
FORM	?
DATE	?

DESIGN AND CONSTRUCTION GUIDE FOR MAKING A T-SQUARE

2 MAKE OUT A TIMBER LIST FOR YOUR T-SQUARE
(GUIDE BELOW)

TIMBER LIST FOR A T — SQUARE							
NAMES OF MEMBERS	VARIETY OF TIMBER TO BE USED	STATE OF TIMBER TO TO BE USED	NUMBER REQUIRED	OVERALL LENGTH OF EACH MEMBER	TOTAL LENGTH REQUIRED FOR THIS TYPE OF MEMBER	OVERALL WIDTH	OVERALL THICKNESS
STOCK	?	?	?	? + 1" P.A.	/	+ ¼" P.A.	?
BLADE	?	?	?	? + 1" P.A.	/	+ ¼" P.A.	?

3 NOW FOLLOW THE INSTRUCTIONS AND ANSWER EACH OF THE QUESTIONS IN TURN

AS YOU PROGRESS FILL IN THE REQUIRED INFORMATION ON YOUR TIMBER LIST AND SKETCH OR TRACING

EVENTUALLY DEVELOP AN ORTHOGRAPHIC DRAWING OF YOUR T-SQUARE

4 WHAT TYPE OF FINISH WILL YOU APPLY TO YOUR T-SQUARE'S SURFACE ?

PAINT   OR   A CLEAR FINISH
EXAMPLE
CELLULOSE
LAQUER
FRENCH POLISH
ETC.

5 WHAT VARIETY OR VARIETIES OF HARDWOOD OR SOFTWOOD WILL YOU USE FOR YOUR T-SQUARE ?
(CONSIDER THE TYPE OF FINISH YOU HAVE CHOSEN)

FOR A CLEAR FINISH USE A HARDWOOD VARIETY

FOR A PAINT FINISH USE A SOFTWOOD VARIETY

DESIGN AND CONSTRUCTION GUIDE FOR MAKING A T-SQUARE

6 PREPARE THE TIMBER FOR THE STOCK AND BLADE
TO THEIR MARKING OUT SIZES
(FOR A PREPARATION GUIDE SEE PAGES Nº 24 TO 28)

STOCK MARKING OUT SIZES

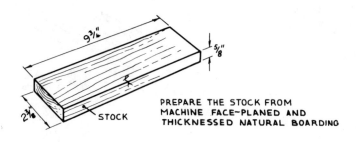

9¾"

5/8"

2⅛"

STOCK

PREPARE THE STOCK FROM
MACHINE FACE-PLANED AND
THICKNESSED NATURAL BOARDING

BLADE MARKING OUT SIZES

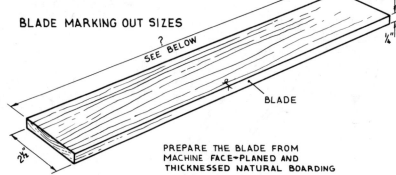

?
SEE BELOW

¼"

BLADE

2½"

PREPARE THE BLADE FROM
MACHINE FACE-PLANED AND
THICKNESSED NATURAL BOARDING

A METHOD FOR FINDING THE LENGTH OF THE BLADE

ADD TOGETHER

WIDTH OF
STOCK

LENGTH OF DRAWING BOARD

1" OVERHANG

NOTE: MAKE THE LENGTH OF
YOUR T-SQUARE TO SUIT
THE DRAWING BOARD AND
PAPER YOU WILL USE

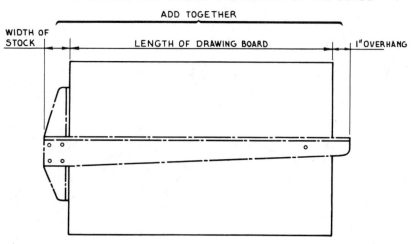

115

DESIGN AND CONSTRUCTION GUIDE FOR MAKING A T-SQUARE

7 MARK OUT THE STOCKS TRENCH
(A METHOD IS GIVEN BELOW)

8 DOT POSITION

LEVEL

2½"

STOCK

BLADE

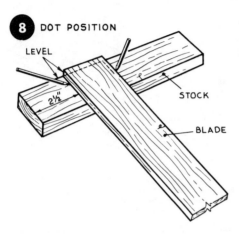

9 SQUARE ACROSS AND
SLIGHTLY DOWN
BOTH EDGES

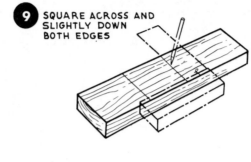

10 GAUGE THE DEPTH OF THE
TRENCH ON BOTH EDGES

⅛"

11 COLOUR IN
THE WASTE

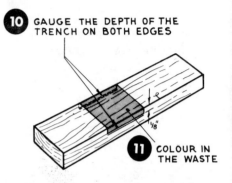

12 SAW THEN CHISEL OUT
THE WASTE THEN LEVEL
THE BOTTOM WITH
A ROUTER

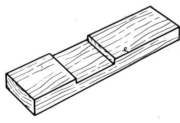

13 NUMBER OFF THE JOINT

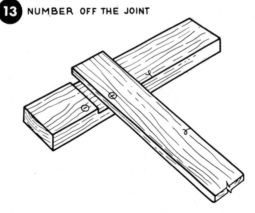

14 FIT THE JOINT

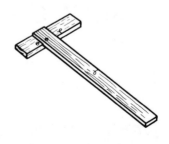

DESIGN AND CONSTRUCTION GUIDE FOR MAKING A T-SQUARE

15 MARK OUT THE SCREW HOLES FOR FASTENING THE BLADE TO THE STOCK
(GUIDE BELOW)

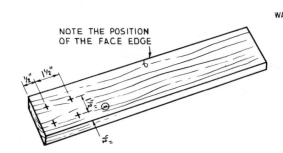

NOTE THE POSITION OF THE FACE EDGE

16 BORE SUITABLY SIZED HOLES FOR RECEIVING THE SHANK OF Nº 4 ⅝" STEEL RAISED COUNTERSUNK SCREWS

WASTE BLOCK

17 MARK OUT THE CHAMFER ON THE FACE EDGE OF THE BLADE

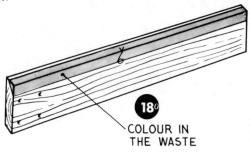

18°

COLOUR IN THE WASTE

19 PLACE THE BLADE IN A SASH CRAMP THAT IS GRIPPED IN A VICE THEN REMOVE THE CHAMFERS WASTE WITH A JACK PLANE
(LEAVE THE LINES JUST IN)

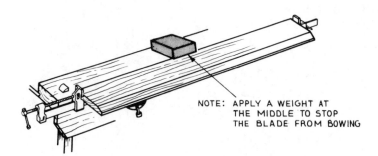

NOTE: APPLY A WEIGHT AT THE MIDDLE TO STOP THE BLADE FROM BOWING

20 REMOVE FROM THE CRAMP AND MARK OUT THE BLADES TAPER

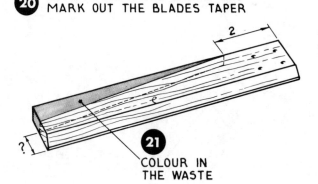

2

?

21

COLOUR IN THE WASTE

117

8*

DESIGN AND CONSTRUCTION GUIDE FOR MAKING A T-SQUARE

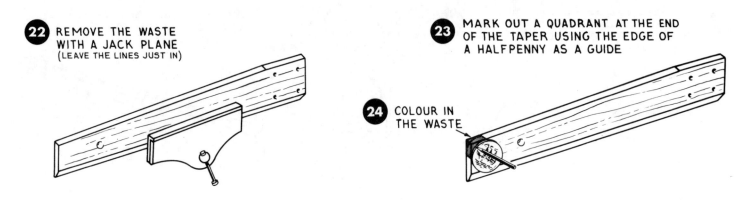

22 REMOVE THE WASTE
WITH A JACK PLANE
(LEAVE THE LINES JUST IN)

23 MARK OUT A QUADRANT AT THE END
OF THE TAPER USING THE EDGE OF
A HALFPENNY AS A GUIDE

24 COLOUR IN
THE WASTE

25 ROUND OFF THE BULK OF THE
WASTE WITH A MEDIUM CUTTING
RASP THEN FINISH OFF WITH A
FINE CUTTING WOOD FILE
(LEAVE THE LINES JUST IN)

26 MARK THE POSITION OF THE HOLE
USED FOR HANGING UP THE T-SQUARE

27 BORE A HOLE WITH
A 5/16" TWIST BIT

WASTE BLOCK

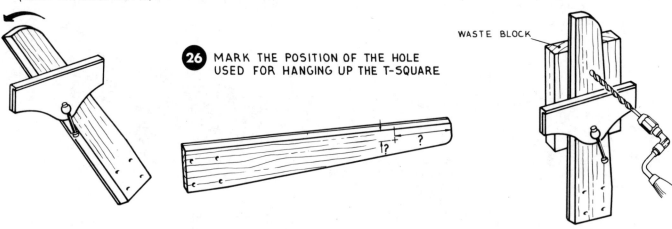

DESIGN AND CONSTRUCTION GUIDE FOR MAKING A T-SQUARE

31 COLOUR IN THE WASTE

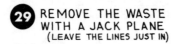

28 MARK OUT THE STOCK'S TAPERS

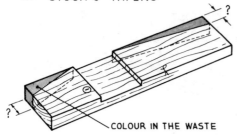

COLOUR IN THE WASTE

29 REMOVE THE WASTE WITH A JACK PLANE
(LEAVE THE LINES JUST IN)

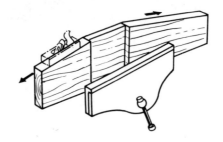

30 MARK OUT QUADRANTS AT THE END OF THE TAPERS USING THE EDGE OF A HALFPENNY AS A GUIDE

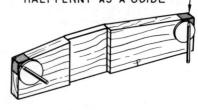

32 ROUND OFF THE BULK OF THE WASTE WITH A MEDIUM CUTTING RASP THEN FINISH OFF WITH A FINE CUTTING WOOD FILE
(LEAVE THE LINES JUST IN)

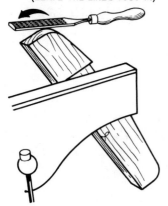

33 MARK OUT THE CHAMFER ON THE FACE EDGE OF THE STOCK

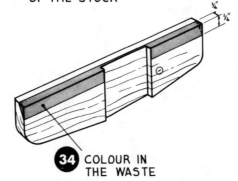

34 COLOUR IN THE WASTE

35 REMOVE THE WASTE WITH A JACK PLANE
(LEAVE THE LINES JUST IN)

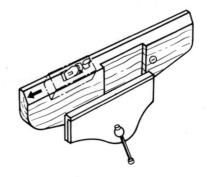

DESIGN AND CONSTRUCTION GUIDE FOR MAKING A T-SQUARE

36 PREPARE AND ASSEMBLE THE T-SQUARE FOR RECEIVING A FINISH
(A METHOD IS GIVEN BELOW AND ON THE NEXT PAGE FOR A CLEAR FINISH)

37 ON BOTH THE BLADE AND THE STOCK REMOVE ANY SERIOUS MARKS WITH A SMOOTH PLANE THEN SCRAPE

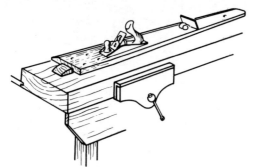

38 RUB DOWN THEN DUST
(GLASS PAPER GRADE Nº 2)
(OR GARNET PAPER GRADE Nº 2/0)

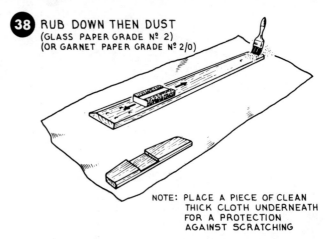

NOTE: PLACE A PIECE OF CLEAN THICK CLOTH UNDERNEATH FOR A PROTECTION AGAINST SCRATCHING

39 POSITION THE BLADE IN THE STOCK THEN BRADAWL AND DRIVE HOME THE SCREWS

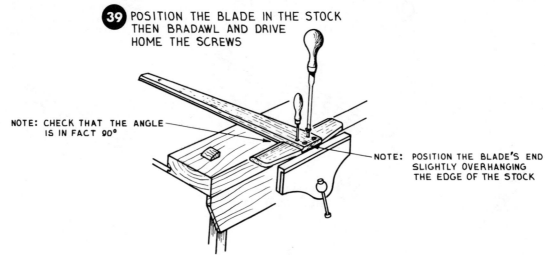

NOTE: CHECK THAT THE ANGLE IS IN FACT 90°

NOTE: POSITION THE BLADE'S END SLIGHTLY OVERHANGING THE EDGE OF THE STOCK

DESIGN AND CONSTRUCTION GUIDE FOR MAKING A T-SQUARE

40 WITH A SMOOTH PLANE TILTED AT A SLIGHT ANGLE CLEAN OFF THE BLADE END BACK TO THE STOCK

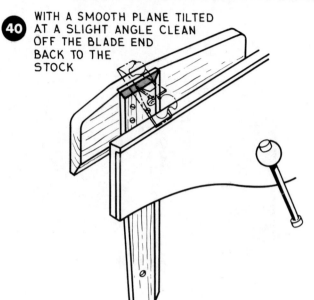

41 DAMP DOWN THEN LEAVE TO DRY

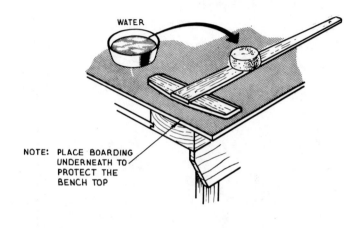

WATER

NOTE: PLACE BOARDING UNDERNEATH TO PROTECT THE BENCH TOP

42 RUB DOWN AGAIN THEN DUST
(GLASS PAPER GRADE № 1)
(OR GARNET PAPER GRADE № 4/0)

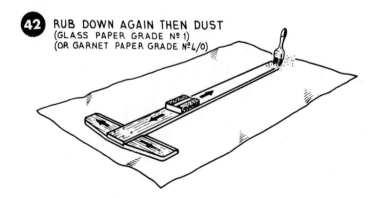

43 APPLY THE FINISH
(FOR A GUIDE SEE BOOK 1)

INTRODUCTION TO MALLETS

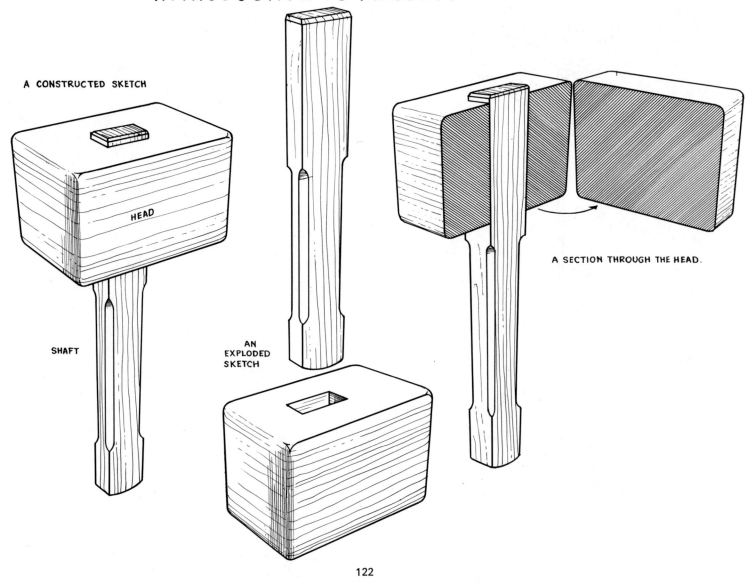

A CONSTRUCTED SKETCH

HEAD

SHAFT

AN EXPLODED SKETCH

A SECTION THROUGH THE HEAD.

122

INTRODUCTION TO MALLETS

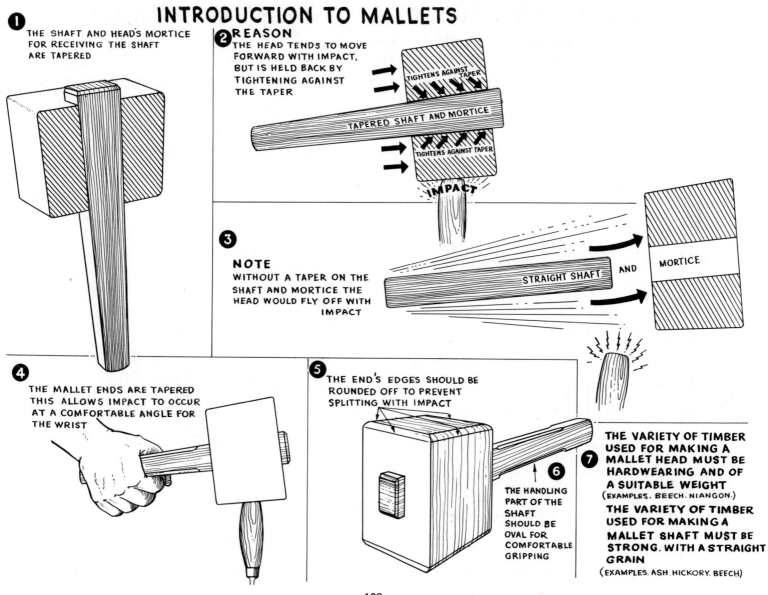

1 THE SHAFT AND HEAD'S MORTICE FOR RECEIVING THE SHAFT ARE TAPERED

2 REASON
THE HEAD TENDS TO MOVE FORWARD WITH IMPACT, BUT IS HELD BACK BY TIGHTENING AGAINST THE TAPER

TIGHTENS AGAINST TAPER

TAPERED SHAFT AND MORTICE

TIGHTENS AGAINST TAPER

IMPACT

3 NOTE
WITHOUT A TAPER ON THE SHAFT AND MORTICE THE HEAD WOULD FLY OFF WITH IMPACT

STRAIGHT SHAFT AND

MORTICE

4 THE MALLET ENDS ARE TAPERED THIS ALLOWS IMPACT TO OCCUR AT A COMFORTABLE ANGLE FOR THE WRIST

5 THE END'S EDGES SHOULD BE ROUNDED OFF TO PREVENT SPLITTING WITH IMPACT

6 THE HANDLING PART OF THE SHAFT SHOULD BE OVAL FOR COMFORTABLE GRIPPING

7 THE VARIETY OF TIMBER USED FOR MAKING A MALLET HEAD MUST BE HARDWEARING AND OF A SUITABLE WEIGHT
(EXAMPLES. BEECH. NIANGON.)

THE VARIETY OF TIMBER USED FOR MAKING A MALLET SHAFT MUST BE STRONG. WITH A STRAIGHT GRAIN
(EXAMPLES. ASH. HICKORY. BEECH)

DESIGN AND CONSTRUCTION GUIDE FOR MAKING A MALLET

❶ ON TO A SHEET OF DRAWING PAPER FAINTLY SKETCH
OR TRACE DETAILS ON THIS PAGE AND THE NEXT PAGE

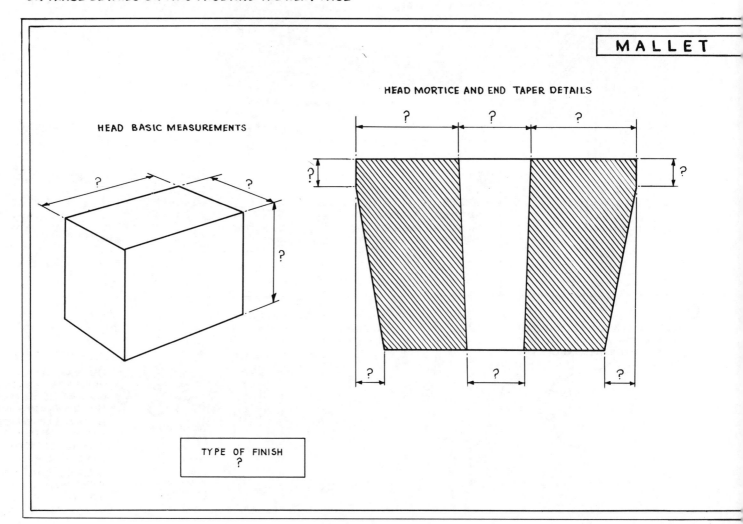

MALLET

HEAD MORTICE AND END TAPER DETAILS

HEAD BASIC MEASUREMENTS

TYPE OF FINISH
?

DESIGN AND CONSTRUCTION GUIDE FOR MAKING A MALLET

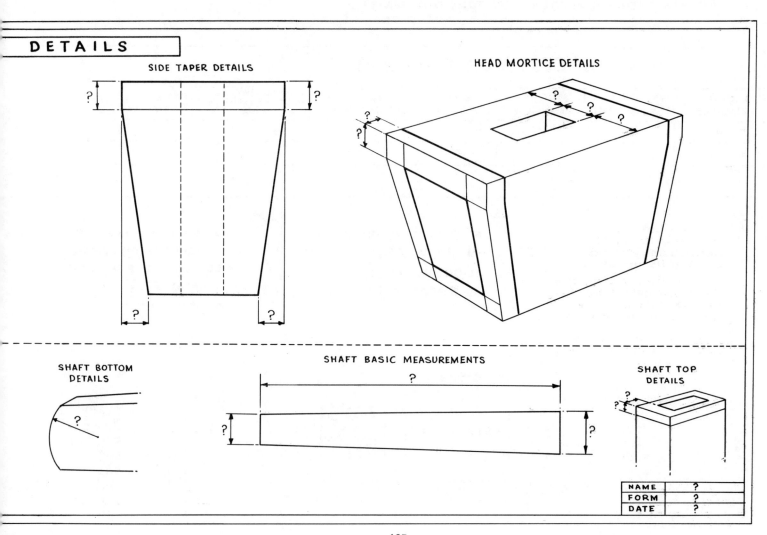

DETAILS

SIDE TAPER DETAILS

HEAD MORTICE DETAILS

SHAFT BOTTOM DETAILS

SHAFT BASIC MEASUREMENTS

SHAFT TOP DETAILS

NAME	?
FORM	?
DATE	?

DESIGN AND CONSTRUCTION GUIDE FOR MAKING A MALLET

2 MARK OUT A TIMBER LIST FOR YOUR MALLET

GUIDE BELOW

TIMBER LIST FOR A MALLET

NAME OF MEMBERS	VARIETY OF TIMBER TO BE USED	STATE OF TIMBER TO BE USED	NUMBER REQUIRED	OVERALL LENGTH OF EACH MEMBER	TOTAL LENGTH OF DIFFERENT TYPES OF TIMBER	OVERALL WIDTH	OVERALL THICKNESS
HEAD	?	?	?	? + 1" P.A.	——	?	?
SHAFT	?	?	?	? + 1" P.A.	——	? + $\frac{1}{4}$" P.A.	?

3 NOW FOLLOW THE INSTRUCTIONS AND ANSWER EACH OF THE QUESTIONS IN TURN.

AS YOU PROGRESS FILL IN THE REQUIRED INFORMATION ON YOUR TIMBER LISTS AND SKETCH OR TRACING.

EVENTUALLY DEVELOP AN ORTHOGRAPHIC DRAWING OF YOUR MALLET

4 WHAT TYPE OF FINISH WILL YOU APPLY TO YOUR MALLET'S SURFACE ?

PAINT   OR   A CLEAR FINISH (EXAMPLES) FRENCH POLISH LINSEED OIL ETC.

5 WHAT VARIETY OR VARIETIES OF HARDWOOD OR SOFTWOOD WILL YOU USE FOR YOUR MALLET ?

CONSIDER THE TYPE OF FINISH YOU HAVE CHOSEN

FOR A CLEAR FINISH USE A HARDWOOD VARIETY

FOR A PAINT FINISH USE A SOFTWOOD VARIETY

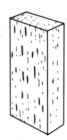

DESIGN AND CONSTRUCTION GUIDE FOR MAKING A MALLET

6 WHAT WILL BE THE LENGTH WIDTH AND THICKNESS OF YOUR MALLET HEAD?

(A METHOD FOR FINDING GIVEN BELOW)

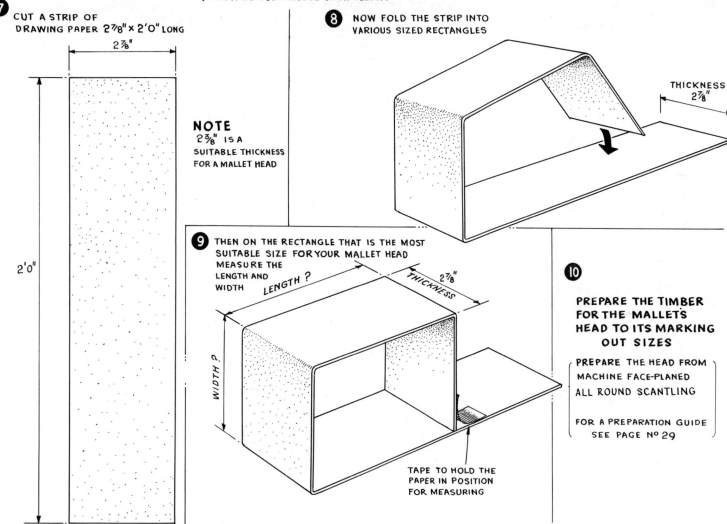

7 CUT A STRIP OF DRAWING PAPER 2⅞" × 2'0" LONG

2⅞"

2'0"

NOTE
2⅜" IS A SUITABLE THICKNESS FOR A MALLET HEAD

8 NOW FOLD THE STRIP INTO VARIOUS SIZED RECTANGLES

THICKNESS 2⅞"

9 THEN ON THE RECTANGLE THAT IS THE MOST SUITABLE SIZE FOR YOUR MALLET HEAD MEASURE THE LENGTH AND WIDTH

LENGTH ?

THICKNESS 2⅞"

WIDTH ?

TAPE TO HOLD THE PAPER IN POSITION FOR MEASURING

10 PREPARE THE TIMBER FOR THE MALLET'S HEAD TO ITS MARKING OUT SIZES

PREPARE THE HEAD FROM MACHINE FACE-PLANED ALL ROUND SCANTLING

FOR A PREPARATION GUIDE SEE PAGE N° 29

DESIGN AND CONSTRUCTION GUIDE FOR MAKING A MALLET

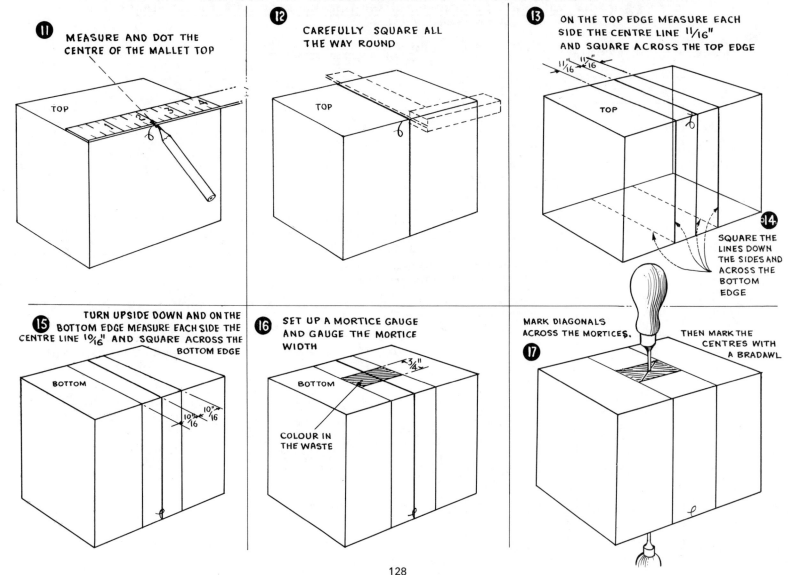

11 MEASURE AND DOT THE CENTRE OF THE MALLET TOP

TOP

12 CAREFULLY SQUARE ALL THE WAY ROUND

TOP

13 ON THE TOP EDGE MEASURE EACH SIDE THE CENTRE LINE 11/16" AND SQUARE ACROSS THE TOP EDGE

TOP

11/16" 11/16"

14 SQUARE THE LINES DOWN THE SIDES AND ACROSS THE BOTTOM EDGE

15 TURN UPSIDE DOWN AND ON THE BOTTOM EDGE MEASURE EACH SIDE THE CENTRE LINE 10/16" AND SQUARE ACROSS THE BOTTOM EDGE

BOTTOM

10"/16 10"/16

16 SET UP A MORTICE GAUGE AND GAUGE THE MORTICE WIDTH

BOTTOM

3/4"

COLOUR IN THE WASTE

17 MARK DIAGONALS ACROSS THE MORTICES. THEN MARK THE CENTRES WITH A BRADAWL

DESIGN AND CONSTRUCTION GUIDE FOR MAKING A MALLET

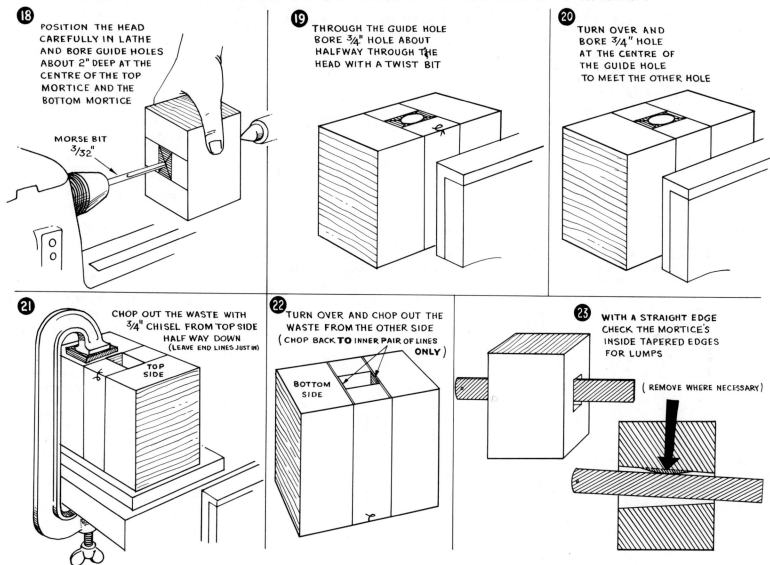

18 POSITION THE HEAD CAREFULLY IN LATHE AND BORE GUIDE HOLES ABOUT 2" DEEP AT THE CENTRE OF THE TOP MORTICE AND THE BOTTOM MORTICE

MORSE BIT 3/32"

19 THROUGH THE GUIDE HOLE BORE 3/4" HOLE ABOUT HALFWAY THROUGH THE HEAD WITH A TWIST BIT

20 TURN OVER AND BORE 3/4" HOLE AT THE CENTRE OF THE GUIDE HOLE TO MEET THE OTHER HOLE

21 CHOP OUT THE WASTE WITH 3/4" CHISEL FROM TOP SIDE HALF WAY DOWN (LEAVE END LINES JUST IN)

TOP SIDE

22 TURN OVER AND CHOP OUT THE WASTE FROM THE OTHER SIDE (CHOP BACK **TO** INNER PAIR OF LINES **ONLY**)

BOTTOM SIDE

23 WITH A STRAIGHT EDGE CHECK THE MORTICE'S INSIDE TAPERED EDGES FOR LUMPS

(REMOVE WHERE NECESSARY)

9

DESIGN AND CONSTRUCTION GUIDE FOR MAKING A MALLET

24 **WHAT WILL BE THE LENGTH OF YOUR MALLET SHAFT ?**
(A METHOD FOR FINDING GIVEN BELOW)

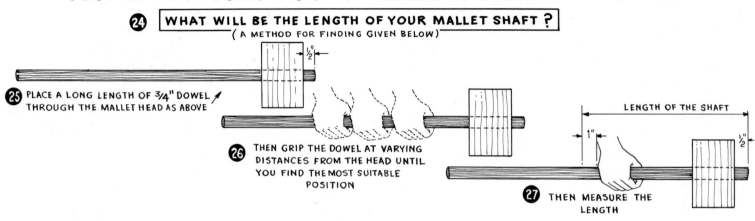

25 PLACE A LONG LENGTH OF ¾" DOWEL THROUGH THE MALLET HEAD AS ABOVE

26 THEN GRIP THE DOWEL AT VARYING DISTANCES FROM THE HEAD UNTIL YOU FIND THE MOST SUITABLE POSITION

LENGTH OF THE SHAFT

27 THEN MEASURE THE LENGTH

---

28 **WHAT WILL BE THE WIDTH OF YOUR MALLET SHAFT ?**
(A METHOD FOR FINDING GIVEN BELOW)

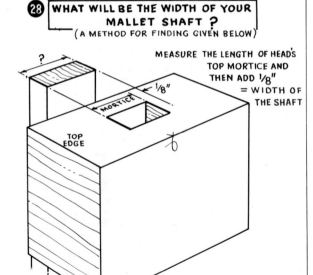

MEASURE THE LENGTH OF HEAD'S TOP MORTICE AND THEN ADD ⅛"
= WIDTH OF THE SHAFT

MORTICE

TOP EDGE

---

29 **WHAT WILL BE THE THICKNESS OF YOUR MALLET SHAFT ?**

THICKNESS OF THE SHAFT IS EQUAL TO THE WIDTH OF THE MORTICE

---

30 **PREPARE THE TIMBER FOR THE SHAFT TO ITS MARKING OUT SIZES**

(PREPARE THE SHAFT FROM MACHINE FACE-PLANED AND THICKNESSED NATURAL BOARDING — FOR A PREPARATION GUIDE SEE PAGES Nº 24 TO PAGE Nº 27)

DESIGN AND CONSTRUCTION GUIDE FOR MAKING A MALLET

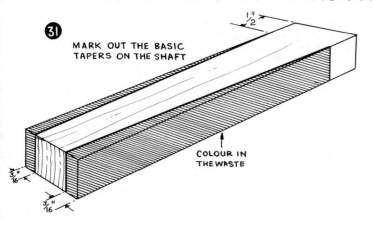

31 MARK OUT THE BASIC TAPERS ON THE SHAFT

½"

COLOUR IN THE WASTE

³⁄₁₆"

³⁄₁₆"

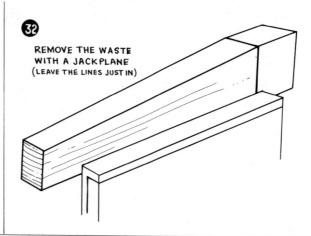

32 REMOVE THE WASTE WITH A JACKPLANE (LEAVE THE LINES JUST IN)

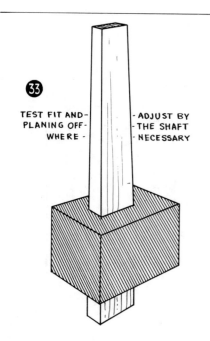

33 TEST FIT AND- PLANING OFF- WHERE -

- ADJUST BY - THE SHAFT - NECESSARY

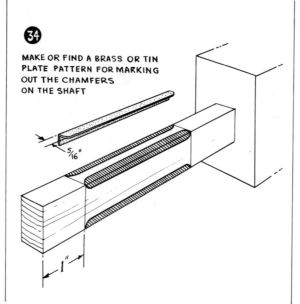

34 MAKE OR FIND A BRASS OR TIN PLATE PATTERN FOR MARKING OUT THE CHAMFERS ON THE SHAFT

⁵⁄₁₆"

1"

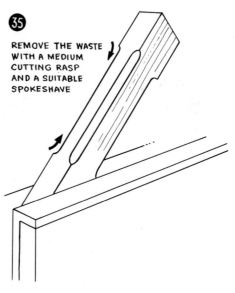

35 REMOVE THE WASTE WITH A MEDIUM CUTTING RASP AND A SUITABLE SPOKESHAVE

DESIGN AND CONSTRUCTION GUIDE FOR MAKING A MALLET

36 MARK OUT AN ARC WITH
THE AID OF A PENNY AT
THE BOTTOM OF THE SHAFT

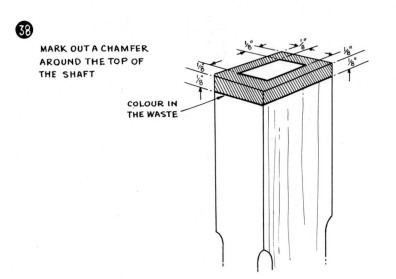

COLOUR IN
THE WASTE

37 REMOVE THE BULK OF THE WASTE
WITH A MEDIUM CUTTING RASP.
THEN FINISH OFF WITH A FINE CUTTING WOOD FILE
(LEAVE THE LINES JUST IN)

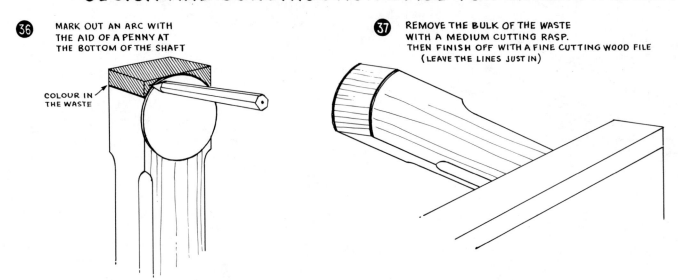

38 MARK OUT A CHAMFER
AROUND THE TOP OF
THE SHAFT

COLOUR IN
THE WASTE

39 REMOVE THE WASTE WITH
A FINE CUTTING WOOD FILE
(LEAVE THE LINES JUST IN)

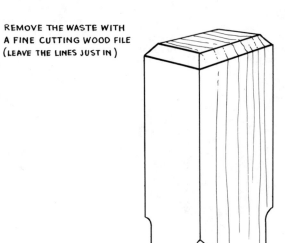

132

DESIGN AND CONSTRUCTION GUIDE FOR MAKING A MALLET

40 | **WHAT WILL BE THE AMOUNT OF TAPER ON YOUR MALLET ENDS?**
(A METHOD FOR FINDING GIVEN BELOW)

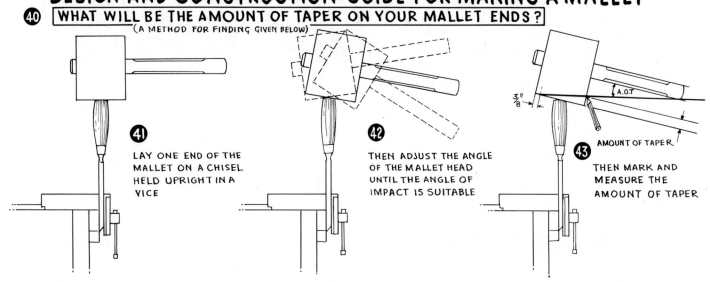

41 LAY ONE END OF THE MALLET ON A CHISEL HELD UPRIGHT IN A VICE

42 THEN ADJUST THE ANGLE OF THE MALLET HEAD UNTIL THE ANGLE OF IMPACT IS SUITABLE

43 THEN MARK AND MEASURE THE AMOUNT OF TAPER

A.O.T

$\frac{3}{8}$"

AMOUNT OF TAPER

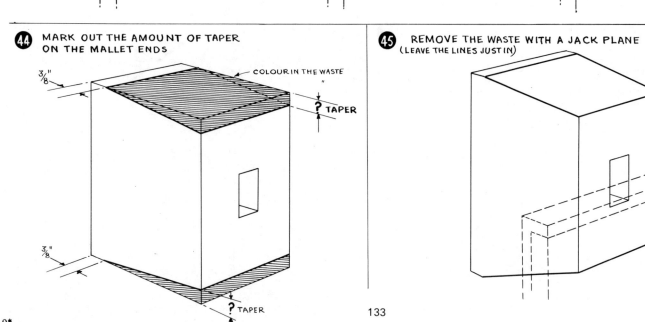

44 MARK OUT THE AMOUNT OF TAPER ON THE MALLET ENDS

$\frac{3}{8}$"

COLOUR IN THE WASTE

? TAPER

$\frac{3}{8}$"

? TAPER

45 REMOVE THE WASTE WITH A JACK PLANE
(LEAVE THE LINES JUST IN)

9*

DESIGN AND CONSTRUCTION GUIDE FOR MAKING A MALLET

46 MARK OUT THE SIDE TAPERS

COLOUR IN THE WASTE

3/8"

3/8"

3/8"

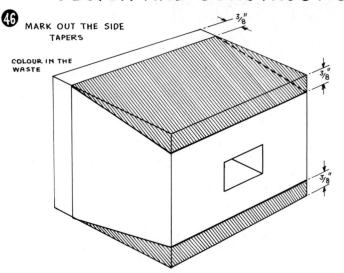

47 REMOVE THE WASTE WITH A JACK PLANE
(LEAVE THE LINES)
(JUST IN)

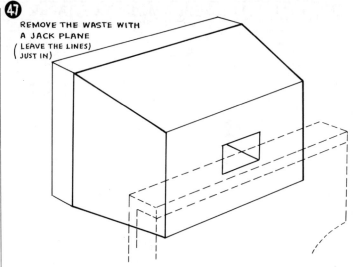

48 MARK OUT THE QUARTER ROUND'S MEASUREMENT LINES ON THE ENDS

3/8"

3/8"

3/8"

COLOUR IN THE WASTE

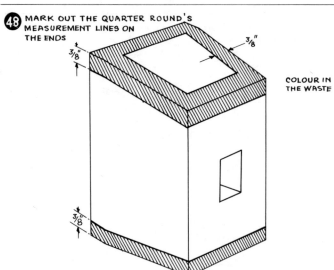

49 WITH A MEDIUM CUTTING RASP ROUND OFF THE BULK OF THE WASTE AND FINISH OFF WITH A FINE CUTTING WOOD FILE
(LEAVE THE LINES JUST IN)

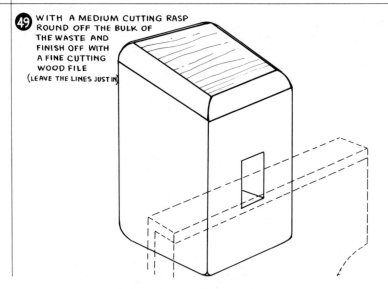

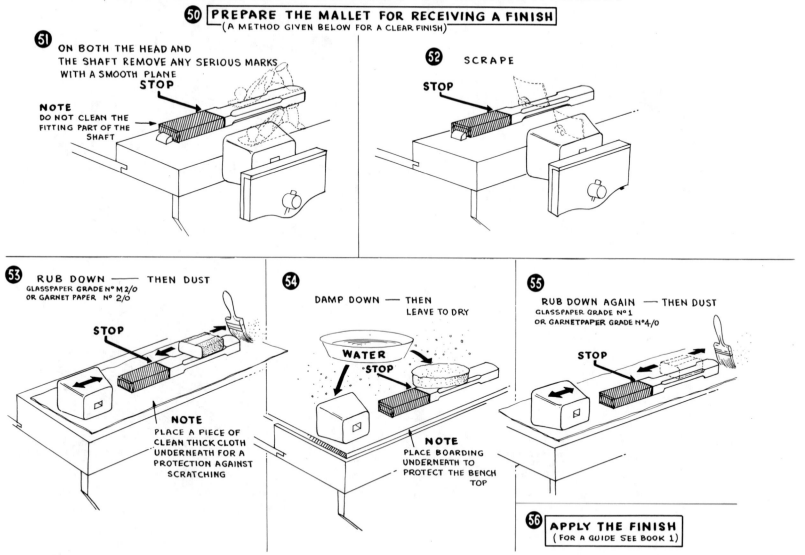

DESIGN AND CONSTRUCTION GUIDE FOR MAKING A MALLET

50 PREPARE THE MALLET FOR RECEIVING A FINISH
(A METHOD GIVEN BELOW FOR A CLEAR FINISH)

51 ON BOTH THE HEAD AND THE SHAFT REMOVE ANY SERIOUS MARKS WITH A SMOOTH PLANE
STOP

NOTE
DO NOT CLEAN THE FITTING PART OF THE SHAFT

52 SCRAPE
STOP

53 RUB DOWN —— THEN DUST
GLASSPAPER GRADE Nº M2/0 OR GARNET PAPER Nº 2/0
STOP

NOTE
PLACE A PIECE OF CLEAN THICK CLOTH UNDERNEATH FOR A PROTECTION AGAINST SCRATCHING

54 DAMP DOWN — THEN LEAVE TO DRY
WATER
STOP

NOTE
PLACE BOARDING UNDERNEATH TO PROTECT THE BENCH TOP

55 RUB DOWN AGAIN — THEN DUST
GLASSPAPER GRADE Nº1 OR GARNETPAPER GRADE Nº4/0
STOP

56 APPLY THE FINISH
(FOR A GUIDE SEE BOOK 1)

INTRODUCTION TO TEA TRAYS

2 AN EXPLODED SKETCH OF THE MAIN PARTS

1

AN EXAMPLE

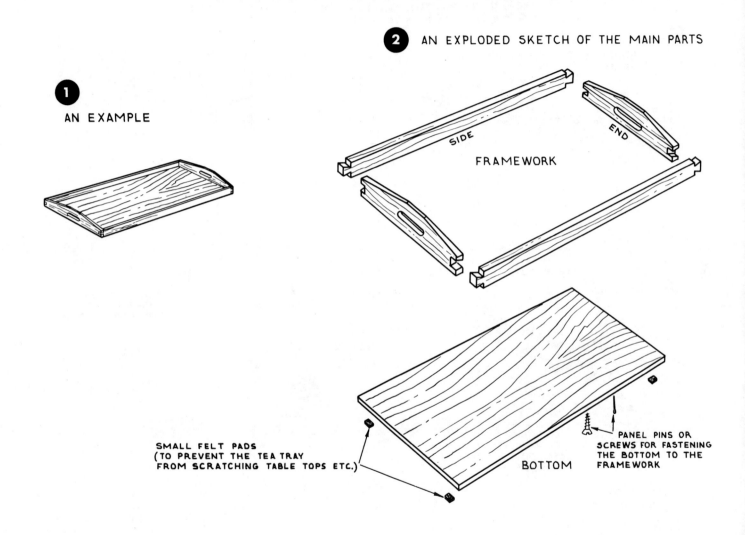

SIDE

END

FRAMEWORK

SMALL FELT PADS
(TO PREVENT THE TEA TRAY
FROM SCRATCHING TABLE TOPS ETC.)

BOTTOM

PANEL PINS OR
SCREWS FOR FASTENING
THE BOTTOM TO THE
FRAMEWORK

INTRODUCTION TO TEA TRAYS

3

<u>THE MAIN FUNCTION</u>
A LIGHT TRAY FOR CARRYING CUPS, SAUCERS,
FOOD, ETC. FROM ONE ROOM TO ANOTHER

4

THE SLOTS FORMING THE HANDLE
MUST BE OF A COMFORTABLE SIZE
THE FRAMEWORK AND BOTTOM
MUST BE LIGHT BUT STRONG

5 FOR THE BOTTOM A PIECE OF
PLYWOOD OF A SUITABLE THICKNESS
IS RECOMMENDED AS IT IS LIGHT
STRONG AND KEEPS ITS SHAPE WELL

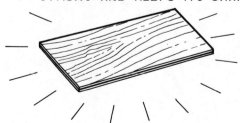

6 WHEREAS IF A PIECE OF NATURAL
BOARDING IS USED IT MAY WARP
TWIST OR SHAKE AND IT IS
COMPARATIVELY HEAVY

INTRODUCTION TO TEA TRAYS

7 IT IS WISE TO KEEP TO A BASIC RECTANGULAR SHAPE

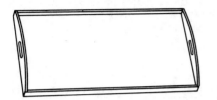

8 REASON
MANY OTHER SHAPES E.G. CIRCLES PENTAGONS ETC. ARE VERY DIFFICULT TO CONSTRUCT

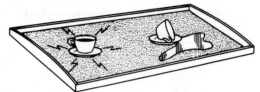

9 IT IS IMPORTANT THAT THE FINISH APPLIED TO A TEA TRAY IS HARDWEARING AND RESISTANT TO HEAT AND LIQUIDS

10 CERTAIN CLEAR FINISHES OR A FORMICA FINISH LOOK AND ARE, MORE HYGENIC THAN A PAINT FINISH

11 FIRST, TO GAIN EXPERIENCE, MAKE THE FRAMEWORK PRACTICE JOINTS AND SHAPES IN THE FOLLOWING PAGES

TEA TRAY FRAMEWORK PRACTICE JOINTS AND SHAPES

EXPLODED DIMENSIONED SKETCH
OF THE FRAMEWORK PRACTICE JOINTS

5/8"

1¾"

10"

SKETCH OF THE
CONSTRUCTED FRAMEWORK
PRACTICE JOINTS

½"

1¾"

11"

PREPARE THE SIDE AND END
FROM MACHINE FACE-
PLANED AND THICKNESSED
NATURAL BOARDING

1 MAKE OUT A TIMBER LIST FOR THE TEA TRAY FRAMEWORK
PRACTICE JOINTS AND SHAPES
(GUIDE BELOW)

TIMBER LIST FOR TEA TRAY FRAMEWORK PRACTICE JOINTS AND SHAPES							
NAMES OF MEMBERS	VARIETY OF TIMBER TO BE USED	STATE OF TIMBER TO BE USED	NUMBER REQUIRED	OVERALL LENGTH OF EACH MEMBER	TOTAL LENGTH REQUIRED FOR THIS TYPE OF MEMBER	OVERALL WIDTH	OVERALL THICKNESS
END	?	?	?	+ 1" P.A.		? + ¼" P.A.	?
SIDE	?	?	?	+ 1 P.A.		? ¼" P.A.	?

2 FILL IN THE REQUIRED INFORMATION

3 PREPARE TIMBER FOR THEIR MARKING OUT SIZES
(FOR A PREPARATION GUIDE SEE PAGES 24 TO 28)

TEA TRAY FRAMEWORK PRACTICE JOINTS AND SHAPES

4 MARK OUT THE SIDE TAILS

LENGTH OF THE TAIL
SAME AS THICKNESS
OF THE END

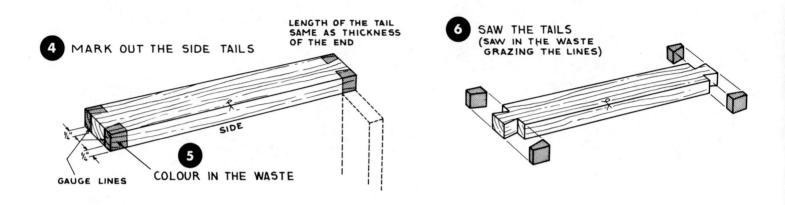

SIDE

GAUGE LINES

5 COLOUR IN THE WASTE

6 SAW THE TAILS
(SAW IN THE WASTE
GRAZING THE LINES)

7 NUMBER OFF THE JOINTS

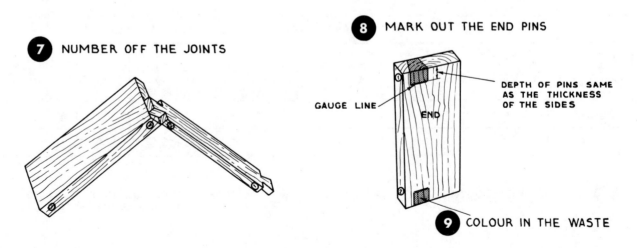

8 MARK OUT THE END PINS

DEPTH OF PINS SAME
AS THE THICKNESS
OF THE SIDES

GAUGE LINE

END

9 COLOUR IN THE WASTE

TEA TRAY FRAMEWORK PRACTICE JOINTS AND SHAPES

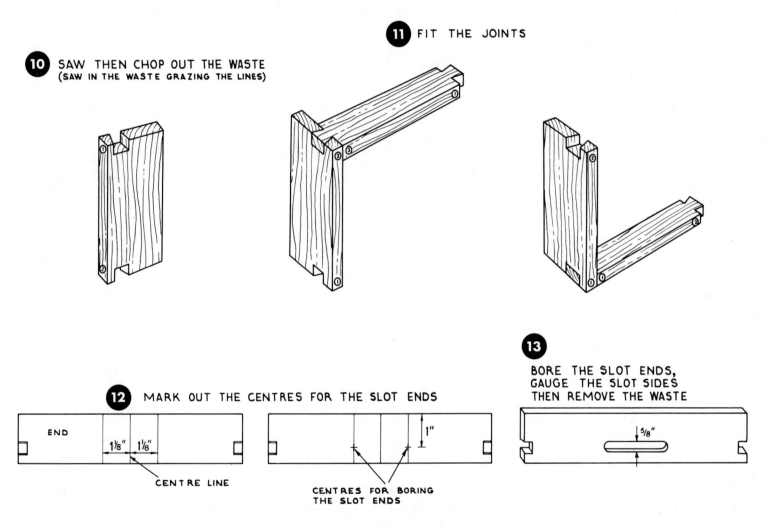

11 FIT THE JOINTS

10 SAW THEN CHOP OUT THE WASTE
(SAW IN THE WASTE GRAZING THE LINES)

13
BORE THE SLOT ENDS,
GAUGE THE SLOT SIDES
THEN REMOVE THE WASTE

5/8"

12 MARK OUT THE CENTRES FOR THE SLOT ENDS

END

1⅛" 1⅛"

CENTRE LINE

1"

CENTRES FOR BORING
THE SLOT ENDS

141

TEA TRAY FRAMEWORK PRACTICE JOINTS AND SHAPES

14 ON TWO LARGE SHEETS OF DRAWING PAPER DRAW A NUMBER
OF SIDE AND END VIEW OUTLINES AROUND YOUR END AND SIDE (EXAMPLES BELOW)

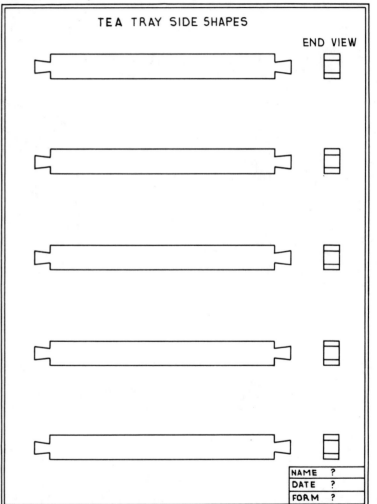

TEA TRAY END SHAPES

END VIEW

NAME	?
DATE	?
FORM	?

TEA TRAY SIDE SHAPES

END VIEW

NAME	?
DATE	?
FORM	?

TEA TRAY FRAMEWORK PRACTICE JOINTS AND SHAPES

15 THEN CONSIDER AND BUILD UP SHAPES ON THE OUTLINES
(SOME EXAMPLES BELOW)

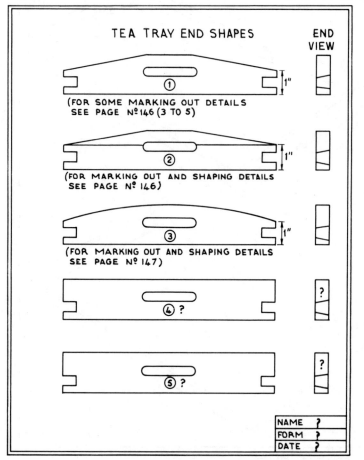

TEA TRAY END SHAPES

END VIEW

①

(FOR SOME MARKING OUT DETAILS
SEE PAGE Nº 146 (3 TO 5)

1"

②

(FOR MARKING OUT AND SHAPING DETAILS
SEE PAGE Nº 146)

1"

③

(FOR MARKING OUT AND SHAPING DETAILS
SEE PAGE Nº 147)

1"

④ ?

?

⑤ ?

?

NAME	?
FORM	?
DATE	?

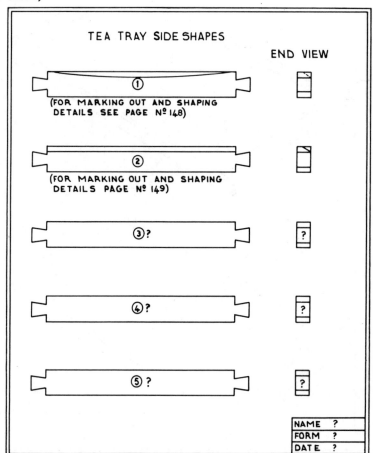

TEA TRAY SIDE SHAPES

END VIEW

①

(FOR MARKING OUT AND SHAPING
DETAILS SEE PAGE Nº 148)

②

(FOR MARKING OUT AND SHAPING
DETAILS PAGE Nº 149)

③?

?

④?

?

⑤ ?

?

NAME	?
FORM	?
DATE	?

TEA TRAY FRAMEWORK PRACTICE JOINTS AND SHAPES

16 ON A SHEET OF DRAWING PAPER SKETCH OR TRACE
FAINT OUTLINES OF A NUMBER OF CONSTRUCTED TEA TRAY FRAMEWORKS
(AN EXAMPLE BELOW)

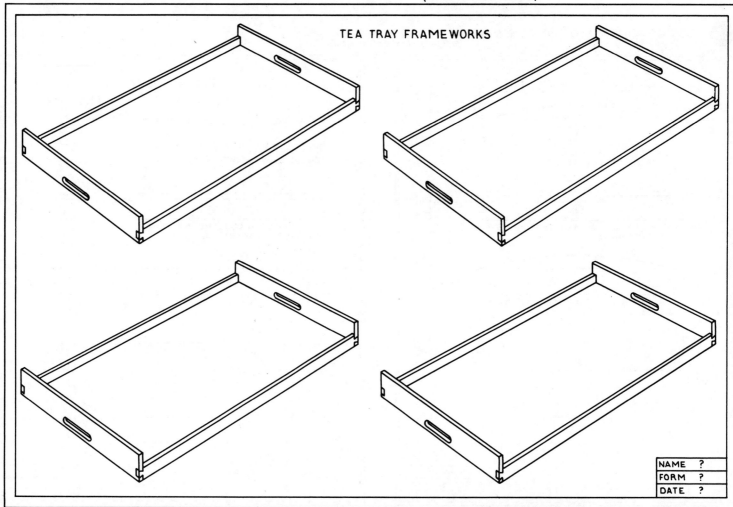

TEA TRAY FRAMEWORKS

NAME	?
FORM	?
DATE	?

TEA TRAY FRAMEWORK PRACTICE JOINTS AND SHAPES

17 THEN BUILD UP DESIGNS WITH THE END SHAPES AND SIDE SHAPES
WHICH WILL BLEND TOGETHER
(SOME EXAMPLES BELOW)

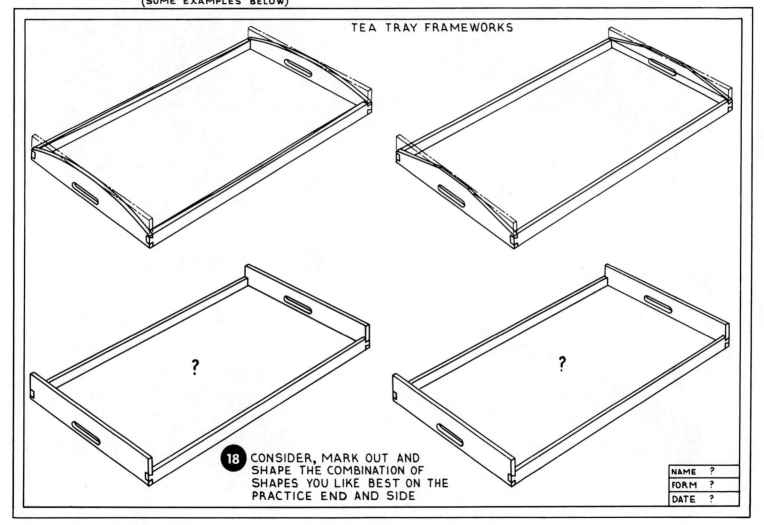

TEA TRAY FRAMEWORKS

18 CONSIDER, MARK OUT AND
SHAPE THE COMBINATION OF
SHAPES YOU LIKE BEST ON THE
PRACTICE END AND SIDE

NAME	?
FORM	?
DATE	?

10

TEA TRAY FRAMEWORK PRACTICE JOINTS AND SHAPES
A METHOD OF MARKING OUT AND SHAPING END Nº 2

1 MARK OUT THE CHAMFER
ON THE INSIDE EDGE

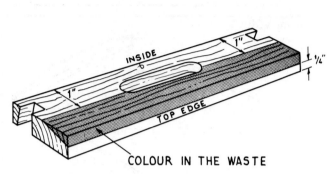

INSIDE

1"

1"

¼"

TOP EDGE

COLOUR IN THE WASTE

2 REMOVE THE WASTE WITH
A JACK PLANE
(LEAVE THE LINES JUST IN)

3 MARK OUT THE TOP EDGE BEVELS

4

COLOUR IN
THE WASTE

5 REMOVE THE WASTE WITH A JACK PLANE
(LEAVE THE LINES JUST IN)

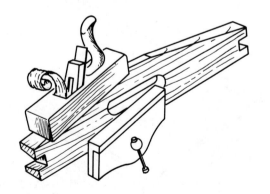

TEA TRAY FRAMEWORK PRACTICE JOINTS AND SHAPES
A METHOD OF MARKING OUT AND SHAPING END Nº 3

ON ONE END MARK THE SPRINGING POSITIONS FOR BENDING A LATH TO, FOR MARKING OUT THE CURVE

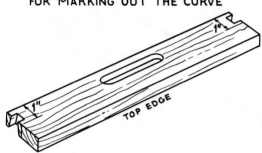

2 BEND A LATH TO THE SPRINGING POSITION AND TO THE TOP EDGE AT THE CENTRE GET SOMEONE TO MARK IN THE CURVES

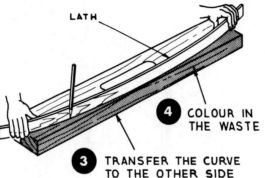

LATH

4 COLOUR IN THE WASTE

3 TRANSFER THE CURVE TO THE OTHER SIDE

5 REMOVE THE WASTE WITH A COPING SAW (SAW IN THE WASTE LEAVING THE LINES WELL IN)

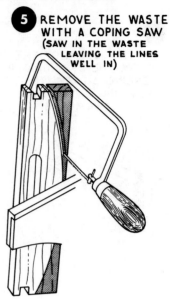

6 REMOVE ANY LUMPS OR MARKS LEFT BY THE SAW WITH A MEDIUM CUTTING RASP

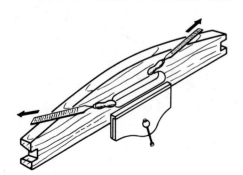

7 FINISH OFF WITH A FLAT FACED SPOKESHAVE (LEAVE THE LINES JUST IN)

NOTE: WHEN SHAPING OPPOSITE ENDS SHAPE ONE FIRST THEN USE IT FOR A PATTERN FOR MARKING AROUND

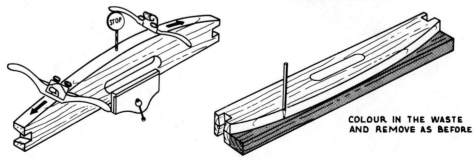

COLOUR IN THE WASTE AND REMOVE AS BEFORE

TEA TRAY FRAMEWORK PRACTICE JOINTS AND SHAPES

A METHOD OF MARKING OUT AND SHAPING SIDE Nº 1

1 ON THE INSIDE OF THE TOP EDGE MARK THE SPRINGING POSITIONS FOR BENDING A LATH TO, FOR MARKING OUT THE WAGGON CHAMFERS

2 BEND A LATH TO THE SPRINGING POSITIONS AND GET SOMEONE TO MARK IN THE CURVES

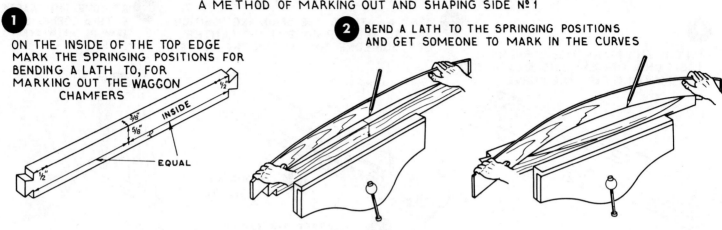

3 COLOUR IN THE WASTE

4 REMOVE THE WASTE WITH A FLAT FACED SPOKESHAVE

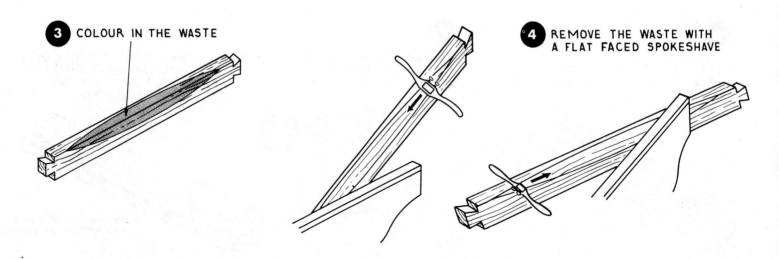

TEA TRAY FRAMEWORK PRACTICE JOINTS AND SHAPES

A METHOD OF MARKING OUT AND SHAPING SIDE Nº 2

1 ON THE INSIDE TOP EDGE MARK OUT THE CHAMFER

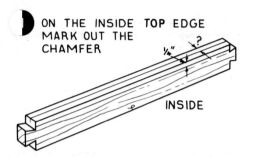

INSIDE

2 COLOUR IN THE WASTE

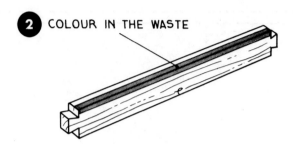

3 REMOVE THE WASTE WITH A JACK PLANE
(LEAVE THE LINES JUST IN)

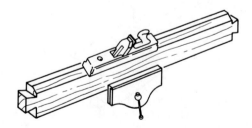

RESULT

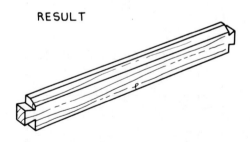

DESIGN AND CONSTRUCTION GUIDE FOR MAKING A TEA TRAY

1 ON A SHEET OF DRAWING PAPER FAINTLY SKETCH
OR TRACE THE DETAILS FROM THIS AND THE NEXT PAGE

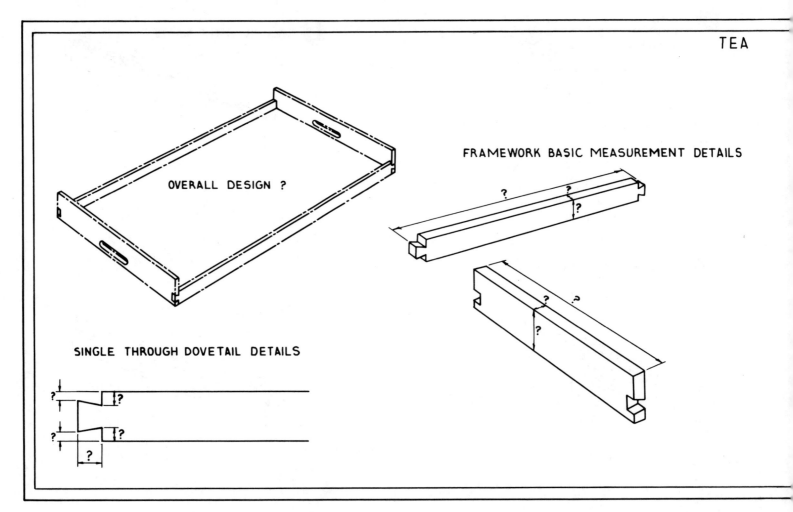

TEA

OVERALL DESIGN ?

FRAMEWORK BASIC MEASUREMENT DETAILS

SINGLE THROUGH DOVETAIL DETAILS

DESIGN AND CONSTRUCTION GUIDE FOR MAKING A TEA TRAY

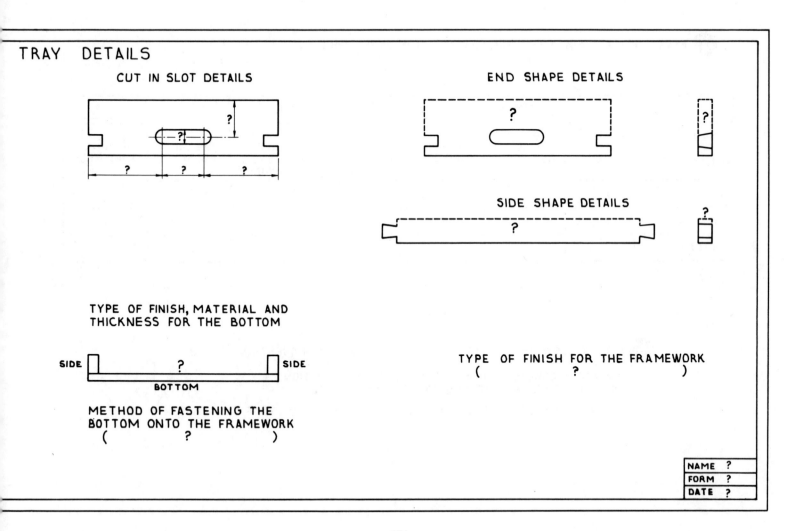

TRAY DETAILS

CUT IN SLOT DETAILS

END SHAPE DETAILS

SIDE SHAPE DETAILS

TYPE OF FINISH, MATERIAL AND
THICKNESS FOR THE BOTTOM

SIDE   ?   SIDE

BOTTOM

METHOD OF FASTENING THE
BOTTOM ONTO THE FRAMEWORK
(?   )

TYPE OF FINISH FOR THE FRAMEWORK
(?   )

NAME	?
FORM	?
DATE	?

DESIGN AND CONSTRUCTION GUIDE FOR MAKING A TEA TRAY

2 MAKE OUT A TIMBER LIST FOR YOUR TEA TRAY FRAMEWORK
(GUIDE BELOW)

TIMBER LIST FOR A TEA TRAY FRAMEWORK							
NAMES OF MEMBERS	VARIETY OF TIMBER TO BE USED	STATE OF TIMBER TO BE USED	NUMBER REQUIRED	OVERALL LENGTH OF EACH MEMBER	TOTAL LENGTH REQUIRED FOR THIS TYPE OF MEMBER	OVERALL WIDTH	OVERALL THICKNESS
END RAILS	?	?	?	? + 1" P.A.	/	? + ¼" P.A.	?
SIDE RAILS	?	?	?	? + 1" P.A.	/	? ¼" P.A.	?
BOTTOM	?	?	?	?	/	?	?

3 NOW FOLLOW THE INSTRUCTIONS AND ANSWER EACH QUESTION IN TURN

AS YOU PROGRESS FILL IN THE REQUIRED INFORMATION
ON YOUR TIMBER LIST AND SKETCH OR TRACING

EVENTUALLY DEVELOP AN ORTHOGRAPHIC DRAWING OF YOUR TEA TRAY

DESIGN AND CONSTRUCTION GUIDE FOR MAKING A TEA TRAY

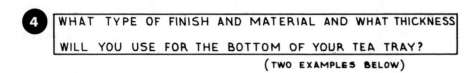

④ WHAT TYPE OF FINISH AND MATERIAL AND WHAT THICKNESS
WILL YOU USE FOR THE BOTTOM OF YOUR TEA TRAY?

(TWO EXAMPLES BELOW)

BOTTOM
FINISH

(A HARDWEARING HEAT AND LIQUID
RESISTANT CLEAR FINISH)

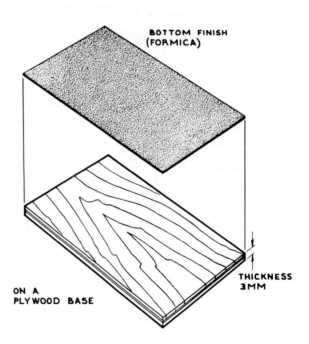

BOTTOM FINISH
(FORMICA)

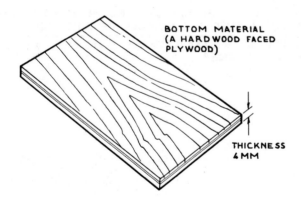

BOTTOM MATERIAL
(A HARDWOOD FACED
PLYWOOD)

THICKNESS
4MM

ON A
PLYWOOD BASE

THICKNESS
3MM

DESIGN AND CONSTRUCTION GUIDE FOR MAKING A TEA TRAY

6 WHAT VARIETY OF HARDWOOD OR SOFTWOOD WILL YOU USE FOR YOUR TEA TRAY'S FRAMEWORK ?

FOR A CLEAR FINISH USE A HARDWOOD OF A TYPE WHICH WILL MATCH THE BOTTOM

FOR A PAINT FINISH USE A SOFTWOOD VARIETY

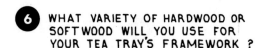

5 WHAT TYPE OF FINISH WILL YOU

APPLY TO YOUR TEA TRAY FRAMEWORK ?

(CONSIDER THE TYPE OF FINISH YOU HAVE CHOSEN FOR THE BOTTOM)

7 WHAT WILL BE THE LENGTH OF YOUR TEA TRAY FRAMEWORK SIDES AND ENDS ?

A METHOD FOR FINDING GIVEN BELOW AND CONTINUED ON THE NEXT PAGE

8 LAY OUT A SHEET OF NEWSPAPER ON THE FLOOR

9 CONSIDER THE NUMBER OF PERSONS AT HOME THEN LAY OUT A SUITABLE NUMBER OF CUPS AND

SAUCERS ETC. IN A RECTANGULAR FASHION IN ONE CORNER

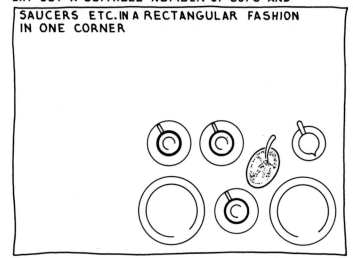

DESIGN AND CONSTRUCTION GUIDE FOR MAKING A TEA TRAY

10 WITH THE LATHS BLOCK IN THE CUPS AND SAUCERS ETC. ALLOWING 1" CLEARANCE ALL ROUND

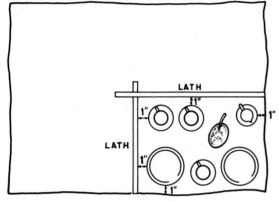

11 TAKE OFF THE CUPS AND SAUCERS ETC. AND SEE IF THE BLOCKED-IN AREA LOOKS RIGHT (DOES IT SEEM IN PROPORTION)

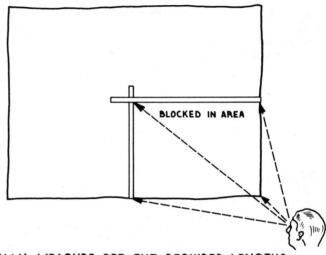

12

NOTE: IF THE PROPORTIONS DO NOT LOOK RIGHT REPLACE THE CUPS AND SAUCERS IN THE BLOCKED AREA. THEN READJUST THE LATHS CAREFULLY ALLOWING AT LEAST 1" CLEARANCE ALL ROUND UNTIL THE AREA LOOKS IN PROPORTION

13 FINALLY MEASURE OFF THE REQUIRED LENGTHS

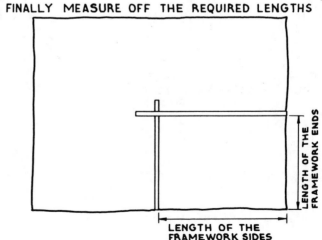

DESIGN AND CONSTRUCTION GUIDE FOR MAKING A TEA TRAY

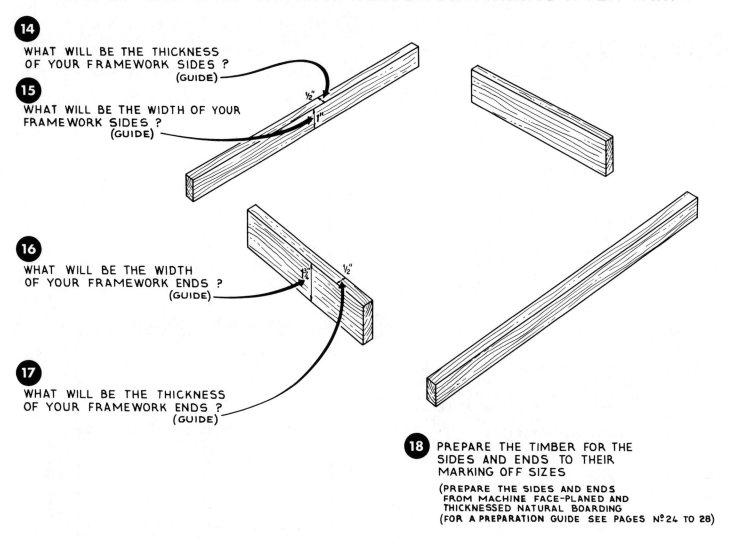

14 WHAT WILL BE THE THICKNESS
OF YOUR FRAMEWORK SIDES ?
(GUIDE)

15 WHAT WILL BE THE WIDTH OF YOUR
FRAMEWORK SIDES ?
(GUIDE)

½"
1"

16 WHAT WILL BE THE WIDTH
OF YOUR FRAMEWORK ENDS ?
(GUIDE)

1¾" ½"

17 WHAT WILL BE THE THICKNESS
OF YOUR FRAMEWORK ENDS ?
(GUIDE)

18 PREPARE THE TIMBER FOR THE
SIDES AND ENDS TO THEIR
MARKING OFF SIZES

(PREPARE THE SIDES AND ENDS
FROM MACHINE FACE-PLANED AND
THICKNESSED NATURAL BOARDING
(FOR A PREPARATION GUIDE SEE PAGES Nº 24 TO 28)

DESIGN AND CONSTRUCTION GUIDE FOR MAKING A TEA TRAY

19 | MARK OUT THE SIDE'S TAILS |
(A METHOD GIVEN BELOW AND
CONTINUED ON THE NEXT PAGE)

20 MEASURE AND SQUARE OVER
THE LENGTH OF THE TAILS

?

LENGTH OF THE TAIL ?
(SAME AS THE THICKNESS
OF THE END)

21 GAUGE THE TAIL ENDS

¼"

22 SET A SLIDING BEVEL
FOR MARKING OUT
THE TAIL BEVELS

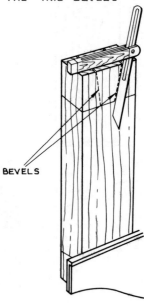

BEVELS

DESIGN AND CONSTRUCTION GUIDE FOR MAKING A TEA TRAY

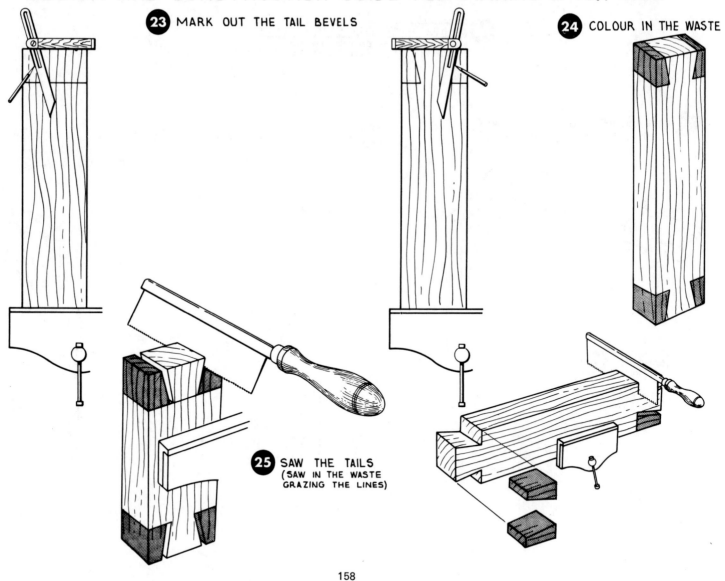

23 MARK OUT THE TAIL BEVELS

24 COLOUR IN THE WASTE

25 SAW THE TAILS
(SAW IN THE WASTE
GRAZING THE LINES)

DESIGN AND CONSTRUCTION GUIDE FOR MAKING A TEA TRAY

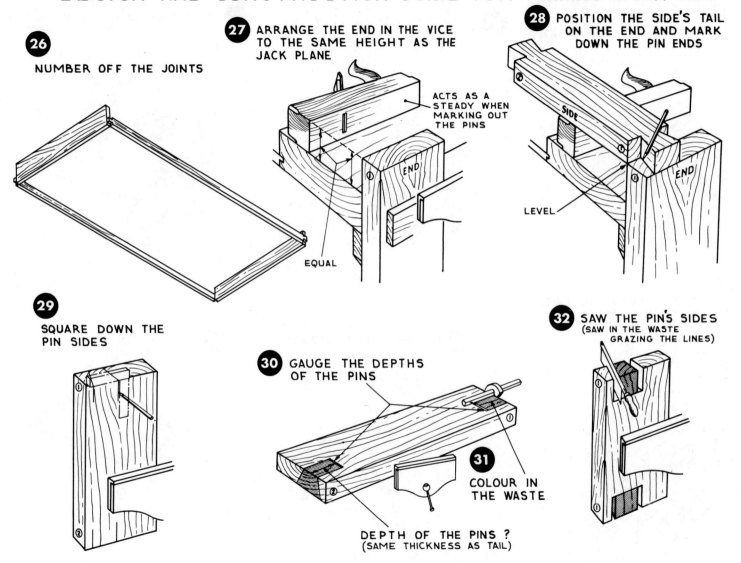

26 NUMBER OFF THE JOINTS

27 ARRANGE THE END IN THE VICE TO THE SAME HEIGHT AS THE JACK PLANE

ACTS AS A STEADY WHEN MARKING OUT THE PINS

EQUAL

END

28 POSITION THE SIDE'S TAIL ON THE END AND MARK DOWN THE PIN ENDS

SIDE

END

LEVEL

29 SQUARE DOWN THE PIN SIDES

30 GAUGE THE DEPTHS OF THE PINS

31 COLOUR IN THE WASTE

DEPTH OF THE PINS ?
(SAME THICKNESS AS TAIL)

32 SAW THE PIN'S SIDES
(SAW IN THE WASTE GRAZING THE LINES)

DESIGN AND CONSTRUCTION GUIDE FOR MAKING A TEA TRAY

33 CHOP OUT HALF THE WASTE

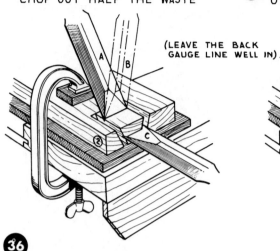

(LEAVE THE BACK GAUGE LINE WELL IN)

34 TURN OVER AND CHOP OUT THE OTHER HALF OF THE WASTE

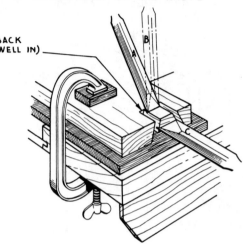

35 LAY THE CHISEL'S EDGE IN THE BACK GAUGE LINE AND CHOP HALF WAY DOWN

36 TURN OVER THEN LAY THE CHISEL'S EDGE IN THE BACK GAUGE LINE AND CHOP HALF WAY DOWN

37 FIT EACH JOINT SEPARATELY

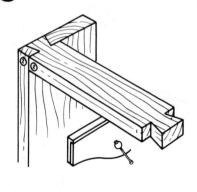

38 FINALLY TRY THEM ALL TOGETHER

DESIGN AND CONSTRUCTION GUIDE FOR MAKING A TEA TRAY

39 | MARK OUT AND FORM THE SLOTS |
(A METHOD GIVEN BELOW)

40

MARK OUT THE SLOT END
CENTRES FOR BORING

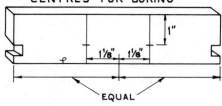

1"

1⅛" 1⅛"

EQUAL

41

BORE THE SLOT END THROUGH
TO A PIECE OF WASTE WOOD

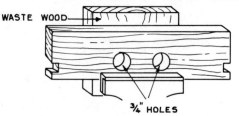

WASTE WOOD

¾" HOLES

42

GAUGE DOWN THE SIDES
OF THE SLOT

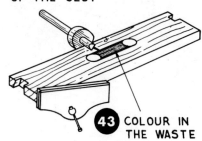

43 COLOUR IN
THE WASTE

44

REMOVE THE WASTE
WITH A COPING SAW
(LEAVE THE LINES WELL IN)

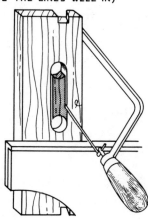

45

CLEAN THE SLOT SIDES DIAGONALLY
WITH A _FINE_ CUTTING WOOD FILE
(CUT THE GAUGE LINES IN TWO)

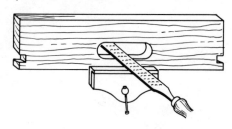

46

CONSIDER, MARK OUT
AND SHAPE THE ENDS
AND SIDES

DESIGN AND CONSTRUCTION GUIDE FOR MAKING A TEA TRAY

47 ASSEMBLE THE FRAMEWORK
(A METHOD GIVEN BELOW AND
CONTINUED ON THE NEXT PAGE)

48

GLUE AND POSITION EACH JOINT CAREFULLY

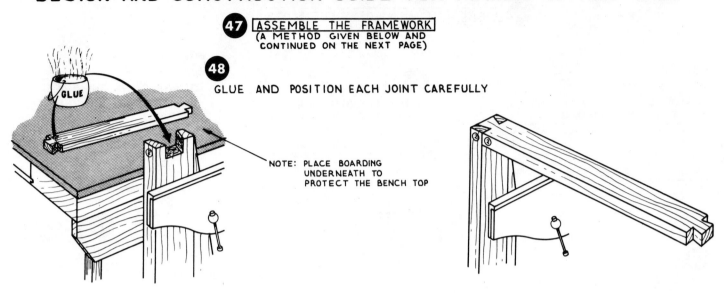

NOTE: PLACE BOARDING
UNDERNEATH TO
PROTECT THE BENCH TOP

49 APPLY THE CRAMPS

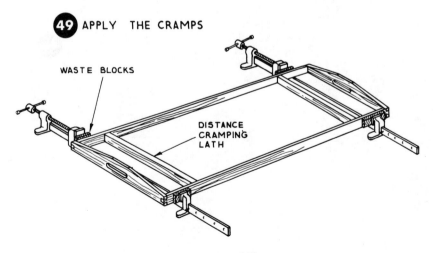

WASTE BLOCKS

DISTANCE
CRAMPING
LATH

DESIGN AND CONSTRUCTION GUIDE FOR MAKING A TEA TRAY

50 TEST FOR SQUARENESS AND THAT THE FRAMEWORK SIDES ARE IN LINE WITH EACH OTHER

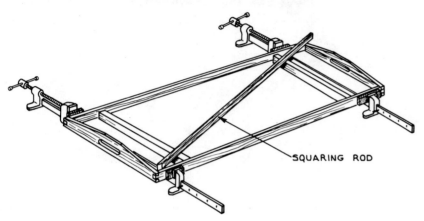

SQUARING ROD

ADJUST WHERE NECESSARY

52 WHERE NECESSARY LEVEL THE FRAMEWORK'S BOTTOM EDGE

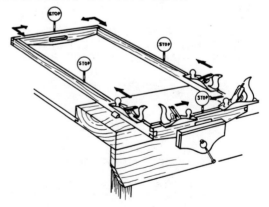

51 THEN LEAVE UNTIL THE GLUE HAS SET

DESIGN AND CONSTRUCTION GUIDE FOR MAKING A TEA TRAY

53 A MARK OUT AND CUT THE BOTTOM
(A METHOD FOR A FORMICA SURFACE FINISH)

54 A ON A SHEET OF PLYWOOD MARK OUT THE BOTTOM OUTLINE AS BELOW

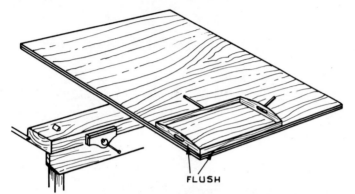

FLUSH

NOTE: OR OBTAIN FROM A SHOP A PIECE OF 3MM PLYWOOD CUT TO AT LEAST THE LENGTH OF THE TRAY + 1/8" AND THE WIDTH OF THE TRAY + 1/8"

55 A SAW OUT LEAVING THE LINES WELL IN

56 A PURCHASE A PIECE OF FORMICA OF SUITABLE TEXTURE 1/8" LARGER ALL ROUND THAN THE PLYWOOD BOTTOM

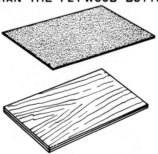

57 A APPLY THE ADHESIVE

58 A TURN UPSIDE DOWN AND APPLY HEAVY WEIGHTS
(OR PLACE IN A CAUL PRESS)

PAINT   LINSEED OIL

DESIGN AND CONSTRUCTION GUIDE FOR MAKING A TEA TRAY

53 B — MARK OUT AND CUT THE BOTTOM THEN PREPARE IT FOR RECEIVING A FINISH
(A METHOD FOR A PLYWOOD SURFACE BOTTOM)

5 B ON A SHEET OF SUITABLE HARDWOOD FACED PLYWOOD MARK OUT THE BOTTOM OUTLINE AS BELOW

55 B SAW OUT LEAVING THE LINES WELL IN

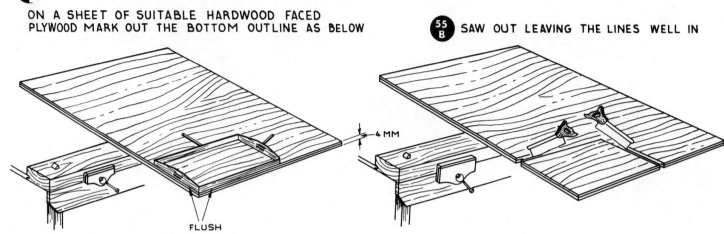

4 MM

FLUSH

NOTE: OR OBTAIN FROM A SHOP A PIECE OF SUITABLE HARDWOOD FACED PLYWOOD CUT TO AT LEAST THE LENGTH OF THE TRAY + 1/8" AND WIDTH OF THE TRAY + 1/8"

5 B SCRAPE IF NECESSARY THEN RUB DOWN
(GLASS PAPER GRADE Nº M2
GARNET PAPER GRADE Nº 2/0)

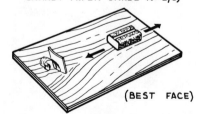

(BEST FACE)

57 B DUST, DAMP DOWN, THEN LEAVE TO DRY

58 B RUB DOWN AGAIN
(GLASS PAPER GRADE Nº 1
OR GARNET PAPER GRADE Nº 4/0)

THEN DUST

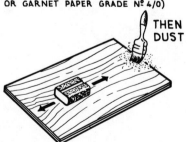

11*

DESIGN AND CONSTRUCTION GUIDE FOR MAKING A TEA TRAY

59 PREPARE THE INSIDE OF THE FRAMEWORK FOR RECEIVING A FINISH
(A METHOD GIVEN BELOW FOR A CLEAR FINISH)

60 SCRAPE

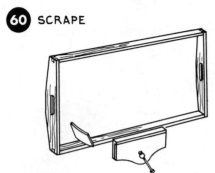

61 RUB DOWN
(GLASS PAPER GRADE Nº M2
GARNET PAPER GRADE
Nº 2/0)

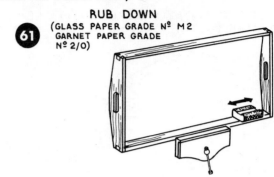

62 DUST

63 DAMP DOWN THEN LEAVE TO DRY

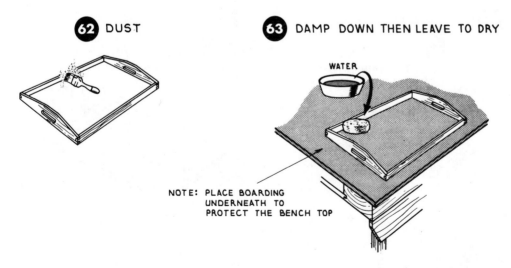

WATER

NOTE: PLACE BOARDING
UNDERNEATH TO
PROTECT THE BENCH TOP

64 RUB DOWN AGAIN
(GLASS PAPER GRADE Nº 1
GARNET PAPER GRADE Nº 4/0)

THEN DUST

DESIGN AND CONSTRUCTION GUIDE FOR MAKING A TEA TRAY

65 FASTEN THE BOTTOM TO THE FRAMEWORK
(A METHOD GIVEN BELOW)

66 CAREFULLY POSITION THE BOTTOM ON
THE FRAMEWORK AND FIX WITH TWO PINS

67 ON THE BOTTOM MARK POSITIONING
LINES FOR PANEL PINS OR SCREWS
ABOVE THE CENTRE OF THE FRAMEWORK

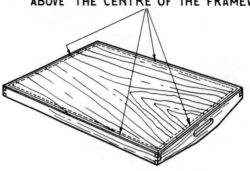

68 APPLY THE PANEL PINS OR SCREWS

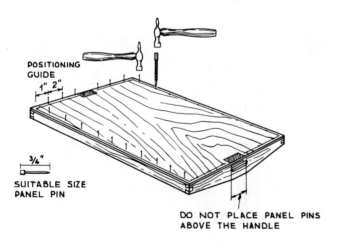

POSITIONING
GUIDE
1" 2"

3/4"

SUITABLE SIZE
PANEL PIN

DO NOT PLACE PANEL PINS
ABOVE THE HANDLE

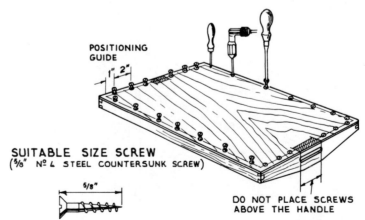

POSITIONING
GUIDE
1" 2"

SUITABLE SIZE SCREW
(5/8" Nº 4 STEEL COUNTERSUNK SCREW)

5/8"

DO NOT PLACE SCREWS
ABOVE THE HANDLE

167

DESIGN AND CONSTRUCTION GUIDE FOR MAKING A TEA TRAY

69 PREPARE THE OUTSIDE OF THE FRAMEWORK FOR RECEIVING A FINISH
(A METHOD GIVEN BELOW FOR A CLEAR FINISH CONTINUED ON THE NEXT PAGE)

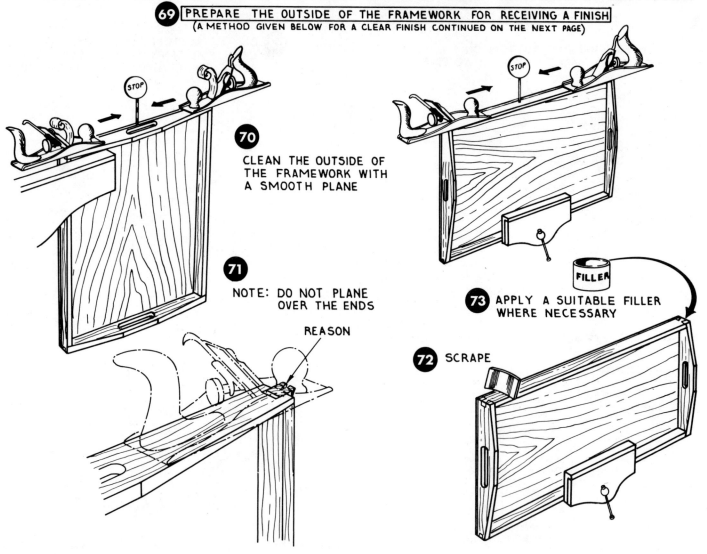

STOP

70 CLEAN THE OUTSIDE OF THE FRAMEWORK WITH A SMOOTH PLANE

STOP

71

NOTE: DO NOT PLANE OVER THE ENDS

REASON

FILLER

73 APPLY A SUITABLE FILLER WHERE NECESSARY

72 SCRAPE

DESIGN AND CONSTRUCTION GUIDE FOR MAKING A TEA TRAY

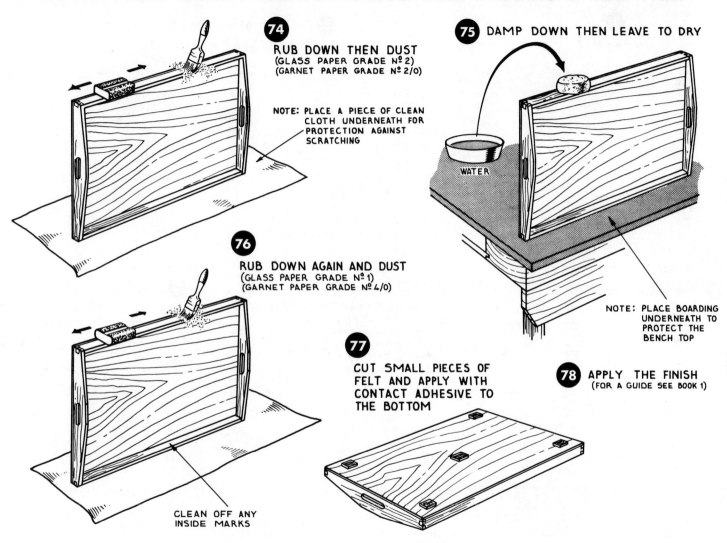

74 RUB DOWN THEN DUST
(GLASS PAPER GRADE Nº 2)
(GARNET PAPER GRADE Nº 2/0)

NOTE: PLACE A PIECE OF CLEAN
CLOTH UNDERNEATH FOR
PROTECTION AGAINST
SCRATCHING

75 DAMP DOWN THEN LEAVE TO DRY

WATER

NOTE: PLACE BOARDING
UNDERNEATH TO
PROTECT THE
BENCH TOP

76 RUB DOWN AGAIN AND DUST
(GLASS PAPER GRADE Nº 1)
(GARNET PAPER GRADE Nº 4/0)

CLEAN OFF ANY
INSIDE MARKS

77 CUT SMALL PIECES OF
FELT AND APPLY WITH
CONTACT ADHESIVE TO
THE BOTTOM

78 APPLY THE FINISH
(FOR A GUIDE SEE BOOK 1)

INTRODUCTION TO SEAGRASS STOOLS

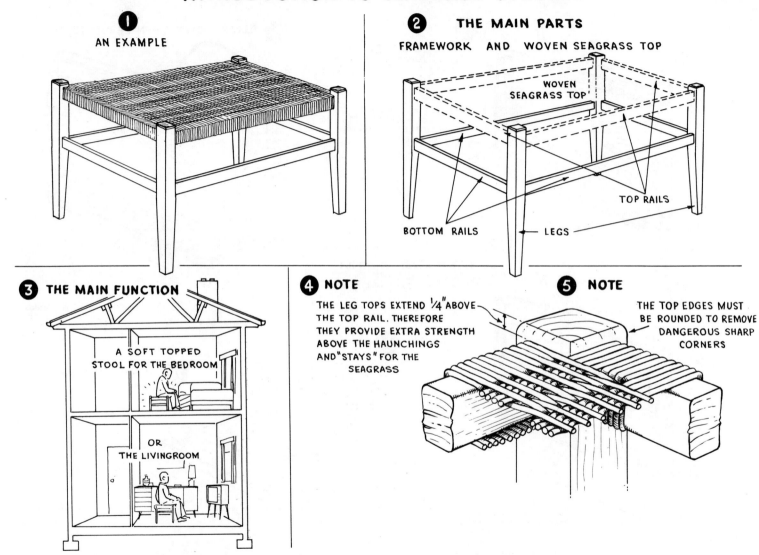

① AN EXAMPLE

② THE MAIN PARTS

FRAMEWORK   AND   WOVEN SEAGRASS TOP

WOVEN SEAGRASS TOP

TOP RAILS

BOTTOM RAILS

LEGS

③ THE MAIN FUNCTION

A SOFT TOPPED STOOL FOR THE BEDROOM

OR THE LIVINGROOM

④ NOTE

THE LEG TOPS EXTEND ¼" ABOVE THE TOP RAIL. THEREFORE THEY PROVIDE EXTRA STRENGTH ABOVE THE HAUNCHINGS AND "STAYS" FOR THE SEAGRASS

⑤ NOTE

THE TOP EDGES MUST BE ROUNDED TO REMOVE DANGEROUS SHARP CORNERS

INTRODUCTION TO SEAGRASS STOOLS

⑥ NOTE
TO PREVENT THE LEGS RACKING — TWO SETS OF RAILS ARE ADVISABLE

REASON
THE SIZE OF THE
TOP RAIL IS
LIMITED
(A WIDE TOP RAIL)
WOULD BE TOO
(BULKY TO WEAVE)
TIGHTLY

⑦ AN EXPLODED SKETCH OF A FRAMEWORK

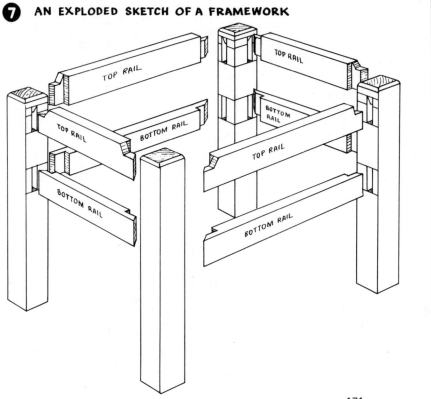

TOP RAIL

TOP RAIL

BOTTOM RAIL

TOP RAIL

BOTTOM RAIL

BOTTOM RAIL

TOP RAIL

BOTTOM RAIL

❽

FIRST, TO GAIN EXPERIENCE,

MAKE THE FRAMEWORK

PRACTICE JOINTS

AND SHAPES

(AS IN THE FOLLOWING PAGES)

SEAGRASS STOOL FRAMEWORK PRACTICE JOINTS AND SHAPES

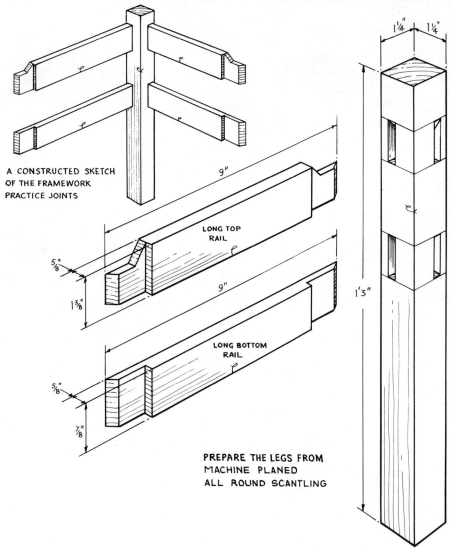

A CONSTRUCTED SKETCH OF THE FRAMEWORK PRACTICE JOINTS

LONG TOP RAIL

9"

5/8"

1 3/8"

LONG BOTTOM RAIL

9"

5/8"

7/8"

PREPARE THE LEGS FROM MACHINE PLANED ALL ROUND SCANTLING

1 1/4" 1 1/4"

1' 3"

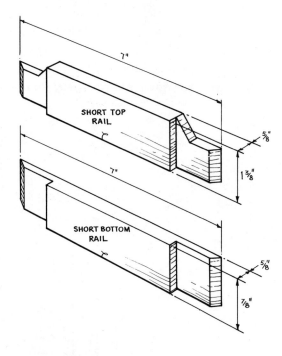

AN EXPLODED SKETCH OF THE FRAMEWORK PRACTICE JOINTS WITH DIMENSIONS

SHORT TOP RAIL

7"

5/8"

1 3/8"

SHORT BOTTOM RAIL

7"

5/8"

7/8"

PREPARE THE RAILS FROM MACHINE FACE-PLANED AND THICKNESSED NATURAL BOARDING

172

SEAGRASS STOOL FRAMEWORK PRACTICE JOINTS AND SHAPES

① MAKE OUT A TIMBER LIST FOR THE FRAMEWORK PRACTICE JOINTS AND SHAPES
(GUIDE BELOW)

TIMBER LIST FOR THE SEAGRASS STOOL FRAMEWORK PRACTICE JOINTS AND SHAPES

NAMES OF MEMBERS	VARIETY OF TIMBER TO BE USED	STATE OF TIMBER TO BE USED	NUMBER REQUIRED	OVERALL LENGTH OF EACH MEMBER	TOTAL LENGTH REQUIRED FOR THIS TYPE OF MEMBER	OVERALL WIDTH	OVER ALL THICKNESS
LEGS	?	?	?	?	?	?	?
LONG TOP RAILS	?	?	?	? + 1" P.A.	?	? + ¼" P.A.	?
LONG BOTTOM RAILS	?	?	?	? + 1" P.A.	?	? + ¼" P.A	?
SHORT TOP RAILS	?	?	?	? + 1" P.A.	?	? + ¼" P.A.	?
SHORT BOTTOM RAILS	?	?	?	? + 1" P.A.	?	? + ¼" P.A.	?

② FILL IN THE REQUIRED INFORMATION

③ PREPARE THE MEMBERS' TIMBER TO THEIR MARKING OUT SIZES.
(FOR PREPARATION GUIDES SEE PAGE N⁰·24 TO PAGE N⁰·29)

SEAGRASS STOOL FRAMEWORK PRACTICE JOINTS AND SHAPES

4 MARK OUT THE MORTICES AND HAUNCHINGS

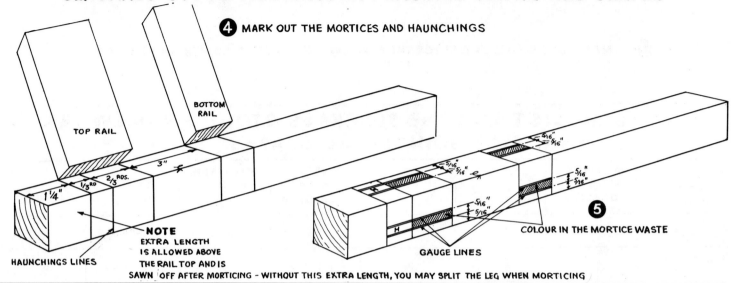

TOP RAIL

BOTTOM RAIL

1¼" 1/3 RD. 2/3 RDS. 3"

HAUNCHINGS LINES

NOTE
EXTRA LENGTH
IS ALLOWED ABOVE
THE RAIL TOP AND IS
SAWN OFF AFTER MORTICING – WITHOUT THIS EXTRA LENGTH, YOU MAY SPLIT THE LEG WHEN MORTICING

5

5/16" 5/16"
5/16" 5/16"
5/16" 5/16"
5/16" 5/16"

COLOUR IN THE MORTICE WASTE

GAUGE LINES

6 CHOP OUT THE MORTICES
(DEPTH OF MORTICES 15/16")

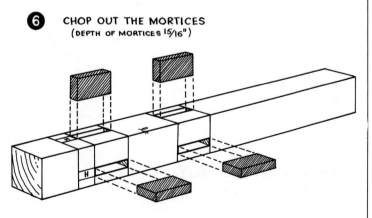

H

7 SAW, THEN CHOP OUT HAUNCHINGS
(DEPTH OF HAUNCHINGS ¼")

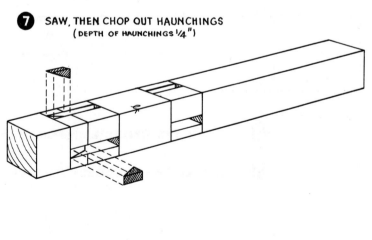

SEAGRASS STOOL FRAMEWORK PRACTICE JOINTS AND SHAPES

8 MARK OUT THE RAIL TENONS

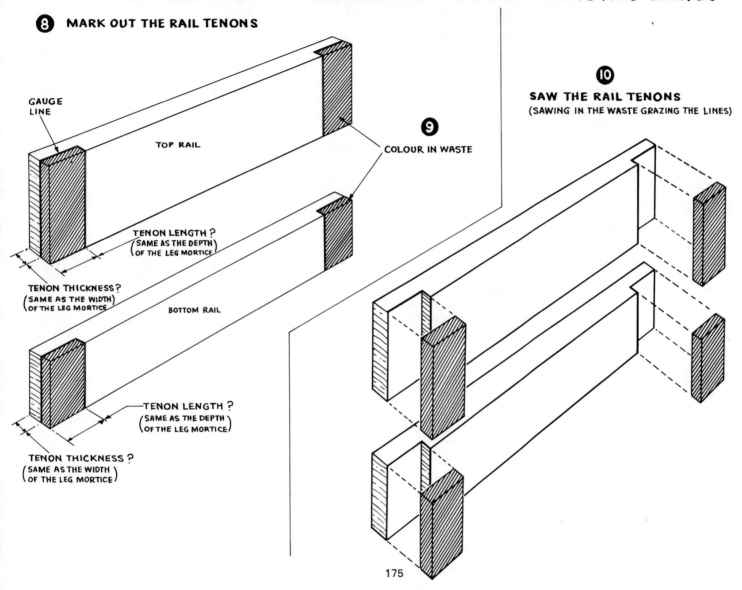

GAUGE LINE

TOP RAIL

TENON LENGTH ?
(SAME AS THE DEPTH)
(OF THE LEG MORTICE)

TENON THICKNESS?
(SAME AS THE WIDTH)
(OF THE LEG MORTICE)

BOTTOM RAIL

TENON LENGTH ?
(SAME AS THE DEPTH)
(OF THE LEG MORTICE)

TENON THICKNESS ?
(SAME AS THE WIDTH)
(OF THE LEG MORTICE)

9

COLOUR IN WASTE

10 SAW THE RAIL TENONS
(SAWING IN THE WASTE GRAZING THE LINES)

175

SEAGRASS STOOL FRAMEWORK PRACTICE JOINTS AND SHAPES

11

MARK OUT THE TOP RAIL HAUNCHES

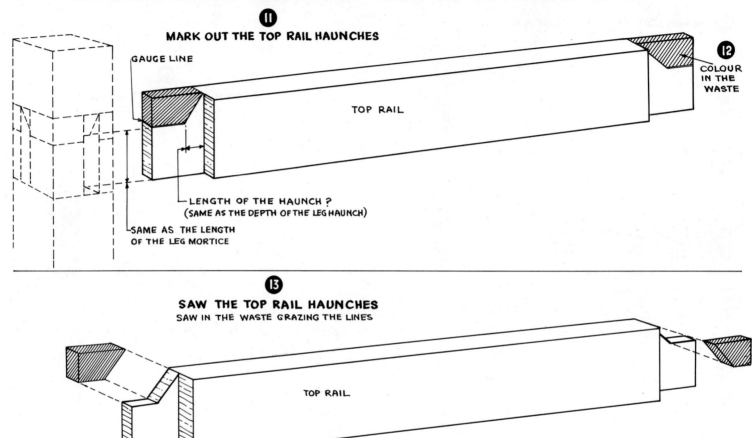

GAUGE LINE

TOP RAIL

12

COLOUR
IN THE
WASTE

LENGTH OF THE HAUNCH ?
(SAME AS THE DEPTH OF THE LEG HAUNCH)

SAME AS THE LENGTH
OF THE LEG MORTICE

13

SAW THE TOP RAIL HAUNCHES
SAW IN THE WASTE GRAZING THE LINES

TOP RAIL

SEAGRASS STOOL FRAMEWORK PRACTICE JOINTS AND SHAPES

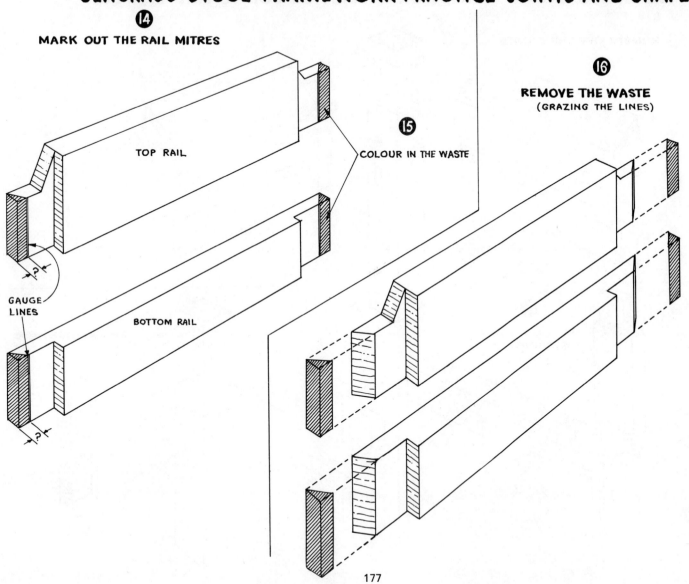

14

MARK OUT THE RAIL MITRES

TOP RAIL

BOTTOM RAIL

GAUGE LINES

?

?

15

COLOUR IN THE WASTE

16

REMOVE THE WASTE
(GRAZING THE LINES)

177

SEAGRASS STOOL FRAMEWORK PRACTICE JOINTS AND SHAPES

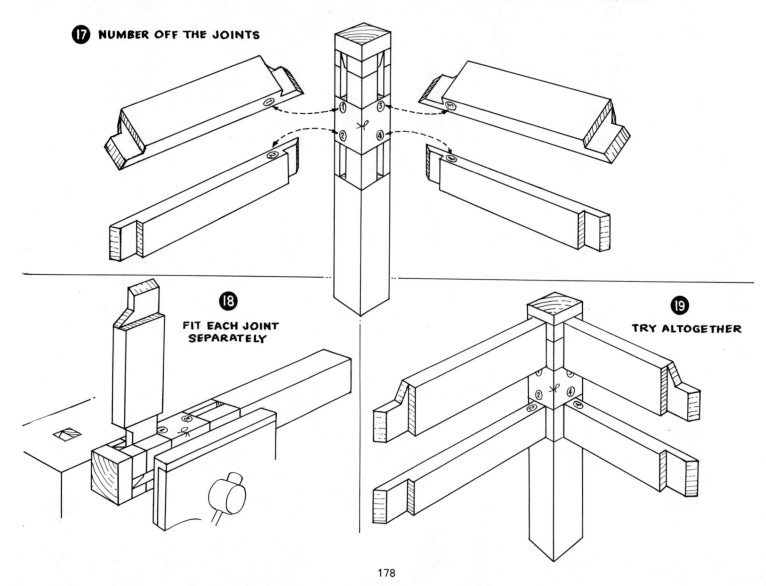

17 NUMBER OFF THE JOINTS

18 FIT EACH JOINT SEPARATELY

19 TRY ALTOGETHER

SEAGRASS STOOL FRAMEWORK PRACTICE JOINTS AND SHAPES

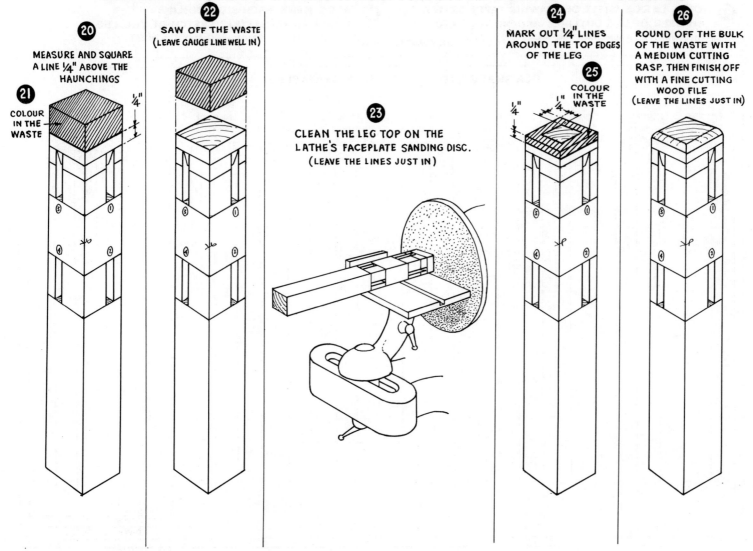

20 MEASURE AND SQUARE A LINE ¼" ABOVE THE HAUNCHINGS

21 COLOUR IN THE WASTE

¼"

22 SAW OFF THE WASTE (LEAVE GAUGE LINE WELL IN)

23 CLEAN THE LEG TOP ON THE LATHE'S FACEPLATE SANDING DISC. (LEAVE THE LINES JUST IN)

24 MARK OUT ¼" LINES AROUND THE TOP EDGES OF THE LEG

25 COLOUR IN THE WASTE

¼" 1" ¼"

26 ROUND OFF THE BULK OF THE WASTE WITH A MEDIUM CUTTING RASP. THEN FINISH OFF WITH A FINE CUTTING WOOD FILE (LEAVE THE LINES JUST IN)

SEAGRASS STOOL FRAMEWORK PRACTICE JOINTS AND SHAPES

27 ON A LARGE SHEET OF DRAWING PAPER DRAW A NUMBER OF SIDE OUTLINES AROUND YOUR LEG
(INCLUDE THE HAUNCHING AND MORTICES)

AN EXAMPLE BELOW

28 ALSO NEAR EACH SIDE OUTLINE DRAW AN ISOMETRIC SKETCH OF THE LEG
(INCLUDE THE HAUNCHING AND MORTICES)

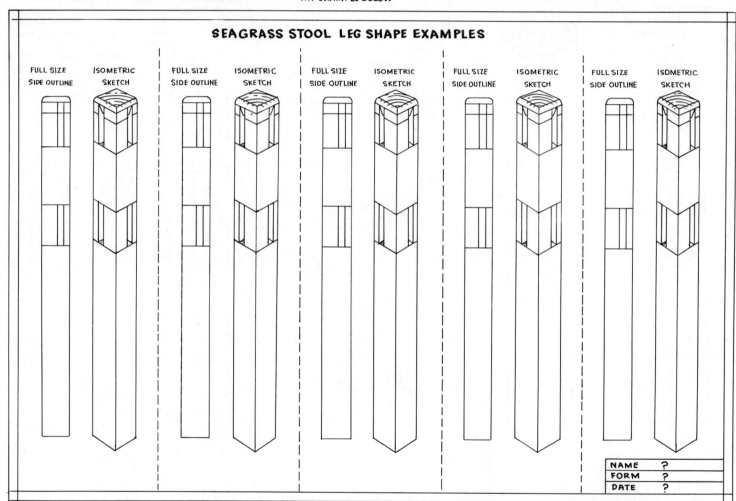

SEAGRASS STOOL LEG SHAPE EXAMPLES

FULL SIZE SIDE OUTLINE   ISOMETRIC SKETCH   FULL SIZE SIDE OUTLINE   ISOMETRIC SKETCH   FULL SIZE SIDE OUTLINE   ISOMETRIC SKETCH   FULL SIZE SIDE OUTLINE   ISOMETRIC SKETCH   FULL SIZE SIDE OUTLINE   ISOMETRIC SKETCH

NAME	?
FORM	?
DATE	?

SEAGRASS STOOL FRAMEWORK PRACTICE JOINTS AND SHAPES

29 THEN CONSIDER AND BUILD UP LEG SHAPES ON THE OUTLINES

(SOME EXAMPLES BELOW)

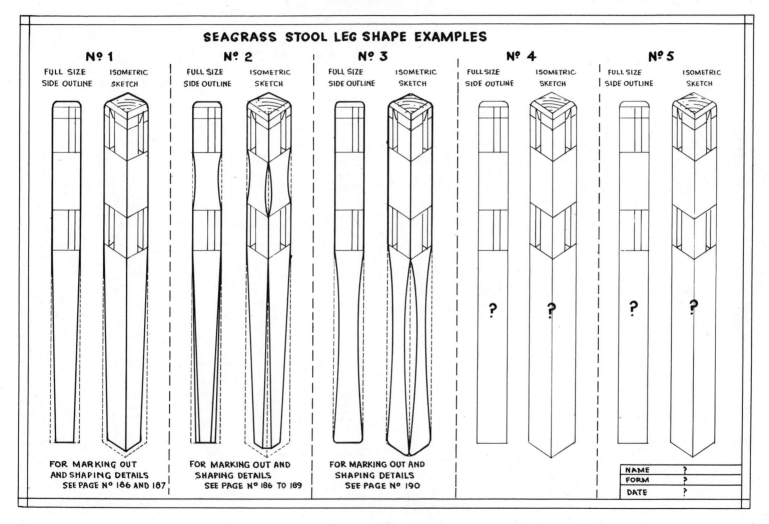

SEAGRASS STOOL LEG SHAPE EXAMPLES

Nº 1	Nº 2	Nº 3	Nº 4	Nº 5
FULL SIZE SIDE OUTLINE / ISOMETRIC SKETCH	FULL SIZE SIDE OUTLINE / ISOMETRIC SKETCH	FULL SIZE SIDE OUTLINE / ISOMETRIC SKETCH	FULL SIZE SIDE OUTLINE / ISOMETRIC SKETCH	FULL SIZE SIDE OUTLINE / ISOMETRIC SKETCH

FOR MARKING OUT AND SHAPING DETAILS SEE PAGE Nº 186 AND 187

FOR MARKING OUT AND SHAPING DETAILS SEE PAGE Nº 186 TO 189

FOR MARKING OUT AND SHAPING DETAILS SEE PAGE Nº 190

NAME	?
FORM	?
DATE	?

12*

SEAGRASS STOOL FRAMEWORK PRACTICE JOINTS AND SHAPES

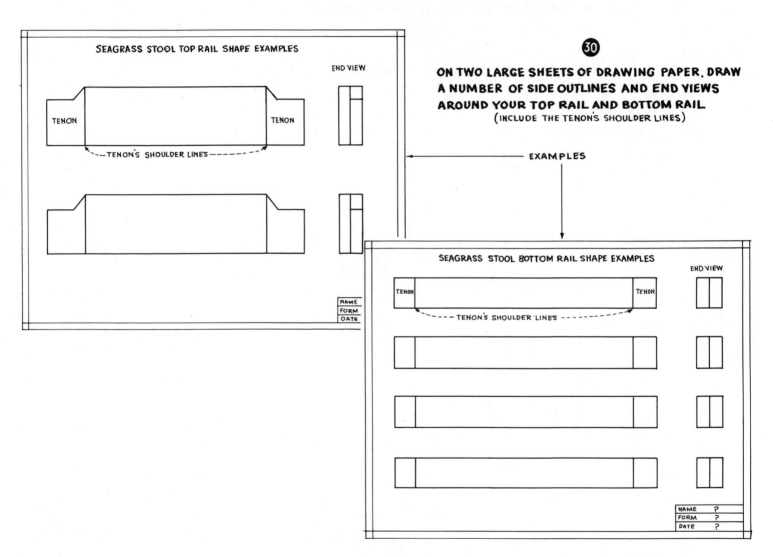

SEAGRASS STOOL TOP RAIL SHAPE EXAMPLES

END VIEW

TENON

TENON

---TENON'S SHOULDER LINES---------

NAME
FORM
DATE

30

ON TWO LARGE SHEETS OF DRAWING PAPER, DRAW
A NUMBER OF SIDE OUTLINES AND END VIEWS
AROUND YOUR TOP RAIL AND BOTTOM RAIL
(INCLUDE THE TENON'S SHOULDER LINES)

EXAMPLES

SEAGRASS STOOL BOTTOM RAIL SHAPE EXAMPLES

END VIEW

TENON

TENON

---TENON'S SHOULDER LINES----------

NAME   ?
FORM   ?
DATE   ?

SEAGRASS STOOL FRAMEWORK PRACTICE JOINTS AND SHAPES

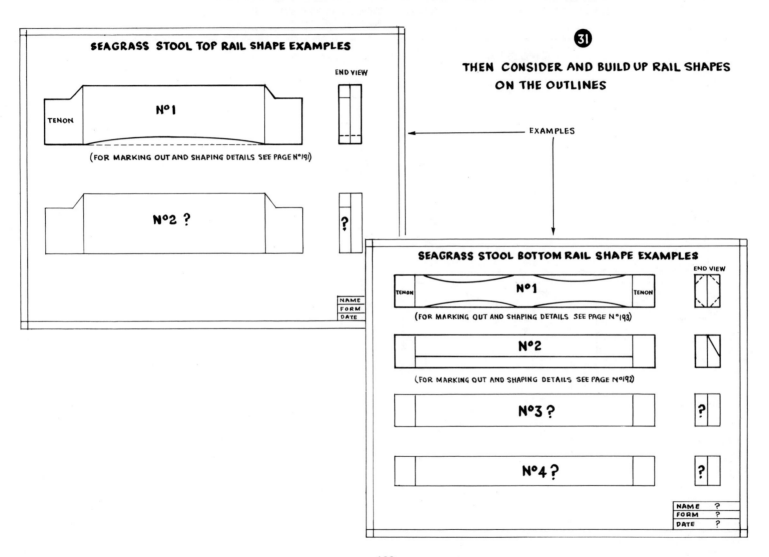

SEAGRASS STOOL TOP RAIL SHAPE EXAMPLES

END VIEW

TENON

Nº1

(FOR MARKING OUT AND SHAPING DETAILS SEE PAGE Nº191)

Nº2 ?

?

NAME
FORM
DATE

31

THEN CONSIDER AND BUILD UP RAIL SHAPES
ON THE OUTLINES

EXAMPLES

SEAGRASS STOOL BOTTOM RAIL SHAPE EXAMPLES

END VIEW

TENON   Nº1   TENON

(FOR MARKING OUT AND SHAPING DETAILS SEE PAGE Nº193)

Nº2

(FOR MARKING OUT AND SHAPING DETAILS SEE PAGE Nº192)

Nº3 ?

?

Nº4 ?

?

NAME   ?
FORM   ?
DATE   ?

SEAGRASS STOOL FRAMEWORK PRACTICE JOINTS AND SHAPES

32 ON A SHEET OF DRAWING PAPER SKETCH OR TRACE FAINT OUTLINES
OF A NUMBER OF CONSTRUCTED SEAGRASS STOOL FRAMEWORKS
(AN EXAMPLE BELOW)

SEAGRASS STOOL FRAMEWORKS

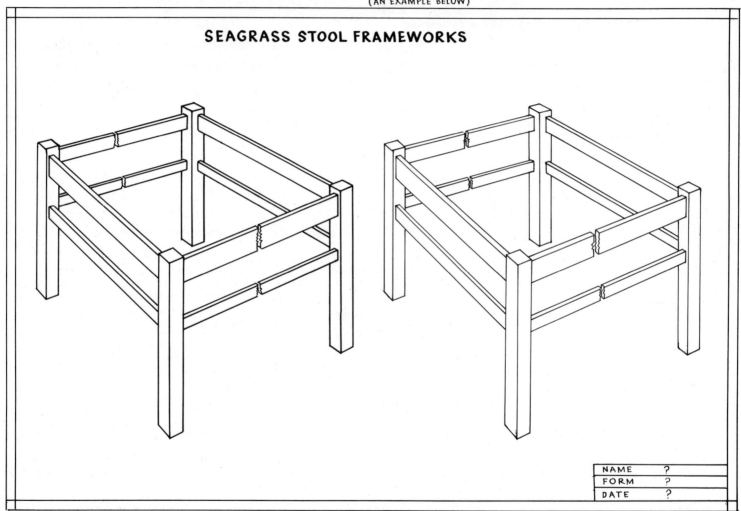

NAME	?
FORM	?
DATE	?

SEAGRASS STOOL FRAMEWORK PRACTICE JOINTS AND SHAPES

33 THEN BUILD UP A DESIGN WITH THE LEG SHAPES AND TOP RAIL SHAPES WHICH BLEND TOGETHER
(AN EXAMPLE BELOW)

SEAGRASS STOOL FRAMEWORKS

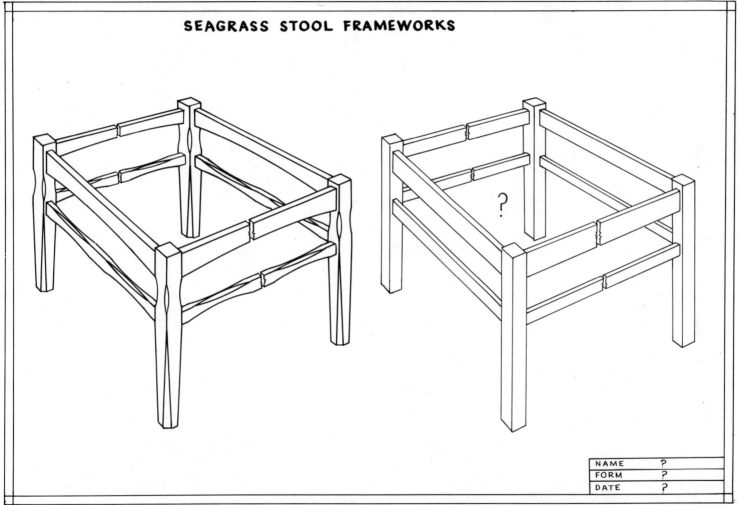

NAME	?
FORM	?
DATE	?

34 CONSIDER, MARK OUT AND SHAPE THE COMBINATION OF SHAPES YOU LIKE BEST ON THE PRACTICE LEG, TOP RAIL, AND BOTTOM RAIL.

SEAGRASS STOOL FRAMEWORK PRACTICE JOINTS AND SHAPES

A METHOD OF MARKING OUT AND SHAPING LEGS Nº1 AND Nº 2

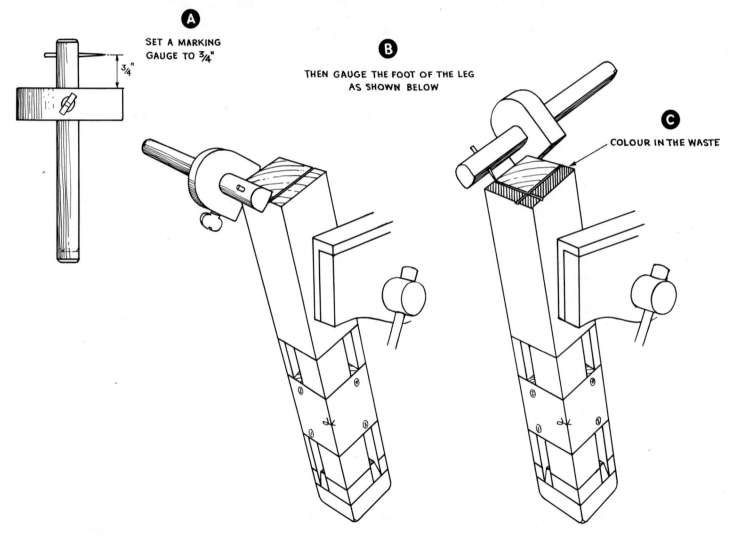

A SET A MARKING GAUGE TO ¾"

¾"

B THEN GAUGE THE FOOT OF THE LEG AS SHOWN BELOW

C COLOUR IN THE WASTE

SEAGRASS STOOL FRAMEWORK PRACTICE JOINTS AND SHAPES

A METHOD OF MARKING AND SHAPING LEGS Nº1 AND Nº2

D MARK TWO OPPOSITE TAPER LINES FROM THE FOOT OF THE LEG TO THE BOTTOM MORTICE LINE

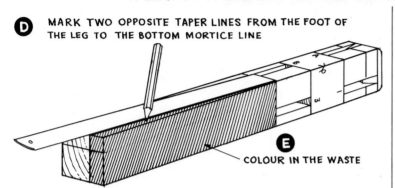

E COLOUR IN THE WASTE

F REMOVE THE WASTE WITH A JACK PLANE
(LEAVE PENCIL LINES JUST IN)

G MARK THE OTHER TWO TAPER LINES

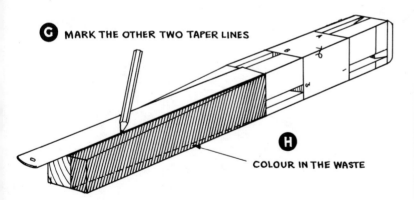

H COLOUR IN THE WASTE

I REMOVE THE WASTE WITH A JACK PLANE
(LEAVE PENCIL LINES JUST IN)

SEAGRASS STOOL FRAMEWORK PRACTICE JOINTS AND SHAPES

A METHOD OF MARKING OUT AND SHAPING LEG Nº 2

J MARK OUT SPLAYED CHAMFERS ON THE LEG CORNERS

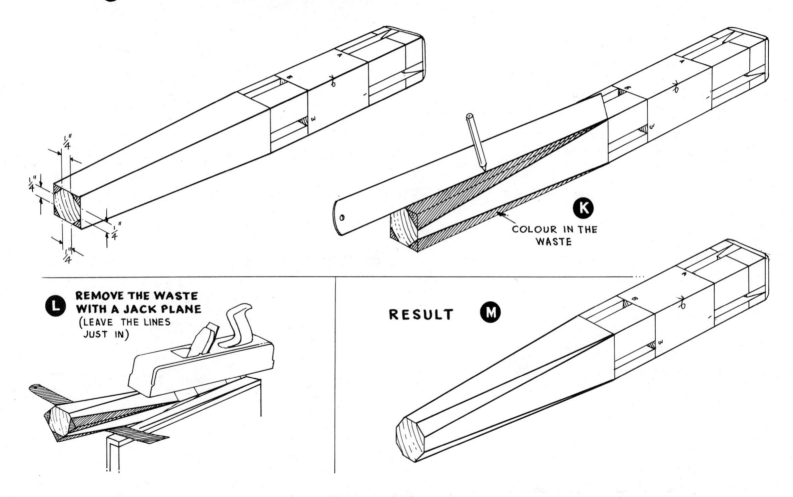

K COLOUR IN THE WASTE

L REMOVE THE WASTE WITH A JACK PLANE (LEAVE THE LINES JUST IN)

RESULT **M**

SEAGRASS STOOL FRAMEWORK PRACTICE JOINTS AND SHAPES

A METHOD OF MARKING OUT AND SHAPING LEG Nº 2

N

MAKE OR FIND A TIN OR BRASS
PATTERN OF A SUITABLE SIZE
TO MARK OUT WAGGON CHAMFERS

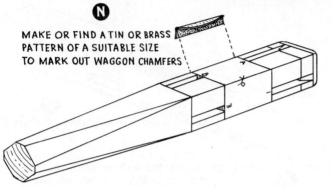

O

POSITION THE PATTERN BETWEEN
THE MORTICES AND MARK
AROUND THE CURVED EDGE

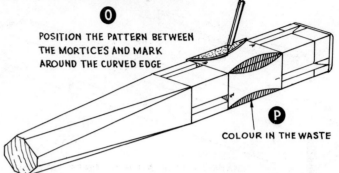

P

COLOUR IN THE WASTE

Q

REMOVE THE WASTE WITH
A ROUND FACED SPOKESHAVE
(LEAVE THE LINES JUST IN)

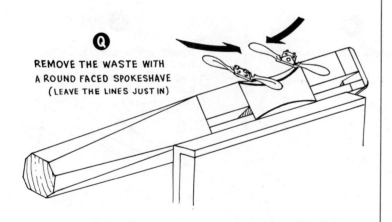

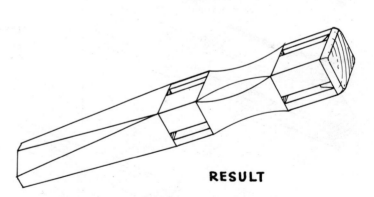

RESULT

SEAGRASS STOOL FRAMEWORK PRACTICE JOINTS AND SHAPES
A METHOD OF MARKING OUT AND SHAPING LEG Nº 3

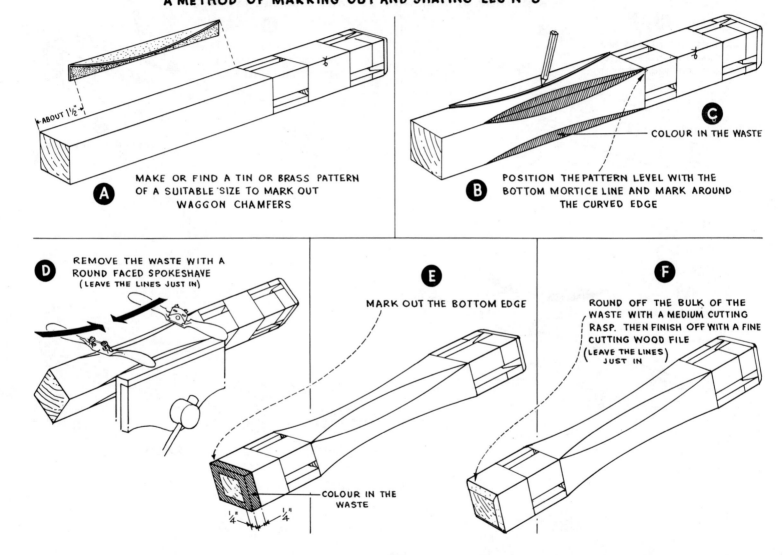

ABOUT 1½

A MAKE OR FIND A TIN OR BRASS PATTERN OF A SUITABLE SIZE TO MARK OUT WAGGON CHAMFERS

B POSITION THE PATTERN LEVEL WITH THE BOTTOM MORTICE LINE AND MARK AROUND THE CURVED EDGE

COLOUR IN THE WASTE

C

D REMOVE THE WASTE WITH A ROUND FACED SPOKESHAVE (LEAVE THE LINES JUST IN)

E MARK OUT THE BOTTOM EDGE

COLOUR IN THE WASTE

¼" ¼"

F ROUND OFF THE BULK OF THE WASTE WITH A MEDIUM CUTTING RASP. THEN FINISH OFF WITH A FINE CUTTING WOOD FILE (LEAVE THE LINES JUST IN)

SEAGRASS STOOL FRAMEWORK PRACTICE JOINTS AND SHAPES

A METHOD OF MARKING OUT AND SHAPING TOP RAIL Nº I

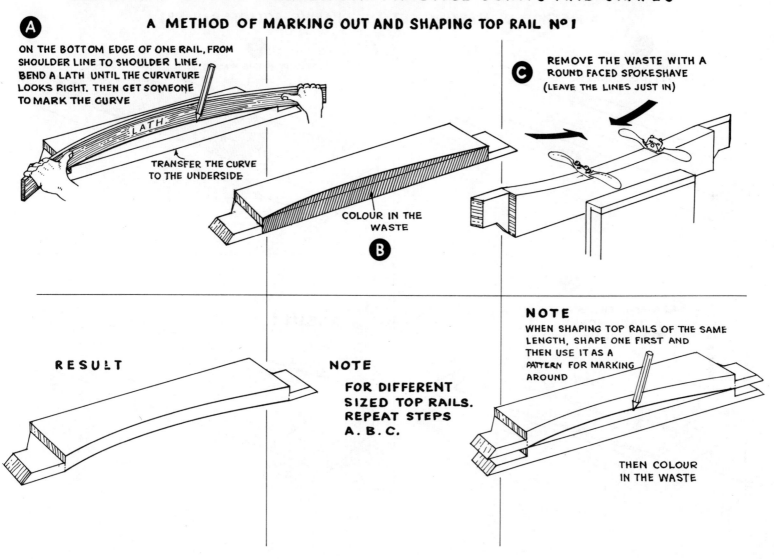

A ON THE BOTTOM EDGE OF ONE RAIL, FROM SHOULDER LINE TO SHOULDER LINE, BEND A LATH UNTIL THE CURVATURE LOOKS RIGHT. THEN GET SOMEONE TO MARK THE CURVE

LATH.

TRANSFER THE CURVE TO THE UNDERSIDE

COLOUR IN THE WASTE

B

C REMOVE THE WASTE WITH A ROUND FACED SPOKESHAVE (LEAVE THE LINES JUST IN)

RESULT

NOTE

FOR DIFFERENT SIZED TOP RAILS. REPEAT STEPS A. B. C.

NOTE

WHEN SHAPING TOP RAILS OF THE SAME LENGTH, SHAPE ONE FIRST AND THEN USE IT AS A PATTERN FOR MARKING AROUND

THEN COLOUR IN THE WASTE

SEAGRASS STOOL FRAMEWORK PRACTICE JOINTS AND SHAPES

A METHOD OF MARKING OUT AND SHAPING BOTTOM RAIL Nº1

A

ON THE INSIDE TOP EDGE
MARK OUT THE CHAMFER

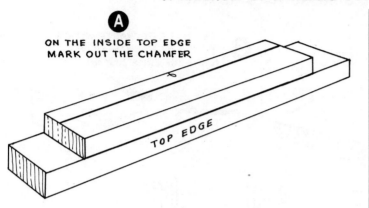

TOP EDGE

B

COLOUR IN THE WASTE

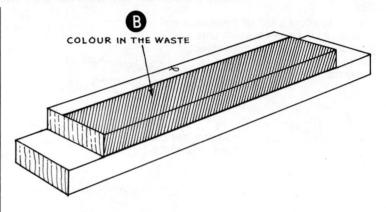

C

REMOVE THE WASTE WITH
A JACK PLANE
(LEAVE THE LINES WELL IN)

RESULT

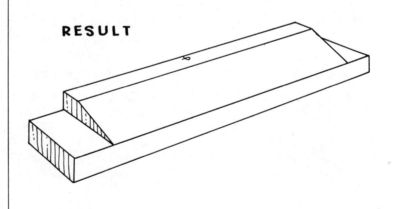

SEAGRASS STOOL FRAMEWORK PRACTICE JOINTS AND SHAPES
A METHOD OF MARKING OUT AND SHAPING BOTTOM RAIL Nº2

A MAKE OR FIND A TIN OR BRASS PATTERN OF A SUITABLE SIZE TO MARK OUT WAGGON CHAMFERS

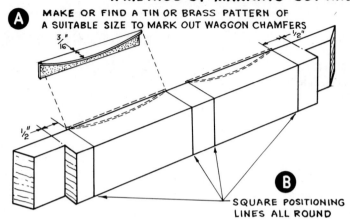

$\frac{3}{16}$"

$\frac{1}{2}$"

$\frac{1}{2}$"

B SQUARE POSITIONING LINES ALL ROUND

C POSITION THE PATTERN BETWEEN THE SQUARED LINES AND MARK AROUND THE CURVED EDGE

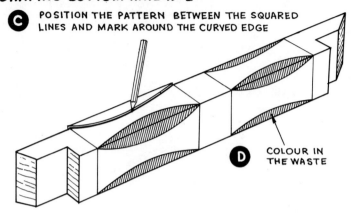

D COLOUR IN THE WASTE

E REMOVE THE WASTE WITH A ROUND FACED SPOKESHAVE (LEAVE THE LINES JUST IN)

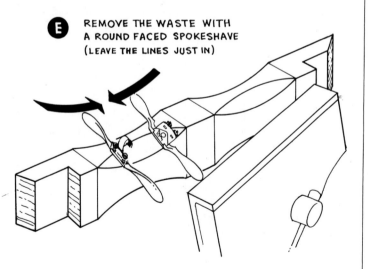

RESULT

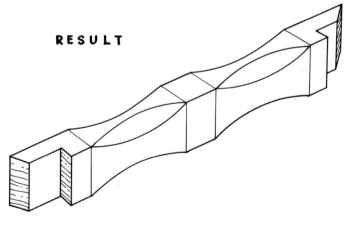

DESIGN AND CONSTRUCTION GUIDE FOR MAKING A SEAGRASS STOOL

1 ON A SHEET OF PAPER FAINTLY SKETCH OR TRACE THE DETAILS ON THESE TWO PAGES

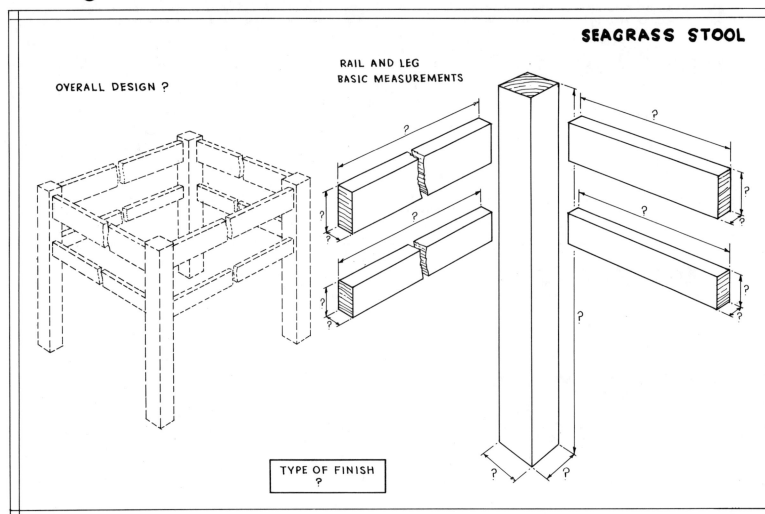

SEAGRASS STOOL

OVERALL DESIGN ?

RAIL AND LEG
BASIC MEASUREMENTS

TYPE OF FINISH
?

DESIGN AND CONSTRUCTION GUIDE FOR MAKING A SEAGRASS STOOL

DETAILS

LEG MORTICE AND HAUNCHING DETAILS

LEG SHAPE ?

TOP RAIL SHAPE

BOTTOM RAIL SHAPE

TENON, HAUNCH AND MITRE DETAILS

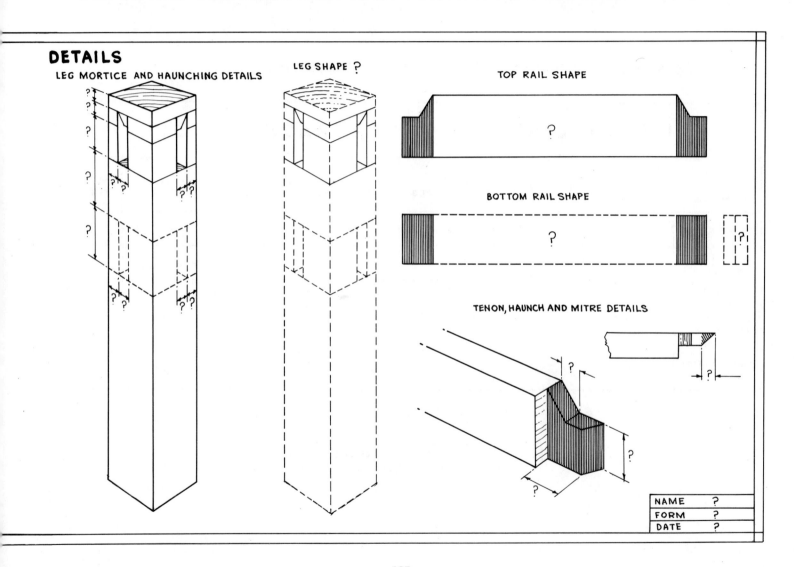

NAME	?
FORM	?
DATE	?

DESIGN AND CONSTRUCTION GUIDE FOR MAKING A SEAGRASS STOOL

2 MAKE OUT A TIMBER LIST FOR YOUR SEAGRASS STOOL

TIMBER LIST FOR A SEAGRASS STOOL

NAMES OF MEMBERS	VARIETY OF TIMBER TO BE USED	STATE OF TIMBER TO BE USED	NUMBER REQUIRED	OVERALL LENGTH OF EACH MEMBER	TOTAL LENGTH REQUIRED FOR THIS TYPE OF MEMBER	OVERALL WIDTH	OVERALL THICKNESS
LEGS	?	?	?	?	?	?	?
LONG TOP RAILS	?	?	?	? + 1" P.A.	?	? + ¼" P.A	?
LONG BOTTOM RAILS	?	?	?	? + 1" P.A.	?	? + ¼" P.A	?
SHORT TOP RAILS	?	?	?	? + 1" P.A.	?	? + ¼" P.A	?
SHORT BOTTOM RAILS	?	?	?	? + 1" P.A	?	? + ¼" P.A	?

NOTE.

(ALLOWANCE HAS BEEN MADE ON THE TIMBER TO MAKE
  A STOOL WITH LONG AND SHORT RAILS. FOR AN EQUAL
  SIDED STOOL DO NOT INCLUDE THE BOTTOM TWO LINES.)

DESIGN AND CONSTRUCTION GUIDE FOR MAKING A SEAGRASS STOOL

❸

NOW FOLLOW THE INSTRUCTIONS AND ANSWER EACH OF THE QUESTIONS IN TURN

AS YOU PROGRESS FILL IN THE REQUIRED INFORMATION ON YOUR TIMBER LIST AND SKETCH OR TRACING

EVENTUALLY DEVELOP AN ORTHO-GRAPHIC DRAWING OF YOUR SEAGRASS STOOL'S FRAMEWORK

❹ WHAT TYPE OF FINISH WILL YOU APPLY TO YOUR SEAGRASS STOOL FRAMEWORK'S SURFACE?

PAINT OR

A CLEAR FINISH
(EXAMPLES)

LINSEED OIL
CELLULOSE
LACQUER
FRENCH POLISH
ETC.

❺ WHAT VARIETY OR VARIETIES OF HARDWOOD OR SOFTWOOD WILL YOU USE FOR YOUR FRAMEWORK'S SURFACE?

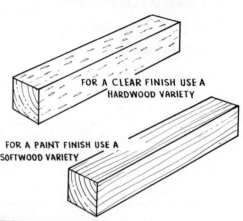

FOR A CLEAR FINISH USE A HARDWOOD VARIETY

FOR A PAINT FINISH USE A SOFTWOOD VARIETY

❻ WHAT WILL BE THE HEIGHT OF YOUR STOOL LEGS ?

A METHOD OF FINDING GIVEN BELOW

CONSIDER THE HEIGHT OF THE PERSON WHO WILL USE IT, AND THROUGH TRIAL AND ERROR FIND THE MOST COMFORTABLE HEIGHT

THEN ADD TO THE MEASURED COMFORTABLE HEIGHT ADD 1" EXTRA

NOTE
WITHOUT THIS EXTRA 1" ALLOWED ABOVE, YOU MAY SPLIT THE LEG TOP WHEN MORTICING

CH

CH CH+1"

13*

DESIGN AND CONSTRUCTION GUIDE FOR MAKING A SEAGRASS STOOL

7

WHAT WILL BE THE
WIDTH AND THE
THICKNESS OF YOUR
STOOL LEGS ?

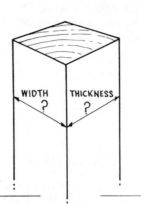

WIDTH
?

THICKNESS
?

8

PREPARE THE TIMBER FOR THE LEGS TO THEIR
MARKING OUT SIZES

(PREPARE THE LEGS FROM MACHINE PLANED
ALL ROUND SCANTLING

(FOR A PREPARATION GUIDE SEE PAGE Nº29)

9 WHAT WILL BE THE LENGTH OF YOUR STOOL RAILS
(A METHOD OF FINDING GIVEN BELOW)

POSITION THE LEGS EVENLY UNTIL THE SIZE
OF THE TOP IS A COMFORTABLE SITTING AREA

AND THE DISTANCE BETWEEN
THE LEGS LOOKS IN TUNE WITH THE HEIGHT

THEN MEASURE THE RAIL LENGTHS

VIEW FROM
ABOUT 10 FT.

IF SQUARE, ONLY
ONE MEASUREMENT
IS REQUIRED

?-5/8"

?-5/8"

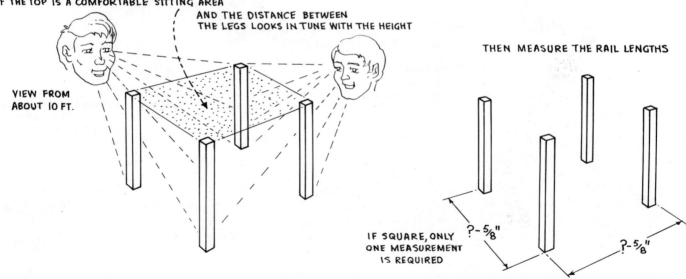

198

DESIGN AND CONSTRUCTION GUIDE FOR MAKING A SEAGRASS STOOL

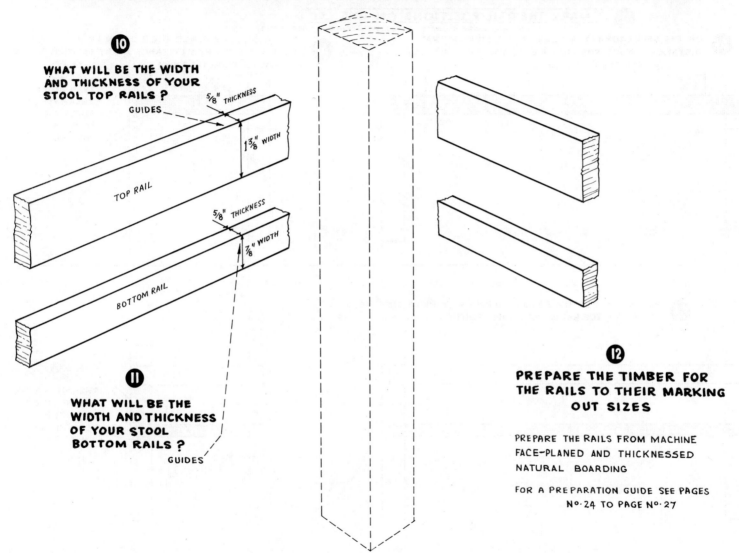

10

WHAT WILL BE THE WIDTH AND THICKNESS OF YOUR STOOL TOP RAILS ?

GUIDES

5/8" THICKNESS

1 3/8" WIDTH

TOP RAIL

5/8" THICKNESS

7/8" WIDTH

BOTTOM RAIL

11

WHAT WILL BE THE WIDTH AND THICKNESS OF YOUR STOOL BOTTOM RAILS ?

GUIDES

12

PREPARE THE TIMBER FOR THE RAILS TO THEIR MARKING OUT SIZES

PREPARE THE RAILS FROM MACHINE FACE-PLANED AND THICKNESSED NATURAL BOARDING

FOR A PREPARATION GUIDE SEE PAGES Nº 24 TO PAGE Nº 27

DESIGN AND CONSTRUCTION GUIDE FOR MAKING A SEAGRASS STOOL

A13 MARK THE RAIL POSITIONS ON ONE LEG
(A METHOD GIVEN BELOW FOR A STOOL WITH LONG AND SHORT RAILS)

A1 ON THE BENCH TOP PLACE 2 LEGS AT THE LONG TOP RAIL DISTANCE APART. POSITION A LONG TOP RAIL 1¼" FROM THE TOP OF THE LEGS

A2 THEN ALONGSIDE PLACE THE 2 OTHER LEGS AT THE SHORT TOP RAIL DISTANCE APART. POSITION A SHORT TOP RAIL 1¼" FROM THE TOP OF THE LEG

A3 THEN WITH A VERY SHARP PENCIL MARK THE POSITION ON THIS LEG

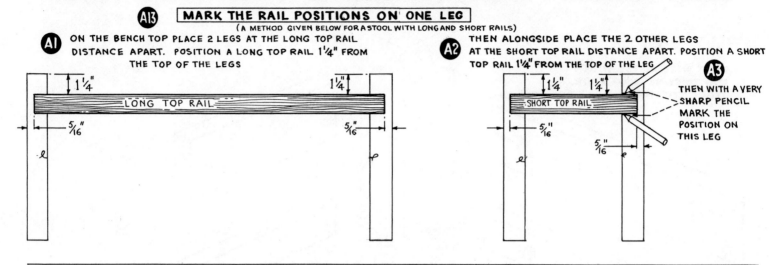

A4 PLACE THE BOTTOM RAILS SQUARELY AT VARIOUS DISTANCES BELOW THE TOP RAILS UNTIL THEIR POSITIONS LOOK RIGHT (IN PROPORTION)

A5 THEN WITH A VERY SHARP PENCIL MARK THE POSITION ON THIS LEG

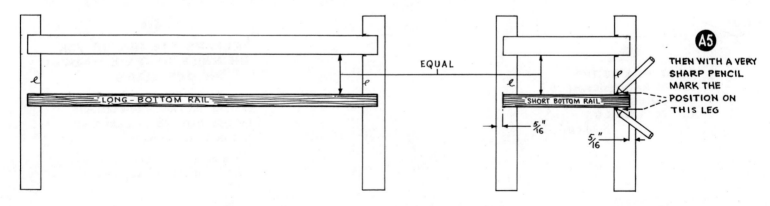

200

DESIGN AND CONSTRUCTION GUIDE FOR MAKING A SEAGRASS STOOL

B13 **MARK THE RAIL POSITIONS ON ONE LEG**
(A METHOD GIVEN BELOW FOR A STOOL WITH ALL THE RAILS OF EQUAL LENGTH)

B1 ON THE BENCH TOP PLACE 2 LEGS AT THE TOP RAIL DISTANCE APART. POSITION A TOP RAIL 1¼" FROM THE TOP OF THE LEGS

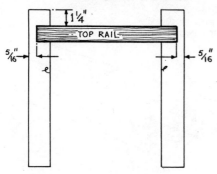

B2 THEN WITH A VERY SHARP PENCIL

MARK THE POSITION ON THE LEG

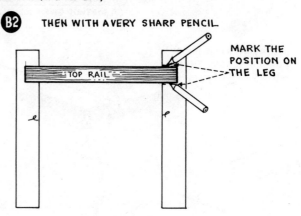

B3 PLACE A BOTTOM RAIL AT VARIOUS DISTANCES BELOW THE TOP RAIL UNTIL ITS POSITION LOOKS RIGHT. (IN PROPORTION)

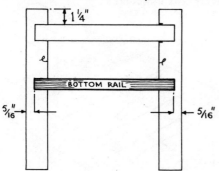

B4

THEN WITH A VERY SHARP PENCIL MARK THE POSITION ON THE LEG

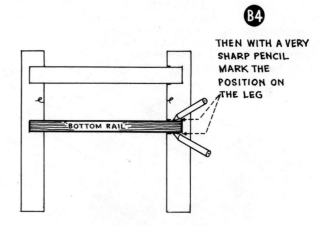

201

DESIGN AND CONSTRUCTION GUIDE FOR MAKING A SEAGRASS STOOL

⑭ MARK OUT THE LEG HAUNCHINGS AND MORTICES
(A METHOD GIVEN BELOW AND CONTINUED ON THE NEXT PAGE)

⑮

ON THE MARKED LEGS
SQUARE ACROSS THE
RAIL POSITIONS

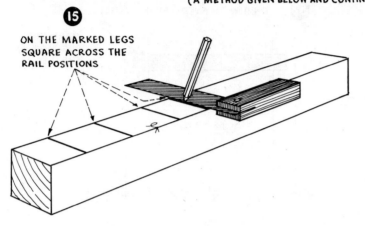

⑯

ON THE SAME LEG
MEASURE AND SQUARE
THE HAUNCHING LINE

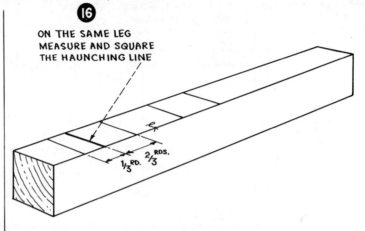

⅓ RD.   ⅔ RDS.

⑰

GET SOMEONE TO GRIP THE LEGS FIRMLY,
OR GRIP THEM IN SASH CRAMPS OR THE
VICE WITH THEIR TOPS SQUARE AT
ONE END AND THEIR FACES LEVEL

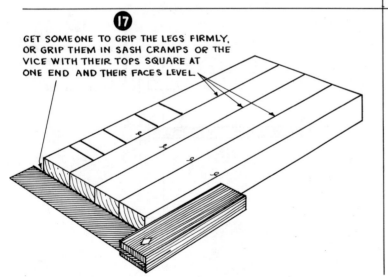

⑱

THEN TRANSFER THE MARKS
OVER ONTO THE UNMARKED
LEGS

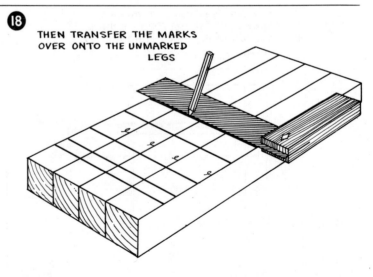

DESIGN AND CONSTRUCTION GUIDE FOR MAKING A SEAGRASS STOOL

19 SQUARE THE MARKS OVER ONTO THE FACE EDGE OF EACH LEG

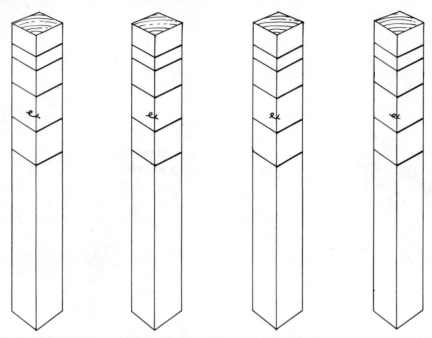

20 SET A MORTICE GAUGE FOR GAUGING THE
LEG MORTICES AND HAUNCHINGS WIDTH

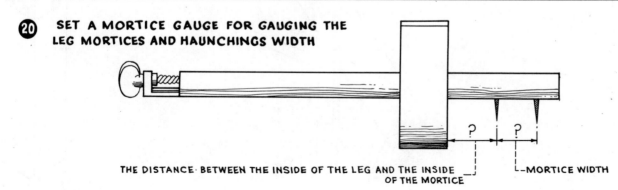

THE DISTANCE BETWEEN THE INSIDE OF THE LEG AND THE INSIDE
OF THE MORTICE

└─MORTICE WIDTH

DESIGN AND CONSTRUCTION GUIDE FOR MAKING A SEAGRASS STOOL

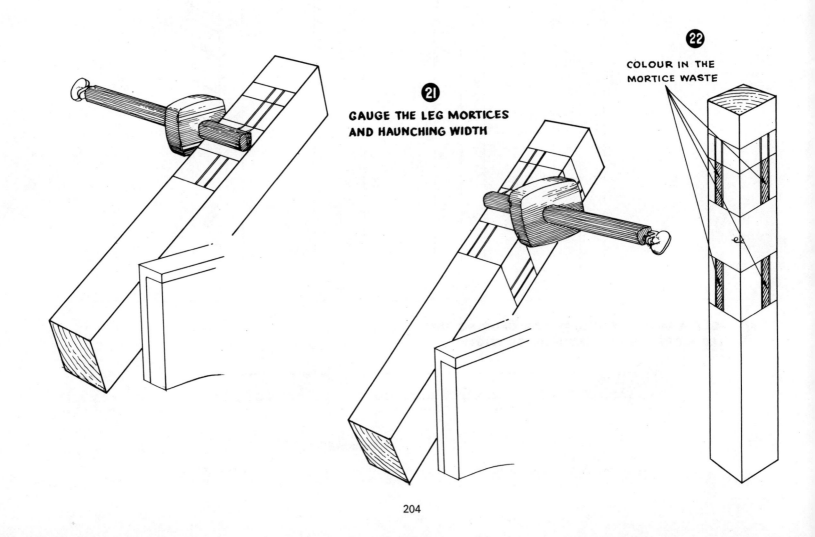

21 GAUGE THE LEG MORTICES AND HAUNCHING WIDTH

22 COLOUR IN THE MORTICE WASTE

DESIGN AND CONSTRUCTION GUIDE FOR MAKING A SEAGRASS STOOL

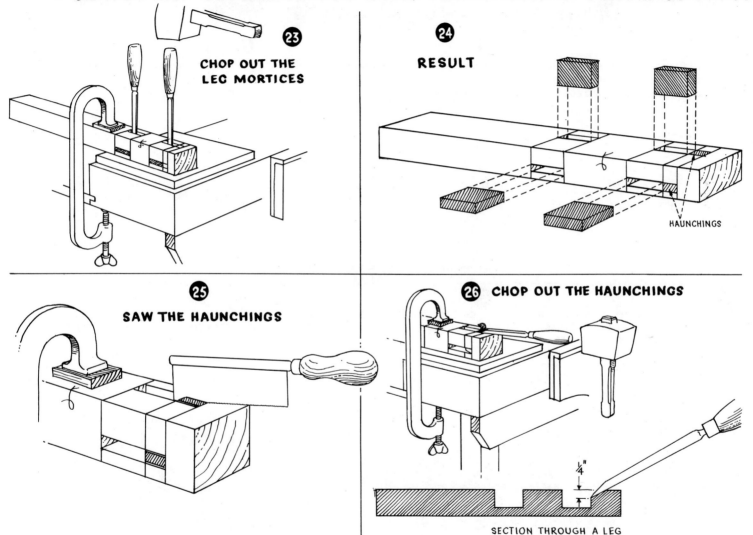

23 CHOP OUT THE LEG MORTICES

24 RESULT

HAUNCHINGS

25 SAW THE HAUNCHINGS

26 CHOP OUT THE HAUNCHINGS

¼"

SECTION THROUGH A LEG

DESIGN AND CONSTRUCTION GUIDE FOR MAKING A SEAGRASS STOOL

27A MARK OUT THE TENON LENGTH ON THE RAILS
(A METHOD GIVEN BELOW FOR A STOOL WITH SHORT AND LONG RAILS)

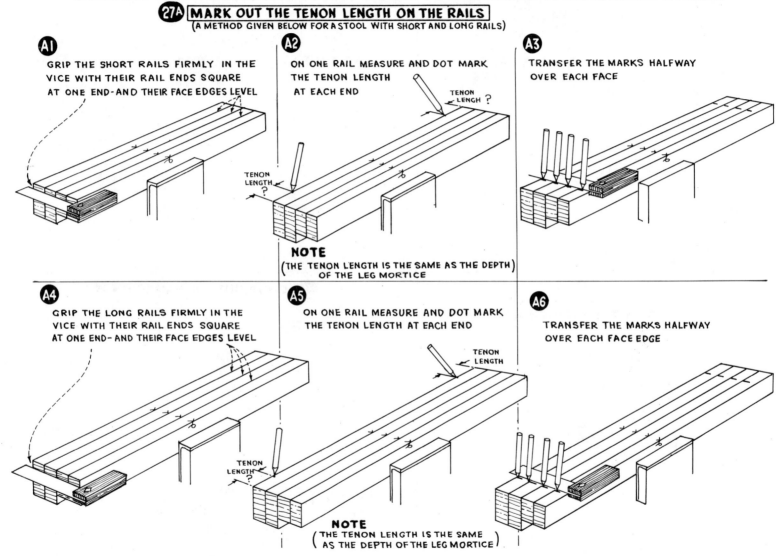

A1 GRIP THE SHORT RAILS FIRMLY IN THE VICE WITH THEIR RAIL ENDS SQUARE AT ONE END - AND THEIR FACE EDGES LEVEL

A2 ON ONE RAIL MEASURE AND DOT MARK THE TENON LENGTH AT EACH END

TENON LENGTH?

TENON LENGTH?

NOTE
(THE TENON LENGTH IS THE SAME AS THE DEPTH) OF THE LEG MORTICE

A3 TRANSFER THE MARKS HALFWAY OVER EACH FACE

A4 GRIP THE LONG RAILS FIRMLY IN THE VICE WITH THEIR RAIL ENDS SQUARE AT ONE END - AND THEIR FACE EDGES LEVEL

A5 ON ONE RAIL MEASURE AND DOT MARK THE TENON LENGTH AT EACH END

TENON LENGTH

TENON LENGTH?

NOTE
(THE TENON LENGTH IS THE SAME) AS THE DEPTH OF THE LEG MORTICE

A6 TRANSFER THE MARKS HALFWAY OVER EACH FACE EDGE

206

DESIGN AND CONSTRUCTION GUIDE FOR MAKING A SEAGRASS STOOL

27B MARK OUT THE TENON LENGTH ON THE RAILS
(A METHOD GIVEN BELOW FOR A STOOL WITH ALL THE RAILS OF EQUAL LENGTH)

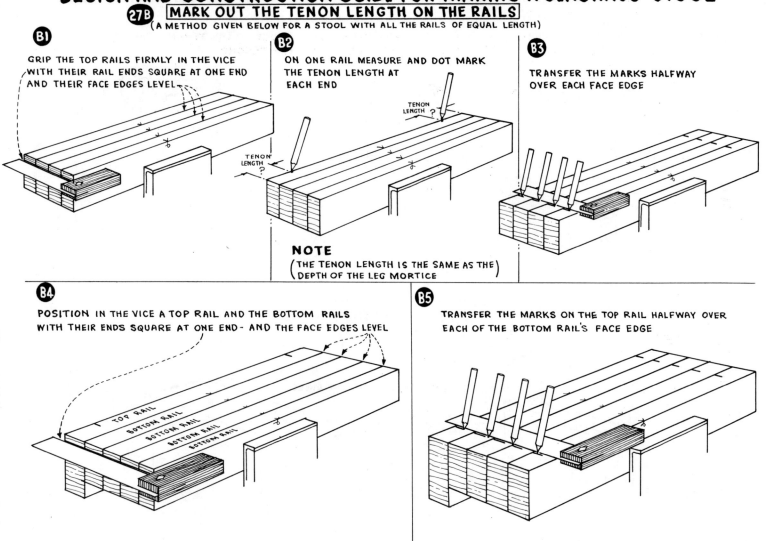

B1 GRIP THE TOP RAILS FIRMLY IN THE VICE WITH THEIR RAIL ENDS SQUARE AT ONE END AND THEIR FACE EDGES LEVEL

B2 ON ONE RAIL MEASURE AND DOT MARK THE TENON LENGTH AT EACH END

TENON LENGTH ?

TENON LENGTH ?

NOTE
(THE TENON LENGTH IS THE SAME AS THE DEPTH OF THE LEG MORTICE)

B3 TRANSFER THE MARKS HALFWAY OVER EACH FACE EDGE

B4 POSITION IN THE VICE A TOP RAIL AND THE BOTTOM RAILS WITH THEIR ENDS SQUARE AT ONE END - AND THE FACE EDGES LEVEL

TOP RAIL
BOTTOM RAIL
BOTTOM RAIL
BOTTOM RAIL
BOTTOM RAIL

B5 TRANSFER THE MARKS ON THE TOP RAIL HALFWAY OVER EACH OF THE BOTTOM RAIL'S FACE EDGE

DESIGN AND CONSTRUCTION DETAIL FOR MAKING A SEAGRASS STOOL

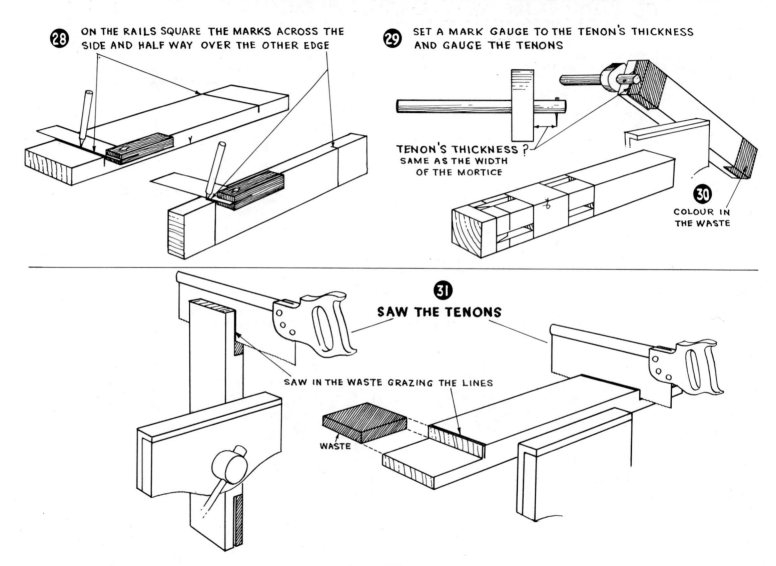

28 ON THE RAILS SQUARE THE MARKS ACROSS THE SIDE AND HALF WAY OVER THE OTHER EDGE

29 SET A MARK GAUGE TO THE TENON'S THICKNESS AND GAUGE THE TENONS

TENON'S THICKNESS ?
SAME AS THE WIDTH
OF THE MORTICE

30 COLOUR IN THE WASTE

31

SAW THE TENONS

SAW IN THE WASTE GRAZING THE LINES

WASTE

DESIGN AND CONSTRUCTION GUIDE FOR MAKING A SEAGRASS STOOL

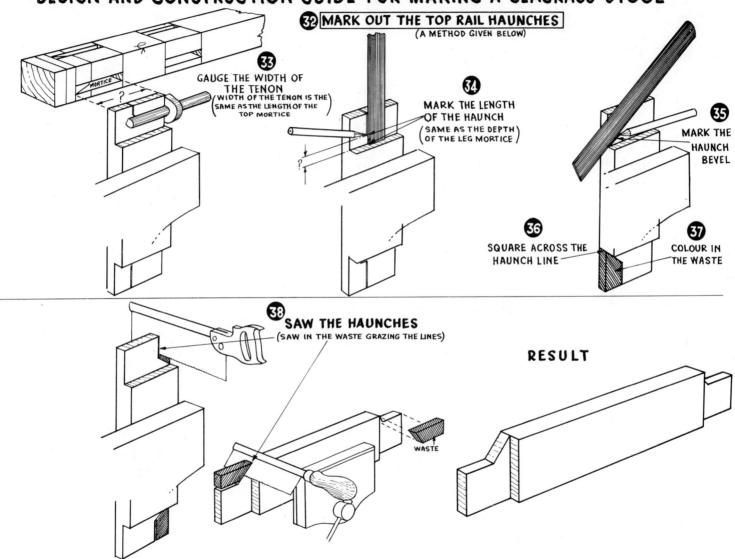

32 MARK OUT THE TOP RAIL HAUNCHES
(A METHOD GIVEN BELOW)

MORTICE

33 GAUGE THE WIDTH OF THE TENON
(WIDTH OF THE TENON IS THE SAME AS THE LENGTH OF THE TOP MORTICE)

34 MARK THE LENGTH OF THE HAUNCH
(SAME AS THE DEPTH OF THE LEG MORTICE)

35 MARK THE HAUNCH BEVEL

36 SQUARE ACROSS THE HAUNCH LINE

37 COLOUR IN THE WASTE

38 SAW THE HAUNCHES
(SAW IN THE WASTE GRAZING THE LINES)

WASTE

RESULT

DESIGN AND CONSTRUCTION GUIDE FOR MAKING A SEAGRASS STOOL

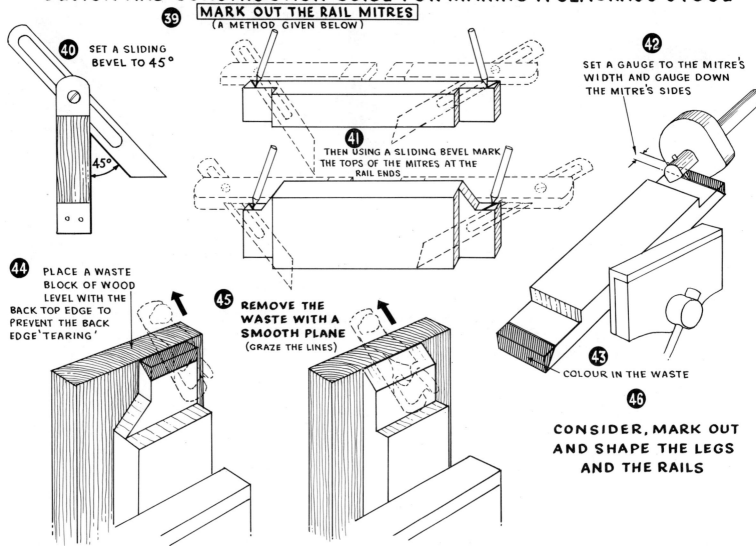

39 MARK OUT THE RAIL MITRES
(A METHOD GIVEN BELOW)

40 SET A SLIDING BEVEL TO 45°

45°

41 THEN USING A SLIDING BEVEL MARK THE TOPS OF THE MITRES AT THE RAIL ENDS

42 SET A GAUGE TO THE MITRE'S WIDTH AND GAUGE DOWN THE MITRE'S SIDES

43 COLOUR IN THE WASTE

44 PLACE A WASTE BLOCK OF WOOD LEVEL WITH THE BACK TOP EDGE TO PREVENT THE BACK EDGE 'TEARING'

45 REMOVE THE WASTE WITH A SMOOTH PLANE
(GRAZE THE LINES)

46 CONSIDER, MARK OUT AND SHAPE THE LEGS AND THE RAILS

DESIGN AND CONSTRUCTION FOR MAKING A SEAGRASS STOOL

47 NUMBER OFF AND FIT THE JOINTS
(A METHOD GIVEN BELOW AND CONTINUED ON THE NEXT PAGE)

48 LAY OUT FOUR LEGS AND TWO SIMILAR SETS OF RAILS
AND NUMBER OFF THE JOINTS

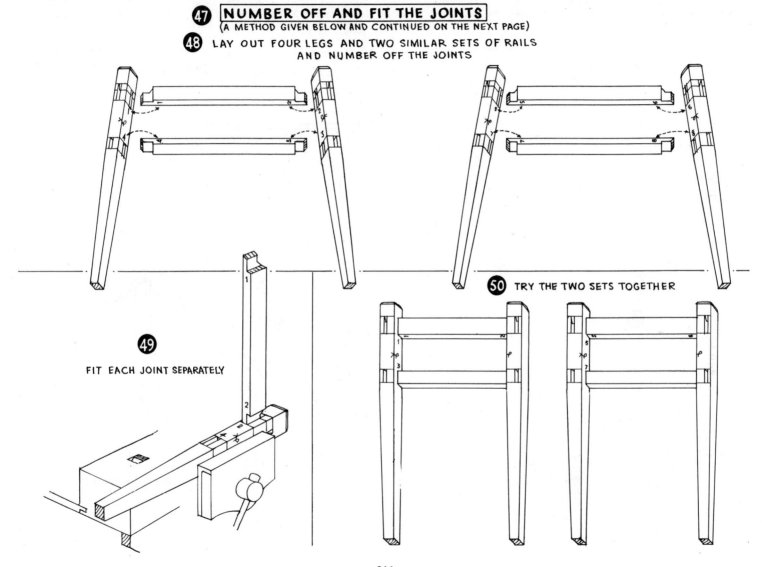

49 FIT EACH JOINT SEPARATELY

50 TRY THE TWO SETS TOGETHER

DESIGN AND CONSTRUCTION DETAILS FOR MAKING A SEAGRASS STOOL

51 LAY OUT THE FITTED RAILS AND LEGS, AND THE RAILS TO BE FITTED, AS SHOWN BELOW – THEN LETTER OFF THE REST OF THE JOINTS

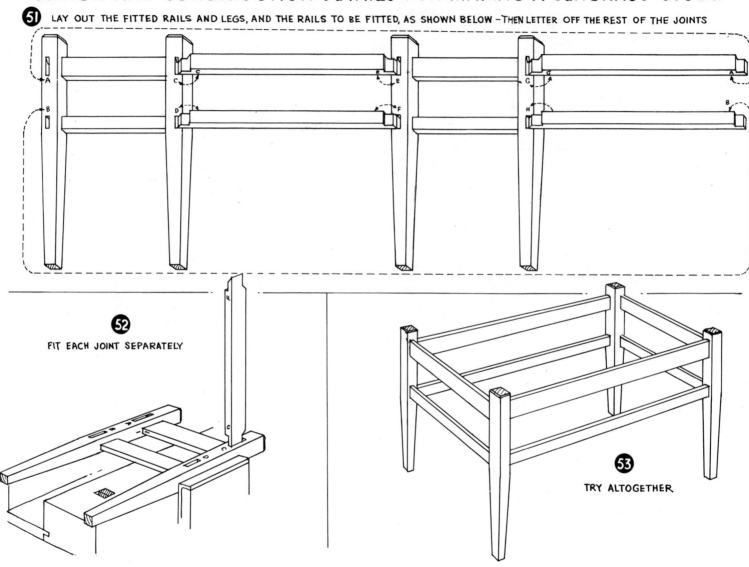

52 FIT EACH JOINT SEPARATELY

53 TRY ALTOGETHER

DESIGN AND CONSTRUCTION GUIDE FOR MAKING A SEAGRASS STOOL

54 MARK OUT AND SHAPE LEG TOPS
(A METHOD GIVEN BELOW)

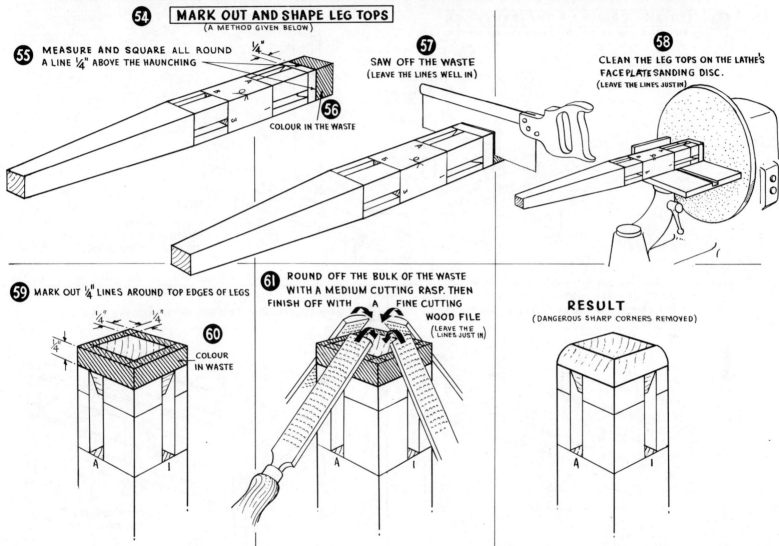

55 MEASURE AND SQUARE ALL ROUND A LINE ¼" ABOVE THE HAUNCHING

56 COLOUR IN THE WASTE

57 SAW OFF THE WASTE
(LEAVE THE LINES WELL IN)

58 CLEAN THE LEG TOPS ON THE LATHE'S FACE PLATE SANDING DISC.
(LEAVE THE LINES JUST IN)

59 MARK OUT ¼" LINES AROUND TOP EDGES OF LEGS

60 COLOUR IN WASTE

61 ROUND OFF THE BULK OF THE WASTE WITH A MEDIUM CUTTING RASP. THEN FINISH OFF WITH A FINE CUTTING WOOD FILE
(LEAVE THE LINES JUST IN)

RESULT
(DANGEROUS SHARP CORNERS REMOVED)

213

14*

DESIGN AND CONSTRUCTION GUIDE FOR MAKING A SEAGRASS STOOL

62 **GLUE AND CRAMP UP THE FRAMEWORK**
(A METHOD GIVEN BELOW AND CONTINUED ON THE NEXT PAGE)

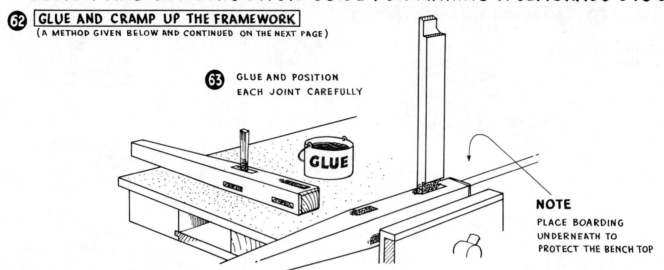

63 GLUE AND POSITION
EACH JOINT CAREFULLY

GLUE

NOTE
PLACE BOARDING
UNDERNEATH TO
PROTECT THE BENCH TOP

64 TIE TWO STRONG LENGTHS OF STRINGS
AT THE CENTRE OF THE RAILS, ALL ROUND THE STOOL

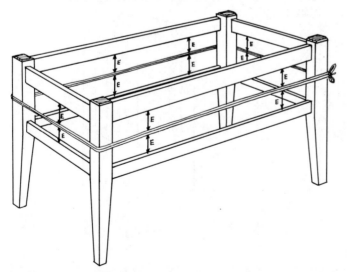

65 CRAMP TOGETHER BY TWISTING WITH WOODEN KEYS

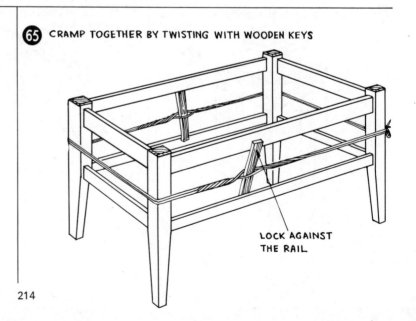

LOCK AGAINST
THE RAIL

DESIGN AND CONSTRUCTION GUIDE FOR MAKING A SEAGRASS STOOL

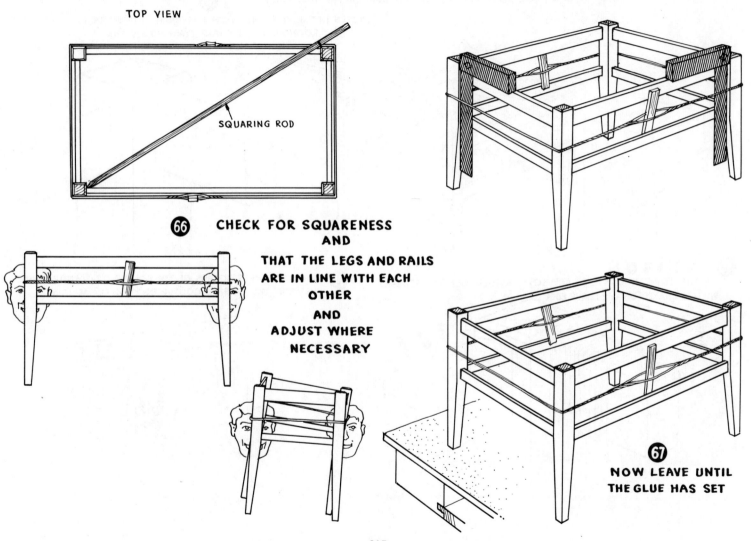

TOP VIEW

SQUARING ROD

66 CHECK FOR SQUARENESS
AND
THAT THE LEGS AND RAILS
ARE IN LINE WITH EACH
OTHER
AND
ADJUST WHERE
NECESSARY

67 NOW LEAVE UNTIL
THE GLUE HAS SET

DESIGN AND CONSTRUCTION GUIDE FOR MAKING A SEAGRASS STOOL

68 **PREPARE FOR WEAVING THE SEAGRASS TOP**
(A METHOD GIVEN BELOW AND CONTINUED ON THE NEXT PAGE)

69 FASTEN IN THE VICE AND WITH A MEDIUM CUTTING RASP ROUND OFF THE SHARP CORNERS OF THE TOP RAILS

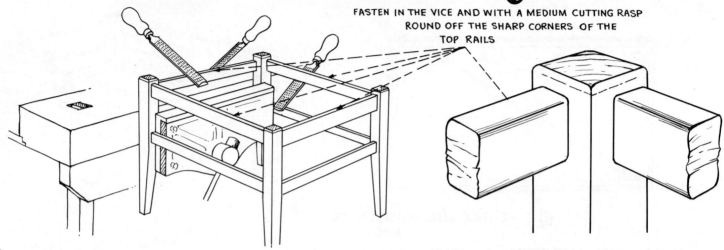

70 **R E A S O N**
IF THE TOP RAIL CORNERS ARE NOT ROUNDED OFF. THE SEAGRASS WILL BE CHAFED ON THE SHARP EDGES

71 PURCHASE THE SEAGRASS OF THE COLOUR OR COLOURS WHICH WILL SUIT THE FINISHED COLOUR OF YOUR FRAMEWORK

HOMECRAFT

216

DESIGN AND CONSTRUCTION GUIDE FOR MAKING A SEAGRASS STOOL

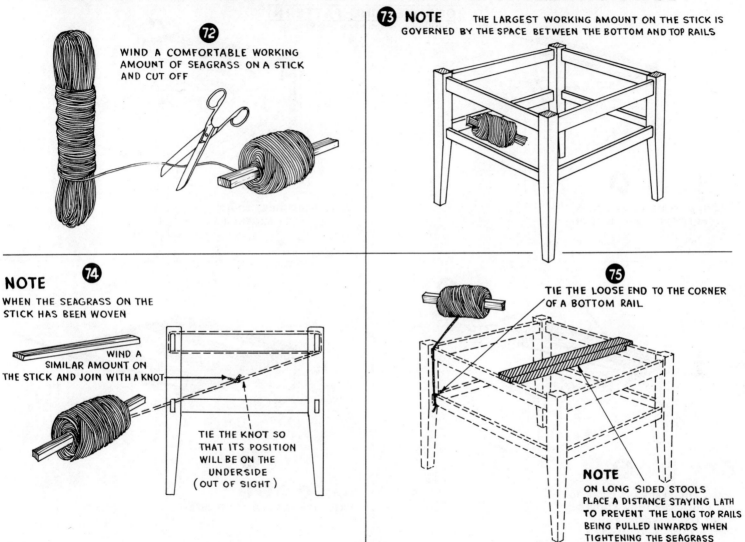

72 WIND A COMFORTABLE WORKING AMOUNT OF SEAGRASS ON A STICK AND CUT OFF

73 NOTE THE LARGEST WORKING AMOUNT ON THE STICK IS GOVERNED BY THE SPACE BETWEEN THE BOTTOM AND TOP RAILS

NOTE 74 WHEN THE SEAGRASS ON THE STICK HAS BEEN WOVEN

WIND A SIMILAR AMOUNT ON THE STICK AND JOIN WITH A KNOT

TIE THE KNOT SO THAT ITS POSITION WILL BE ON THE UNDERSIDE (OUT OF SIGHT)

75 TIE THE LOOSE END TO THE CORNER OF A BOTTOM RAIL

NOTE ON LONG SIDED STOOLS PLACE A DISTANCE STAYING LATH TO PREVENT THE LONG TOP RAILS BEING PULLED INWARDS WHEN TIGHTENING THE SEAGRASS

217

DESIGN AND CONSTRUCTION GUIDE FOR MAKING A SEAGRASS STOOL

ONE WEAVING PATTERN
(CONTINUED ON THE NEXT TWO PAGES)

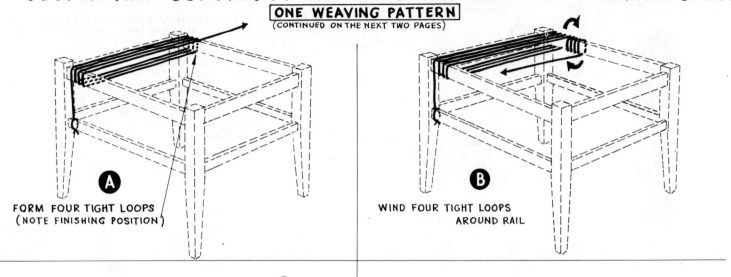

A FORM FOUR TIGHT LOOPS
(NOTE FINISHING POSITION)

B WIND FOUR TIGHT LOOPS
AROUND RAIL

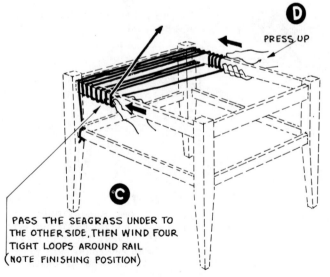

D PRESS UP

C PASS THE SEAGRASS UNDER TO
THE OTHER SIDE, THEN WIND FOUR
TIGHT LOOPS AROUND RAIL
(NOTE FINISHING POSITION)

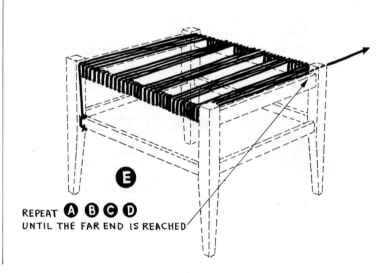

E REPEAT **A** **B** **C** **D**
UNTIL THE FAR END IS REACHED

DESIGN AND CONSTRUCTION GUIDE FOR MAKING A SEAGRASS STOOL

① **NOTE** IF THIS OCCURS — TO BALANCE THE PATTERN, EASE BACK THE WEAVING UNTIL THERE IS SUFFICIENT SPACE TO ALLOW FOUR LONG LOOPS AT THE FINISH

FOUR SHORT LOOPS AT THE FINISH

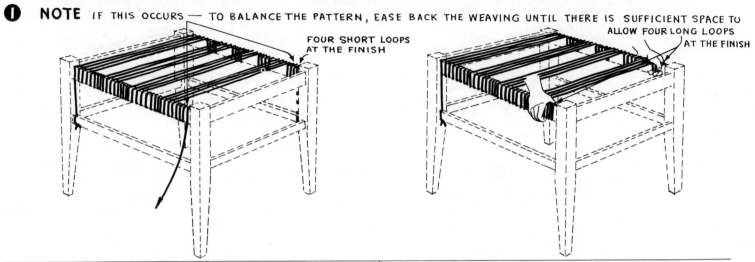

ⓖ **NOTE** IF A DIFFERENT CROSS-COLOUR IS TO BE USED

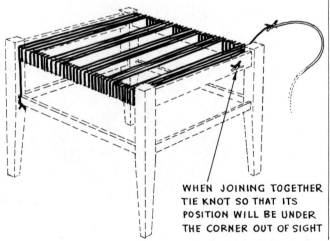

WHEN JOINING TOGETHER TIE KNOT SO THAT ITS POSITION WILL BE UNDER THE CORNER OUT OF SIGHT

ⓗ

PULL THE SEAGRASS UNDER THE CORNER AND THROUGH THE END

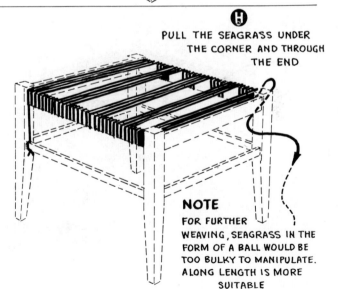

NOTE
FOR FURTHER WEAVING, SEAGRASS IN THE FORM OF A BALL WOULD BE TOO BULKY TO MANIPULATE. ALONG LENGTH IS MORE SUITABLE

DESIGN AND CONSTRUCTION GUIDE FOR MAKING A SEAGRASS STOOL

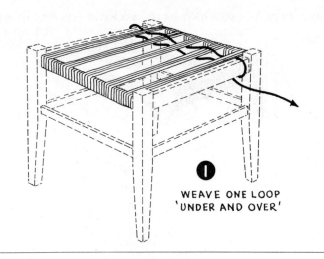

I WEAVE ONE LOOP 'UNDER AND OVER'

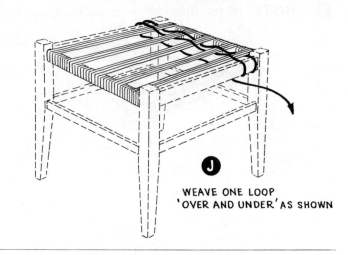

J WEAVE ONE LOOP 'OVER AND UNDER' AS SHOWN

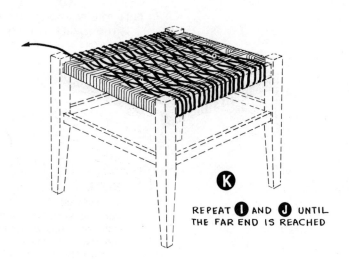

K REPEAT **I** AND **J** UNTIL THE FAR END IS REACHED

L FINALLY TURN UPSIDE DOWN AND ANCHOR THE LOOSE ENDS UNDERNEATH WITH A KNOT

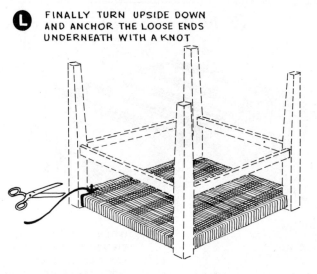

DESIGN AND CONSTRUCTION GUIDE FOR MAKING A SEAGRASS STOOL

(76) **PREPARE THE FRAMEWORK FOR RECEIVING A FINISH**
(A METHOD GIVEN BELOW FOR A CLEAR FINISH)

(77) REMOVE ANY SERIOUS MARKS WITH A
SMOOTH PLANE THEN SCRAPE

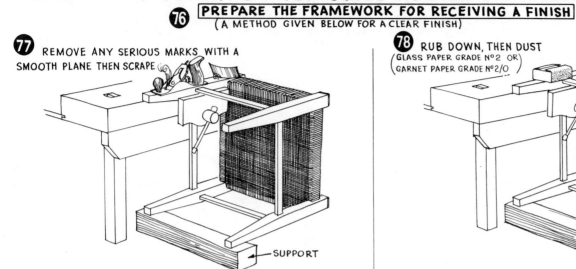

SUPPORT

(78) RUB DOWN, THEN DUST
(GLASS PAPER GRADE N°2 OR)
(GARNET PAPER GRADE N°2/0)

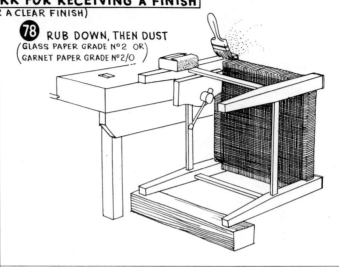

(79) DAMP DOWN, THEN LEAVE TO DRY

SPONGE

WATER

(80) RUB DOWN, THEN DUST
(GLASS PAPER GRADE N°1
(OR GARNET PAPER GRADE N°4/0)

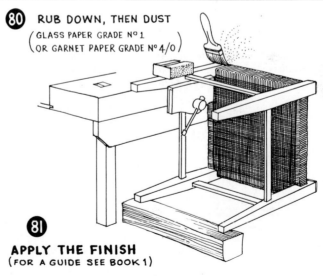

(81)

APPLY THE FINISH
(FOR A GUIDE SEE BOOK 1)

INTRODUCTION TO COFFEE TABLES

❶

THE MAIN FUNCTION

COFFEE TABLES ARE LOW TABLES USED MAINLY
IN LIVING ROOM FOR FOR SUPPORTING
DRINKS, SNACKS ETC.

A COFFEE TABLE

❷ AN EXPLODED SKETCH OF
THE MAIN PARTS

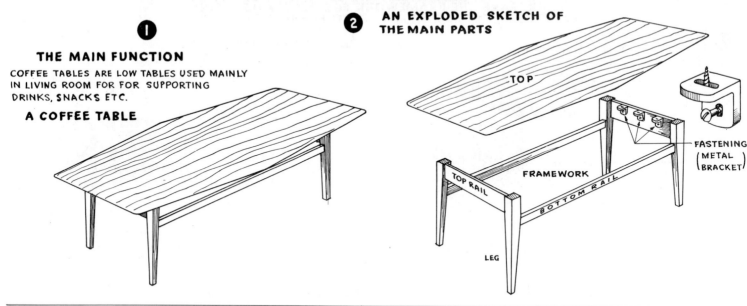

TOP

FASTENING
(METAL
BRACKET)

TOP RAIL

FRAMEWORK

BOTTOM RAIL

LEG

❸ IT IS IMPORTANT WHEN MAKING A COFFEE TABLE
TO DESIGN ITS BASIC SHAPE AND SIZE TO SUIT THE
AVAILABLE SPACE IN YOUR LIVING ROOM

AND TO HOLD THE
REQUIRED NUMBER
OF ARTICLES

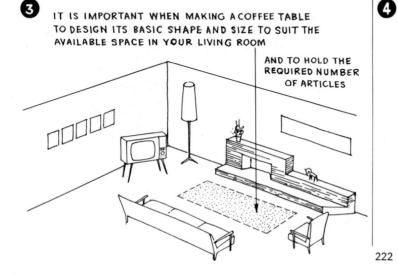

❹ ALSO IT IS IMPORTANT THAT
THE FINISH ON THE TOP IS
HARDWEARING AND LIQUID
AND HEAT RESISTANT

REASONS
IT IS QUITE POSSIBLE
THAT SOMEONE WILL
FORGET TO USE A TABLE
MAT OR SPILL SOME
HOT DRINK ON THE TABLE

INTRODUCTION TO COFFEE TABLES

❺ EXAMPLES OF THREE TYPES OF COFFEE TABLE TOPS

NATURAL BOARDING

(WITH A HARDWEARING, HEAT
AND LIQUID RESISTANT CLEAR
FINISH)

**FORMICA ON A
PLYWOOD BASE**

**VENEER ON A BLOCKBOARD BASE
EDGED WITH EXTERNAL LIPPING**

(WITH A HARDWEARING, HEAT AND LIQUID
RESISTANT CLEAR
FINISH)

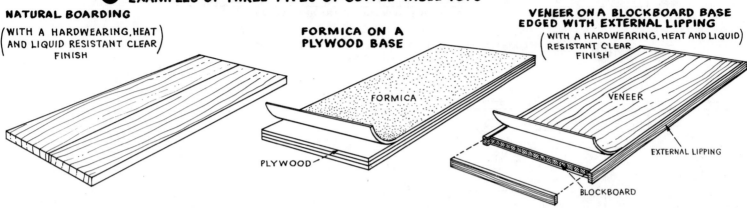

FORMICA

VENEER

PLYWOOD

EXTERNAL LIPPING

BLOCKBOARD

NOTE ❻

WHERE LIPPING IS USED
WHEN CHOOSING THE SHAPE
OF THE TOP KEEP TO
A PLAIN RECTANGULAR
OR SQUARE SHAPE

REASON

IT IS VERY DIFFICULT
TO APPLY LIPPING
AROUND CURVED EDGES

❼

NOW FIRST DESIGN THE
BASIC SHAPE AND SIZE
OF YOUR COFFEE TABLE
TOP AND THE TYPE OF
FRAMEWORK
CONSTRUCTION

(PAGE N° 224 TO PAGE N° 229)

DESIGN AND CONSTRUCTION GUIDE FOR MAKING A COFFEE TABLE

① WHAT WILL BE THE BASIC SIZE AND SHAPE OF YOUR TABLE TOP?
(A METHOD OF FINDING GIVEN BELOW AND ON THE NEXT PAGE)

② AT HOME IN THE LIVINGROOM LAY OUT NEWSPAPERS
IN THE SPACE AVAILABLE

(EXAMPLES)

DESIGN AND CONSTRUCTION GUIDE FOR MAKING A COFFEE TABLE

3 THEN FOLD THE NEWSPAPERS TO A SIZE THAT SUITS THE SPACE,
TAKES THE NUMBER OF ARTICLES REQUIRED, AND LOOKS IN PROPORTION TO ROOM AND FURNITURE
(EXAMPLES)

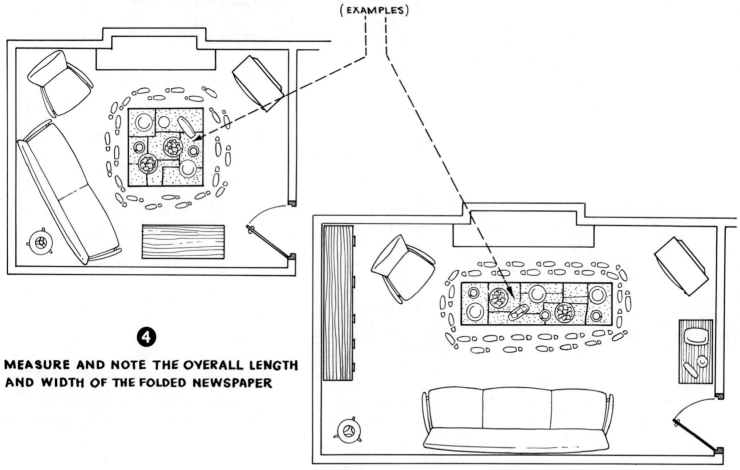

4

**MEASURE AND NOTE THE OVERALL LENGTH
AND WIDTH OF THE FOLDED NEWSPAPER**

225

DESIGN AND CONSTRUCTION GUIDE FOR MAKING A COFFEE TABLE

5 ON A SHEET OF DRAWING PAPER SKETCH OR TRACE FAINT OUTLINES OF A NUMBER OF TOPS

(FOR A SQUARE BASIC SHAPE) ←———————————— TWO EXAMPLES

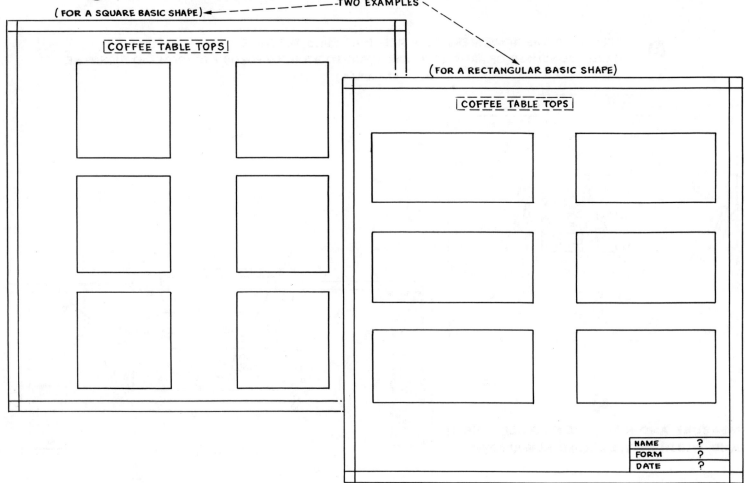

COFFEE TABLE TOPS

(FOR A RECTANGULAR BASIC SHAPE)

COFFEE TABLE TOPS

NAME	?
FORM	?
DATE	?

226

DESIGN AND CONSTRUCTION GUIDE FOR MAKING A COFFEE TABLE

6 CONSIDER, THEN BUILD UP ON THE OUTLINE SHAPES

SEE THE EXAMPLES BELOW

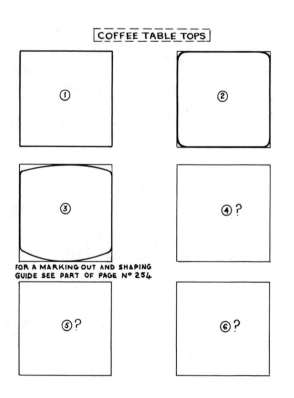

COFFEE TABLE TOPS

① ② ③ ④? ⑤? ⑥?

FOR A MARKING OUT AND SHAPING
GUIDE SEE PART OF PAGE N° 254

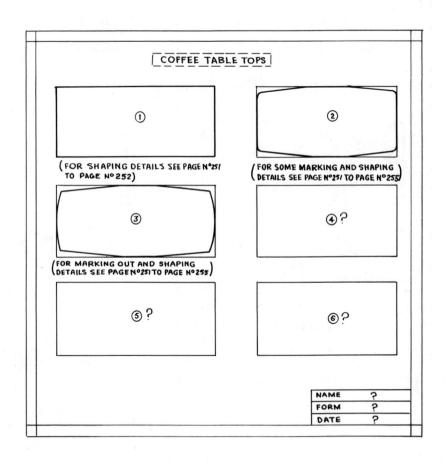

COFFEE TABLE TOPS

①

(FOR SHAPING DETAILS SEE PAGE N°251
TO PAGE N°252)

②

FOR SOME MARKING AND SHAPING
DETAILS SEE PAGE N°251 TO PAGE N°255

③

FOR MARKING OUT AND SHAPING
DETAILS SEE PAGE N°251 TO PAGE N°255

④?

⑤?

⑥?

NAME	?
FORM	?
DATE	?

DESIGN AND CONSTRUCTION GUIDE FOR MAKING A COFFEE TABLE

7 SKETCHED EXAMPLES OF THREE TYPES
OF COFFEE TABLE FRAMEWORK AND THEIR JOINTS

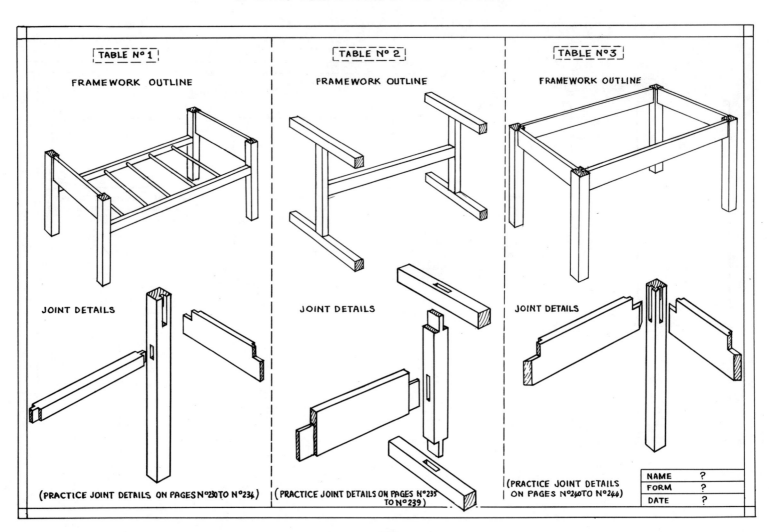

TABLE Nº 1

FRAMEWORK OUTLINE

JOINT DETAILS

(PRACTICE JOINT DETAILS ON PAGES Nº230TO Nº234)

TABLE Nº 2

FRAMEWORK OUTLINE

JOINT DETAILS

(PRACTICE JOINT DETAILS ON PAGES Nº235 TO Nº239)

TABLE Nº 3

FRAMEWORK OUTLINE

JOINT DETAILS

(PRACTICE JOINT DETAILS ON PAGES Nº240TO Nº244)

NAME	?
FORM	?
DATE	?

DESIGN AND CONSTRUCTION GUIDE FOR MAKING A COFFEE TABLE

8 ON A SHEET OF DRAWING PAPER
SKETCH THREE OTHER COFFEE TABLE FRAMEWORKS AND THEIR JOINTS

COFFEE TABLE Nº4	COFFEE TABLE Nº5	COFFEE TABLE Nº 6
?	?	?
?	?	?

NAME	?
FORM	?
DATE	?

9 FAINTLY SKETCH VARIOUS TOP SHAPES OVER THE FRAMEWORKS AND CHOOSE THE TOP AND FRAMEWORK COMBINATION YOU WOULD LIKE TO MAKE

10 THEN MAKE THE PRACTICE JOINTS OF THE FRAMEWORK YOU HAVE CHOSEN

11 THEN DESIGN, MARK OUT AND SHAPE THE PRACTICE JOINTS, LEGS AND RAILS

229

15*

Nº1 COFFEE TABLE FRAMEWORK PRACTICE JOINTS

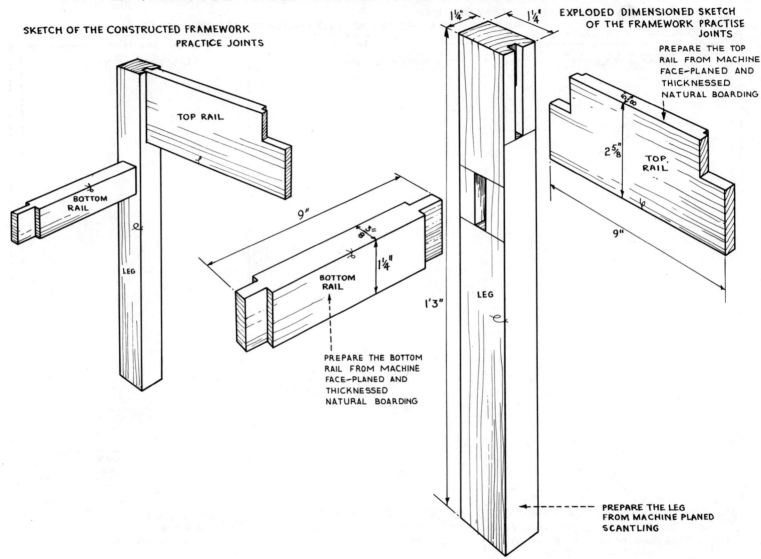

SKETCH OF THE CONSTRUCTED FRAMEWORK
PRACTICE JOINTS

TOP RAIL

BOTTOM RAIL

LEG

EXPLODED DIMENSIONED SKETCH
OF THE FRAMEWORK PRACTISE
JOINTS

PREPARE THE TOP
RAIL FROM MACHINE
FACE-PLANED AND
THICKNESSED
NATURAL BOARDING

TOP. RAIL

$2\frac{5}{8}$"

9"

1¼"   1¼"

LEG

1'3"

9"

$1\frac{3}{4}$"

BOTTOM RAIL

1¼"

PREPARE THE BOTTOM
RAIL FROM MACHINE
FACE-PLANED AND
THICKNESSED
NATURAL BOARDING

PREPARE THE LEG
FROM MACHINE PLANED
SCANTLING

Nº1 COFFEE TABLE FRAMEWORK PRACTICE JOINT

1 MAKE OUT A TIMBER LIST FOR Nº1 COFFEE TABLE FRAMEWORK PRACTICE JOINTS
GUIDE BELOW

TIMBER LIST FOR Nº1 COFFEE TABLE FRAMEWORK PRACTICE JOINTS

NAMES OF MEMBERS	VARIETY OF TIMBER TO BE USED	STATE OF TIMBER TO BE USED	NUMBER REQUIRED	OVERALL LENGTH OF EACH MEMBER	TOTAL LENGTH REQ'D FOR THIS TYPE OF MEMBER	OVERALL WIDTH	OVERALL THICKNESS
LEG	?	?	?	?	?	?	?
TOP RAIL	?	?	?	? + 1" P.A.	?	? + ¼" P.A.	?
BOTTOM RAIL	?	?	?	? + 1" P.A.	?	? + ¼" P.A.	?

2 FILL IN THE REQUIRED INFORMATION

3 PREPARE THE TIMBER FOR THE MEMBERS TO THEIR MARKING OUT SIZES
(FOR PREPARATION GUIDES SEE PAGES Nº24 TO Nº28)

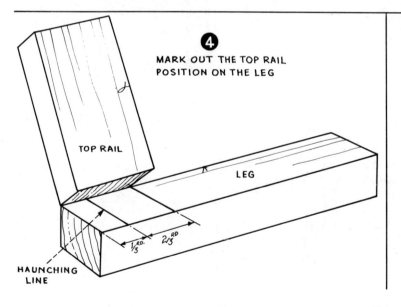

4 MARK OUT THE TOP RAIL POSITION ON THE LEG

TOP RAIL

LEG

$\frac{1}{3}$ RD. 2/3 RD.

HAUNCHING LINE

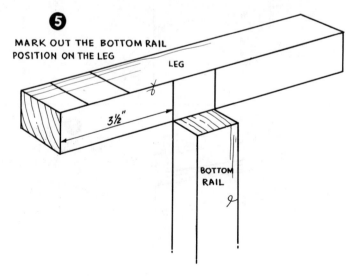

5 MARK OUT THE BOTTOM RAIL POSITION ON THE LEG

LEG

3½"

BOTTOM RAIL

Nº 1 COFFEE TABLE FRAMEWORK PRACTICE JOINT

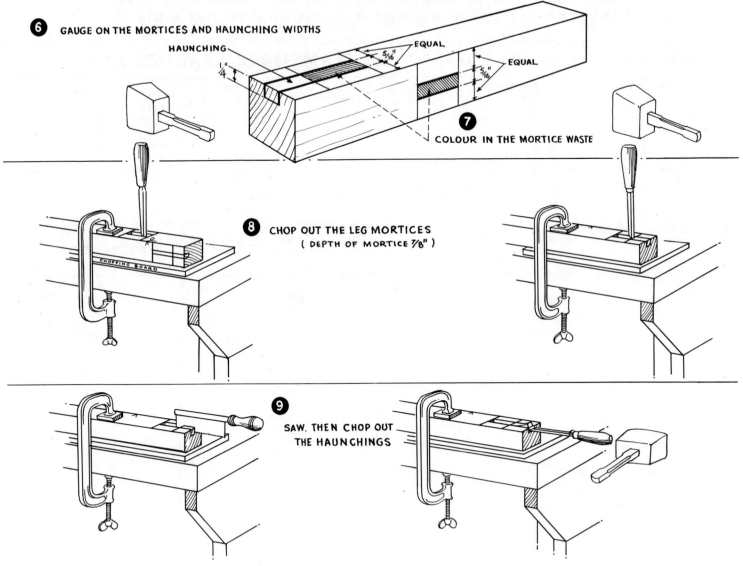

6 GAUGE ON THE MORTICES AND HAUNCHING WIDTHS

HAUNCHING

EQUAL

5/16"

EQUAL

1/4"

5/16"

7 COLOUR IN THE MORTICE WASTE

8 CHOP OUT THE LEG MORTICES
(DEPTH OF MORTICE 7/8")

CHOPPING BOARD

9 SAW. THEN CHOP OUT
THE HAUNCHINGS

232

Nº1 COFFEE TABLE FRAMEWORK PRACTICE JOINTS

10 MARK OUT THE TOP RAIL TENONS

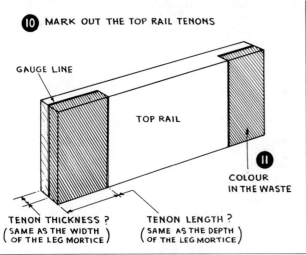

GAUGE LINE

TOP RAIL

11 COLOUR IN THE WASTE

TENON THICKNESS ?
(SAME AS THE WIDTH)
(OF THE LEG MORTICE)

TENON LENGTH ?
(SAME AS THE DEPTH)
(OF THE LEG MORTICE)

12 SAW THE TOP RAIL TENONS
(SAW IN THE WASTE GRAZING THE LINES)

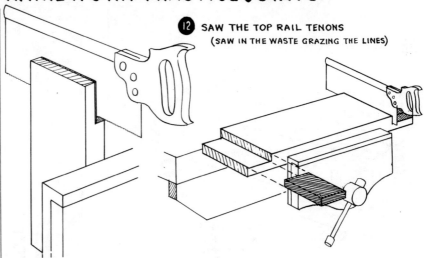

13 MARK OUT THE HAUNCHES

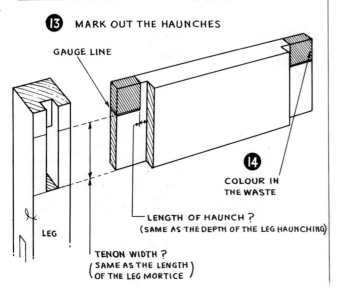

GAUGE LINE

14 COLOUR IN THE WASTE

LEG

LENGTH OF HAUNCH ?
(SAME AS THE DEPTH OF THE LEG HAUNCHING)

TENON WIDTH ?
(SAME AS THE LENGTH)
(OF THE LEG MORTICE)

15 SAW THE HAUNCHES
(SAW IN THE WASTE GRAZING THE LINES)

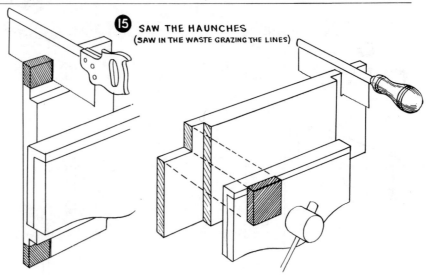

233

N°I COFFEE TABLE FRAMEWORK PRACTICE JOINTS

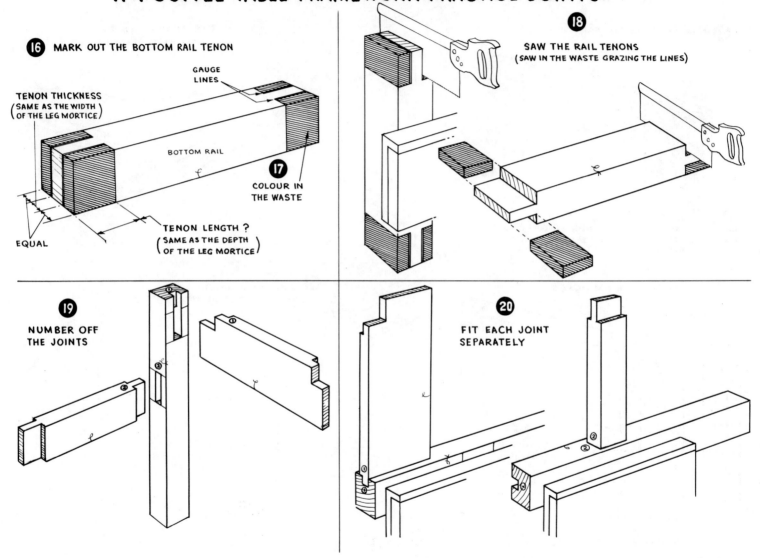

16 MARK OUT THE BOTTOM RAIL TENON

GAUGE LINES

TENON THICKNESS
(SAME AS THE WIDTH)
(OF THE LEG MORTICE)

BOTTOM RAIL

17

COLOUR IN THE WASTE

TENON LENGTH ?
(SAME AS THE DEPTH)
(OF THE LEG MORTICE)

EQUAL

18 SAW THE RAIL TENONS
(SAW IN THE WASTE GRAZING THE LINES)

19 NUMBER OFF THE JOINTS

20 FIT EACH JOINT SEPARATELY

N° 2 COFFEE TABLE FRAMEWORK PRACTICE JOINTS

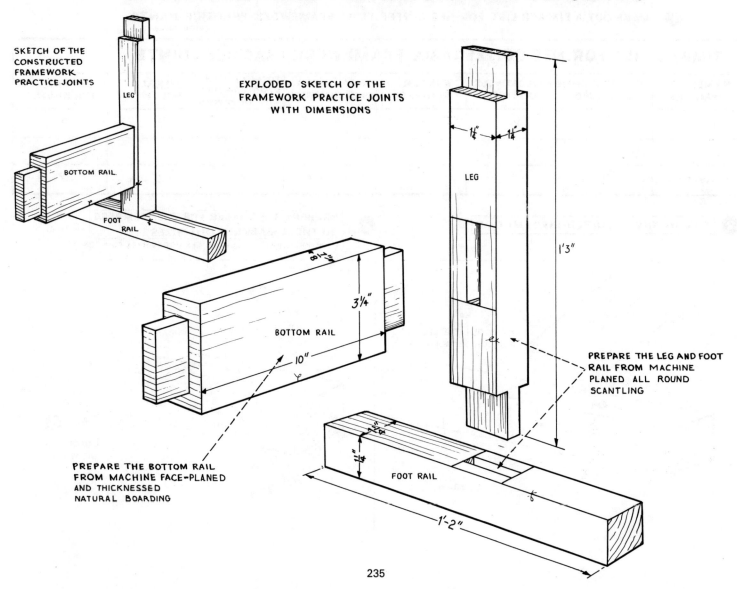

SKETCH OF THE
CONSTRUCTED
FRAMEWORK
PRACTICE JOINTS

LEG

BOTTOM RAIL.

FOOT
RAIL

EXPLODED SKETCH OF THE
FRAMEWORK PRACTICE JOINTS
WITH DIMENSIONS

LEG

$1\frac{1}{4}''$ $1\frac{1}{4}''$

$1'3''$

BOTTOM RAIL

$3\frac{1}{4}''$

$1\frac{1}{8}''$

$10''$

PREPARE THE BOTTOM RAIL
FROM MACHINE FACE-PLANED
AND THICKNESSED
NATURAL BOARDING

PREPARE THE LEG AND FOOT
RAIL FROM MACHINE
PLANED ALL ROUND
SCANTLING

FOOT RAIL

$1\frac{1}{4}''$

$1'-2''$

235

Nº 2 COFFEE TABLE FRAMEWORK PRACTICE JOINT

① MAKE OUT A TIMBER LIST FOR Nº2 COFFEE TABLE FRAMEWORK PRACTICE JOINTS
GUIDE BELOW

TIMBER LIST FOR Nº 2 COFFEE TABLE FRAMEWORK PRACTICE JOINTS

NAMES OF MEMBERS	VARIETY OF TIMBER TO BE USED	STATE OF TIMBER TO BE USED	NUMBER REQUIRED	OVERALL LENGTH OF EACH MEMBER	TOTAL LENGTH REQ'D FOR THIS TYPE OF MEMBER	OVERALL WIDTH	OVERALL THICKNESS
LEG	?	?	?	?	?	?	?
FOOT RAIL	?	?	?	?	?	?	?
BOTTOM RAIL	?	?	?	? + 1" P.A.	?	? + 1/4" P.A.	?

② FILL IN THE REQUIRED INFORMATION

③ PREPARE THE TIMBER FOR THE MEMBERS TO THEIR MARKING OUT SIZES
(FOR PREPARATION GUIDES SEE PAGES Nº24 TO Nº28)

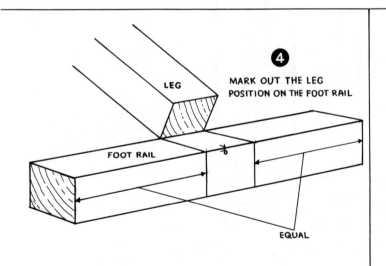

④ MARK OUT THE LEG POSITION ON THE FOOT RAIL

LEG

FOOT RAIL

EQUAL

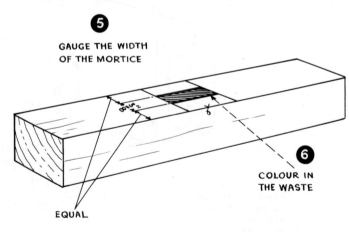

⑤ GAUGE THE WIDTH OF THE MORTICE

⑥ COLOUR IN THE WASTE

EQUAL

N° 2 COFFEE TABLE FRAMEWORK PRACTICE JOINTS

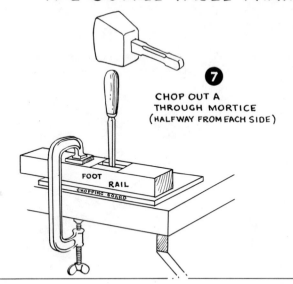

7

CHOP OUT A
THROUGH MORTICE
(HALFWAY FROM EACH SIDE)

FOOT RAIL

CHOPPING BOARD

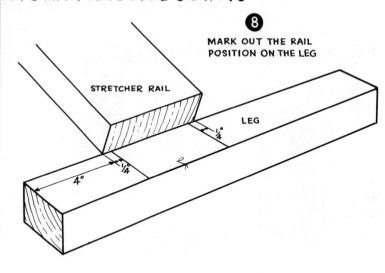

8

MARK OUT THE RAIL
POSITION ON THE LEG

STRETCHER RAIL

LEG

$\frac{1}{4}$"

$\frac{1}{4}$"

4"

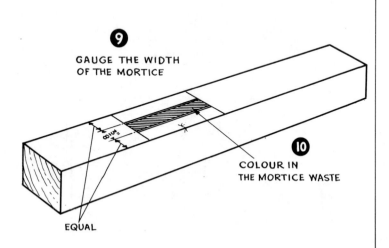

9

GAUGE THE WIDTH
OF THE MORTICE

10

COLOUR IN
THE MORTICE WASTE

EQUAL

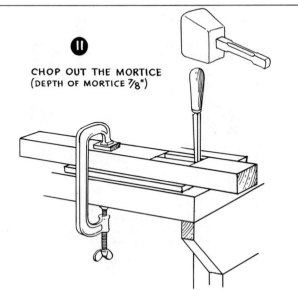

11

CHOP OUT THE MORTICE
(DEPTH OF MORTICE $\frac{7}{8}$")

Nº2 COFFEE TABLE FRAMEWORK PRACTICE JOINTS

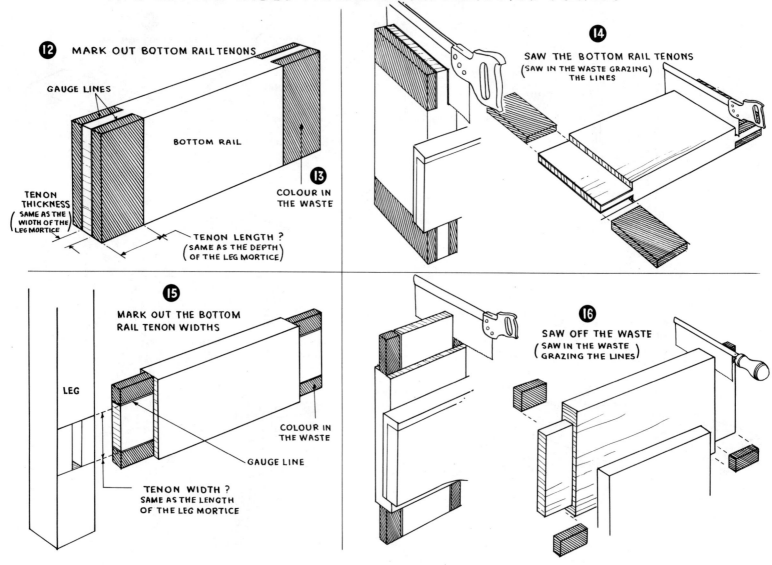

12 MARK OUT BOTTOM RAIL TENONS

GAUGE LINES

BOTTOM RAIL

TENON THICKNESS
(SAME AS THE WIDTH OF THE LEG MORTICE)

13 COLOUR IN THE WASTE

TENON LENGTH ?
(SAME AS THE DEPTH OF THE LEG MORTICE)

14 SAW THE BOTTOM RAIL TENONS
(SAW IN THE WASTE GRAZING THE LINES)

15 MARK OUT THE BOTTOM RAIL TENON WIDTHS

LEG

COLOUR IN THE WASTE

GAUGE LINE

TENON WIDTH ?
SAME AS THE LENGTH OF THE LEG MORTICE

16 SAW OFF THE WASTE
(SAW IN THE WASTE GRAZING THE LINES)

Nº2 COFFEE TABLE FRAMEWORK PRACTICE JOINTS

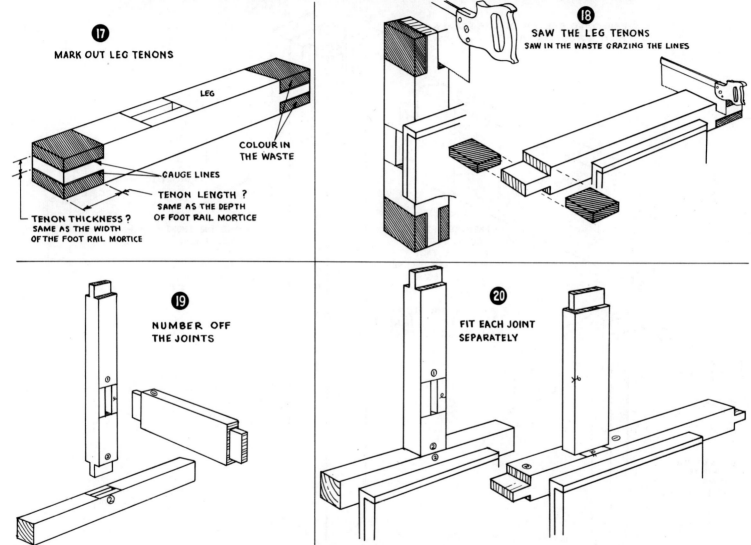

17 MARK OUT LEG TENONS

LEG

COLOUR IN THE WASTE

GAUGE LINES

TENON LENGTH ?
SAME AS THE DEPTH
OF FOOT RAIL MORTICE

TENON THICKNESS ?
SAME AS THE WIDTH
OF THE FOOT RAIL MORTICE

18 SAW THE LEG TENONS
SAW IN THE WASTE GRAZING THE LINES

19 NUMBER OFF
THE JOINTS

20 FIT EACH JOINT
SEPARATELY

N°3 COFFEE TABLE FRAMEWORK PRACTICE JOINTS

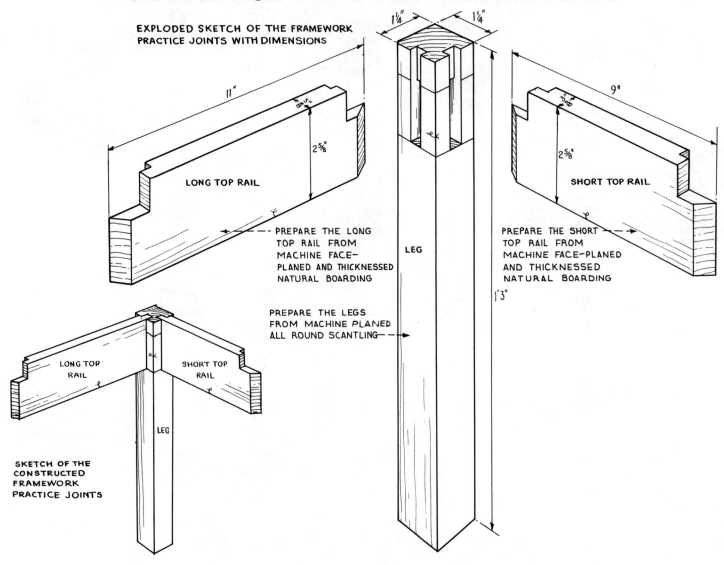

EXPLODED SKETCH OF THE FRAMEWORK
PRACTICE JOINTS WITH DIMENSIONS

1¼"   1¼"

11"

2⅝"

LONG TOP RAIL

— PREPARE THE LONG
TOP RAIL FROM
MACHINE FACE-
PLANED AND THICKNESSED
NATURAL BOARDING

LEG

9"

2⅝"

SHORT TOP RAIL

PREPARE THE SHORT
TOP RAIL FROM
MACHINE FACE-PLANED
AND THICKNESSED
NATURAL BOARDING

PREPARE THE LEGS
FROM MACHINE PLANED
ALL ROUND SCANTLING —

1'3"

LONG TOP
RAIL

SHORT TOP
RAIL

LEG

SKETCH OF THE
CONSTRUCTED
FRAMEWORK
PRACTICE JOINTS

Nº3 COFFEE TABLE FRAMEWORK PRACTICE JOINT

① MAKE OUT A TIMBER LIST FOR Nº3 COFFEE TABLE FRAMEWORK PRACTICE JOINTS

GUIDE BELOW

TIMBER LIST FOR Nº3 COFFEE TABLE FRAMEWORK PRACTICE JOINTS

NAMES OF MEMBERS	VARIETY OF TIMBER TO BE USED	STATE OF TIMBER TO BE USED	NUMBER REQUIRED	OVERALL LENGTH OF EACH MEMBER	TOTAL LENGTH REQ'D. FOR THIS TYPE OF MEMBER	OVERALL WIDTH	OVERALL THICKNESS
LEG	?	?	?	?	?	?	?
LONG TOP RAIL	?	?	?	? + 1" P·A·	?	? + ¼" P·A·	?
LONG BOTTOM RAIL	?	?	?	? + 1" P·A·	?	? + ¼" P·A·	?

② FILL IN REQUIRED INFORMATION

③ PREPARE THE TIMBER FOR THE MEMBERS TO THEIR MARKING OUT SIZES

(FOR PREPARATION GUIDES SEE PAGES Nº24 TO Nº28)

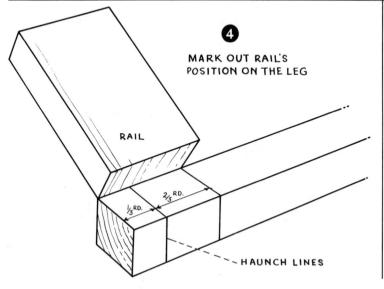

④ MARK OUT RAIL'S POSITION ON THE LEG

RAIL

⅔ RD.

⅓ RD.

— HAUNCH LINES

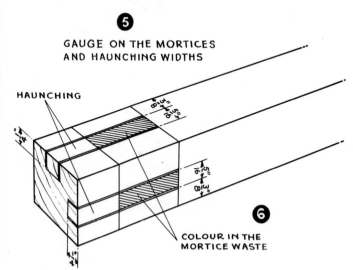

⑤ GAUGE ON THE MORTICES AND HAUNCHING WIDTHS

HAUNCHING

⑥

COLOUR IN THE MORTICE WASTE

16

Nº 3 COFFEE TABLE FRAMEWORK PRACTICE JOINTS

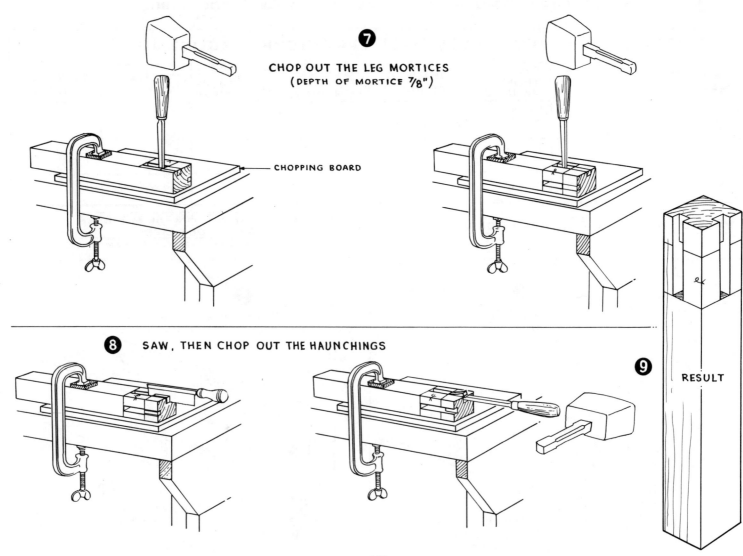

7 CHOP OUT THE LEG MORTICES
(DEPTH OF MORTICE 7/8")

CHOPPING BOARD

8 SAW, THEN CHOP OUT THE HAUNCHINGS

9 RESULT

Nº 3 COFFEE TABLE FRAMEWORK PRACTICE JOINTS

⑩ MARK OUT THE RAIL TENONS

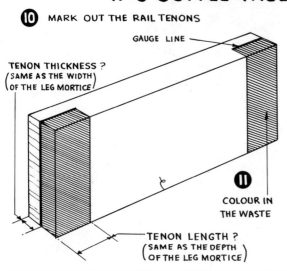

GAUGE LINE

TENON THICKNESS ?
(SAME AS THE WIDTH)
(OF THE LEG MORTICE)

⑪
COLOUR IN
THE WASTE

TENON LENGTH ?
(SAME AS THE DEPTH)
(OF THE LEG MORTICE)

⑫

SAW IN RAIL TENONS
(SAW IN THE WASTE GRAZING THE LINES)

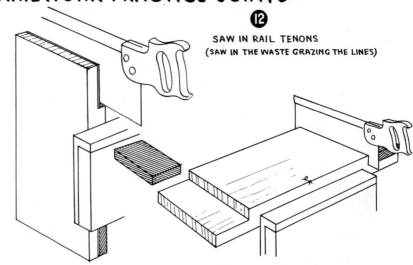

⑬ MARK OUT THE HAUNCHES

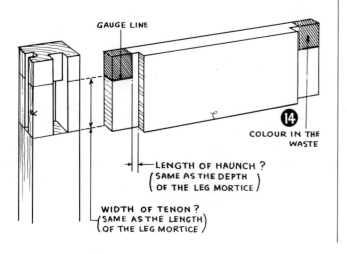

GAUGE LINE

⑭
COLOUR IN THE
WASTE

LENGTH OF HAUNCH ?
(SAME AS THE DEPTH)
(OF THE LEG MORTICE)

WIDTH OF TENON ?
(SAME AS THE LENGTH)
(OF THE LEG MORTICE)

⑮

SAW IN THE HAUNCHES
(SAW IN THE WASTE GRAZING THE LINES)

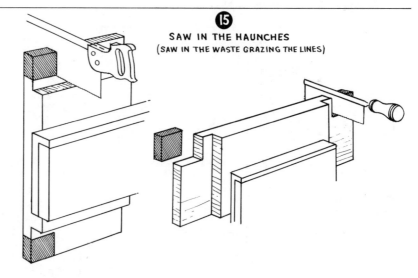

Nº 3 COFFEE TABLE FRAMEWORK PRACTICE JOINTS

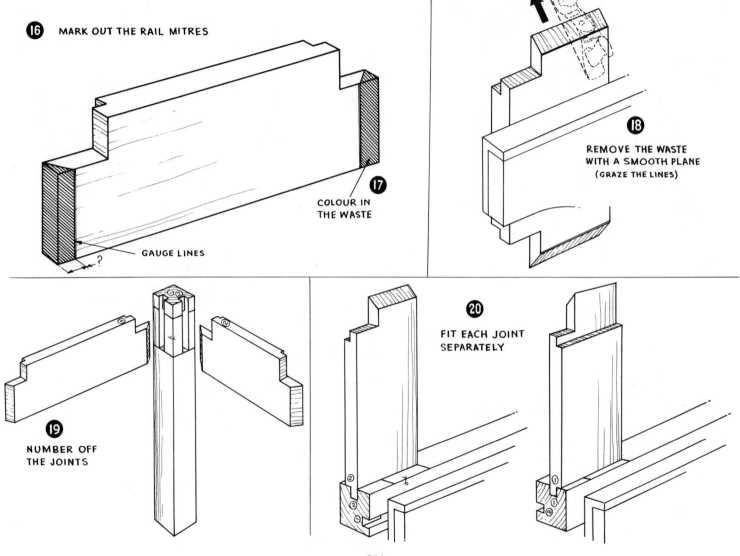

16 MARK OUT THE RAIL MITRES

17 COLOUR IN THE WASTE

GAUGE LINES

?

18 REMOVE THE WASTE WITH A SMOOTH PLANE
(GRAZE THE LINES)

19 NUMBER OFF THE JOINTS

20 FIT EACH JOINT SEPARATELY

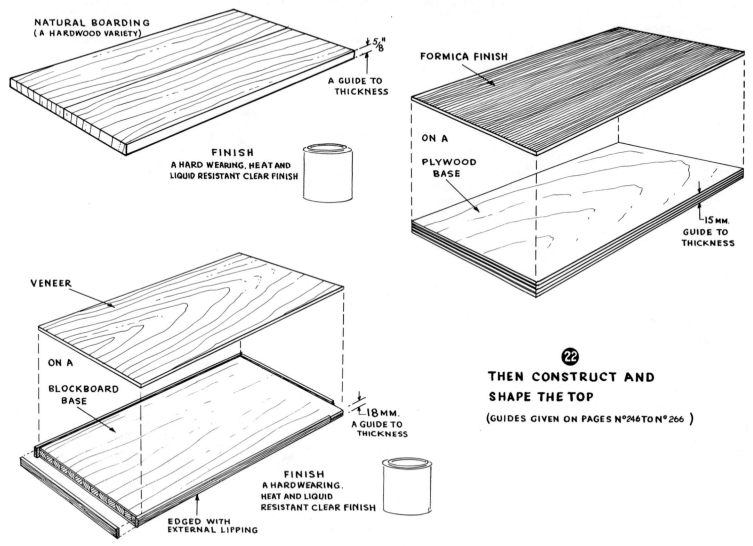

㉑ CONSIDER WHAT TYPE OF TOP AND TOP FINISH YOU WILL HAVE

(THREE EXAMPLES BELOW)

NATURAL BOARDING
(A HARDWOOD VARIETY)

5/8"

A GUIDE TO THICKNESS

FINISH
A HARD WEARING, HEAT AND
LIQUID RESISTANT CLEAR FINISH

FORMICA FINISH

ON A

PLYWOOD
BASE

15 MM.
GUIDE TO THICKNESS

VENEER

ON A

BLOCKBOARD
BASE

18 MM.
A GUIDE TO THICKNESS

FINISH
A HARD WEARING,
HEAT AND LIQUID
RESISTANT CLEAR FINISH

EDGED WITH
EXTERNAL LIPPING

㉒

**THEN CONSTRUCT AND
SHAPE THE TOP**

(GUIDES GIVEN ON PAGES N°246 TO N°266)

A METHOD FOR MAKING A TABLE TOP WITH NATURAL BOARDING

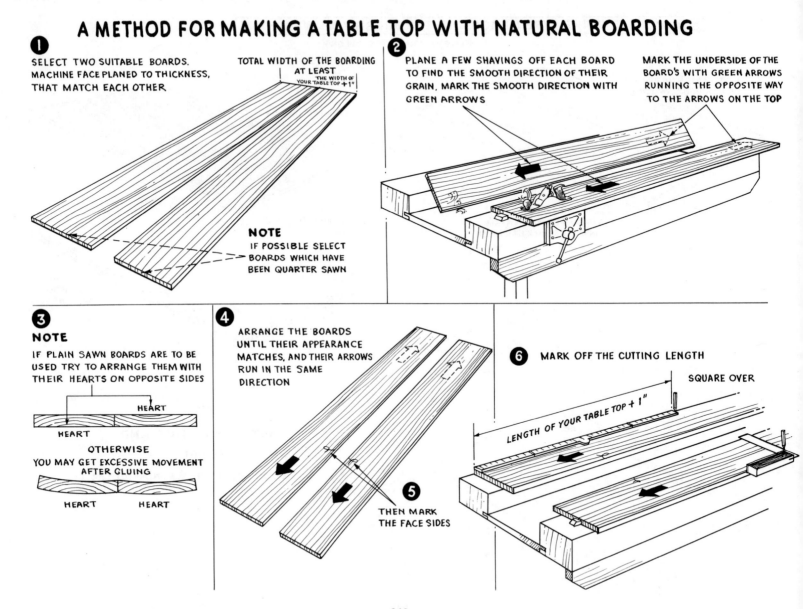

1 SELECT TWO SUITABLE BOARDS. MACHINE FACE PLANED TO THICKNESS, THAT MATCH EACH OTHER

TOTAL WIDTH OF THE BOARDING AT LEAST THE WIDTH OF YOUR TABLE TOP +1"

NOTE
IF POSSIBLE SELECT BOARDS WHICH HAVE BEEN QUARTER SAWN

2 PLANE A FEW SHAVINGS OFF EACH BOARD TO FIND THE SMOOTH DIRECTION OF THEIR GRAIN, MARK THE SMOOTH DIRECTION WITH GREEN ARROWS

MARK THE UNDERSIDE OF THE BOARD'S WITH GREEN ARROWS RUNNING THE OPPOSITE WAY TO THE ARROWS ON THE TOP

3 **NOTE**
IF PLAIN SAWN BOARDS ARE TO BE USED TRY TO ARRANGE THEM WITH THEIR HEARTS ON OPPOSITE SIDES

HEART

HEART

OTHERWISE
YOU MAY GET EXCESSIVE MOVEMENT AFTER GLUING

HEART   HEART

4 ARRANGE THE BOARDS UNTIL THEIR APPEARANCE MATCHES, AND THEIR ARROWS RUN IN THE SAME DIRECTION

5 THEN MARK THE FACE SIDES

6 MARK OFF THE CUTTING LENGTH

SQUARE OVER

LENGTH OF YOUR TABLE TOP + 1"

A METHOD FOR MAKING A TABLE TOP WITH NATURAL BOARDING

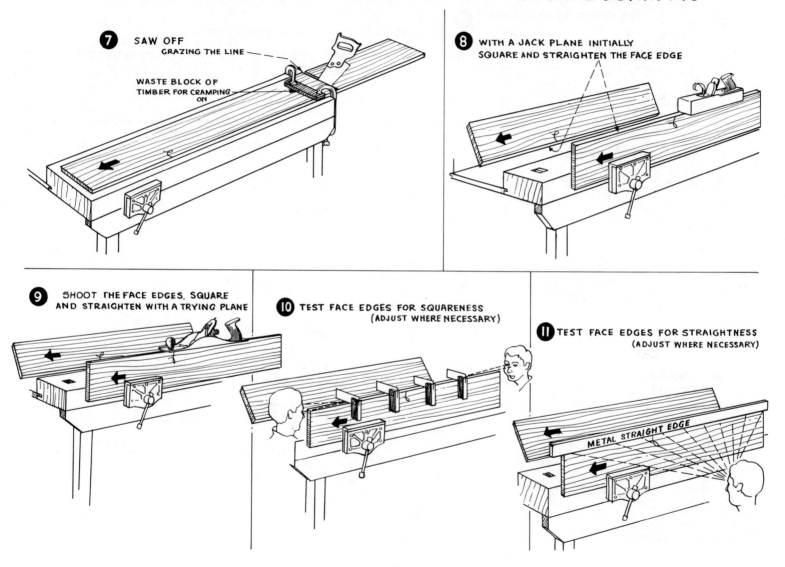

7 SAW OFF
GRAZING THE LINE

WASTE BLOCK OF TIMBER FOR CRAMPING ON

8 WITH A JACK PLANE INITIALLY SQUARE AND STRAIGHTEN THE FACE EDGE

9 SHOOT THE FACE EDGES. SQUARE AND STRAIGHTEN WITH A TRYING PLANE

10 TEST FACE EDGES FOR SQUARENESS (ADJUST WHERE NECESSARY)

11 TEST FACE EDGES FOR STRAIGHTNESS (ADJUST WHERE NECESSARY)

METAL STRAIGHT EDGE

A METHOD FOR MAKING A TABLE TOP WITH NATURAL BOARDING

12 TRY THE FACE EDGES TOGETHER

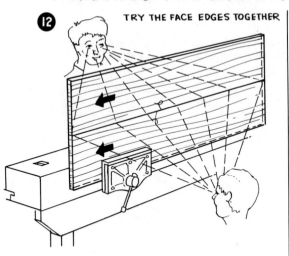

13 NOTE
THE JOINT MUST HAVE NO GAPS WHATSOEVER
(ADJUST WHERE NECESSARY)

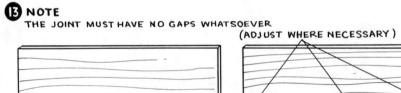

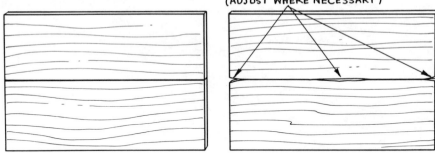

14 PLACE IN THE VICE AS BELOW AND
APPLY THE GLUE TO THE FACE EDGES

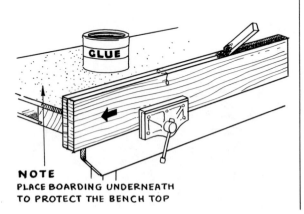

NOTE
PLACE BOARDING UNDERNEATH
TO PROTECT THE BENCH TOP

GLUE

15 HEAVILY RUB THE FACE EDGES TOGETHER
TO PUSH IN THE GLUE AND EASE OUT THE
SURPLUS GLUE

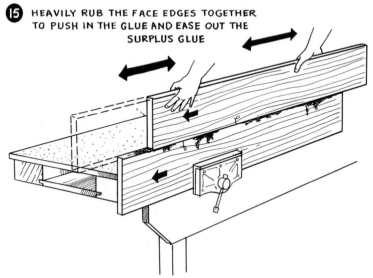

A METHOD FOR MAKING A TABLE TOP WITH NATURAL BOARDING

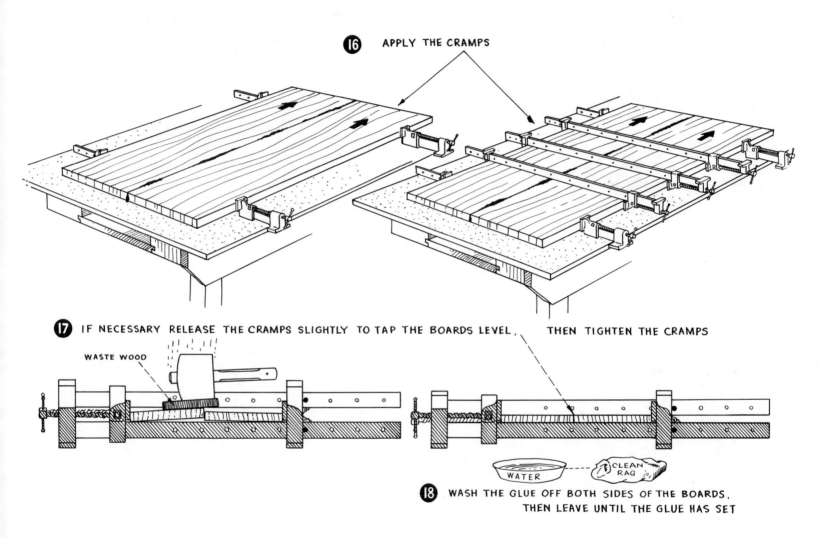

16 APPLY THE CRAMPS

17 IF NECESSARY RELEASE THE CRAMPS SLIGHTLY TO TAP THE BOARDS LEVEL, THEN TIGHTEN THE CRAMPS

WASTE WOOD

WATER   CLEAN RAG

18 WASH THE GLUE OFF BOTH SIDES OF THE BOARDS. THEN LEAVE UNTIL THE GLUE HAS SET

A METHOD FOR MAKING A TABLE TOP WITH NATURAL BOARDING

19 TAKE THE CRAMPS OFF THE EDGES, THEN FASTEN DOWN ON TO THE BENCH TOP AND SCRAPE OFF ANY HARD SURPLUS GLUE ON THE UNDERSIDE

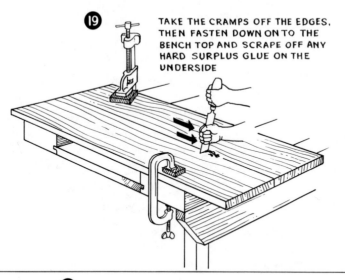

20 PLANE THE UNDERSIDE FLAT AND SMOOTH

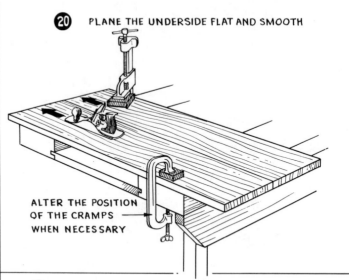

ALTER THE POSITION OF THE CRAMPS WHEN NECESSARY

21 TURN OVER AND SCRAPE OFF THE SURPLUS GLUE THEN PLANE THE FACE SIDE FLAT AND SMOOTH

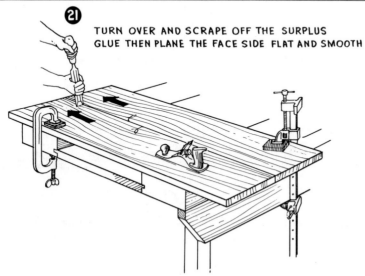

22 FASTEN LOW DOWN IN THE VICE. USING A TRYING PLANE SHOOT ONE EDGE

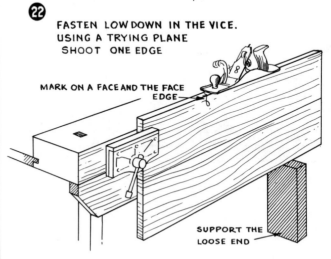

MARK ON A FACE AND THE FACE EDGE

SUPPORT THE LOOSE END

A METHOD FOR MAKING A TABLE TOP WITH NATURAL BOARDING

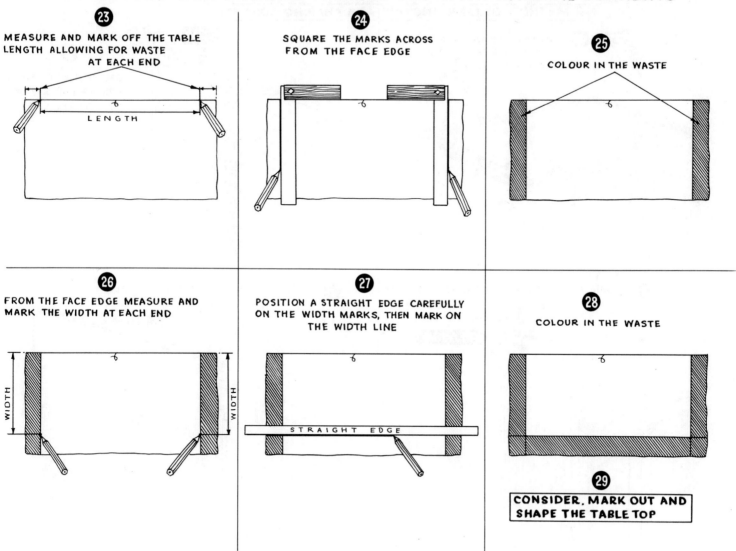

23 MEASURE AND MARK OFF THE TABLE LENGTH ALLOWING FOR WASTE AT EACH END

LENGTH

24 SQUARE THE MARKS ACROSS FROM THE FACE EDGE

25 COLOUR IN THE WASTE

26 FROM THE FACE EDGE MEASURE AND MARK THE WIDTH AT EACH END

WIDTH

WIDTH

27 POSITION A STRAIGHT EDGE CAREFULLY ON THE WIDTH MARKS, THEN MARK ON THE WIDTH LINE

STRAIGHT EDGE

28 COLOUR IN THE WASTE

29 CONSIDER, MARK OUT AND SHAPE THE TABLE TOP

A METHOD FOR MAKING A TABLE TOP WITH NATURAL BOARDING

A METHOD OF MARKING OUT AND SHAPING TOP Nº1

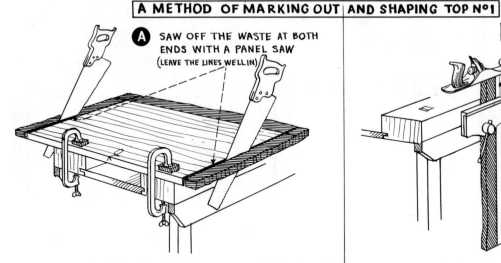

A SAW OFF THE WASTE AT BOTH ENDS WITH A PANEL SAW
(LEAVE THE LINES WELL IN)

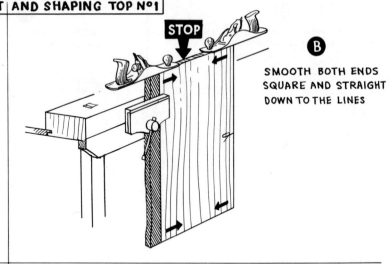

B

SMOOTH BOTH ENDS SQUARE AND STRAIGHT DOWN TO THE LINES

STOP

NOTE

C PLANE AS THE ARROWS INDICATE AND NEVER PLANE OVER THE FAR ENDS

REASON

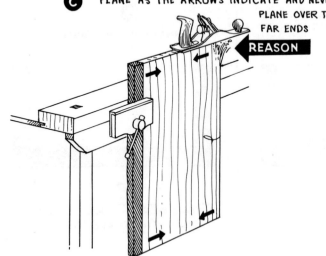

D REMOVE THE SIDE WASTE WITH A JACK PLANE
(LEAVE THE LINES JUST IN)

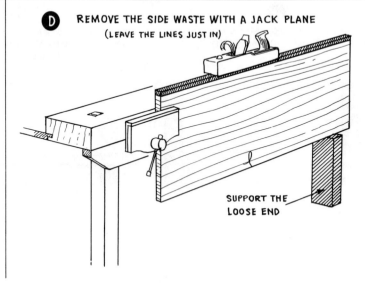

SUPPORT THE LOOSE END

A METHOD FOR MAKING A TABLE TOP WITH NATURAL BOARDING
A METHOD OF MARKING OUT TOPS Nº2 AND Nº3

A ON THE TOP OUTLINE, ADJUST FOUR THIN LATHS EQUALLY UNTIL THE INSIDE SHAPE LOOKS RIGHT

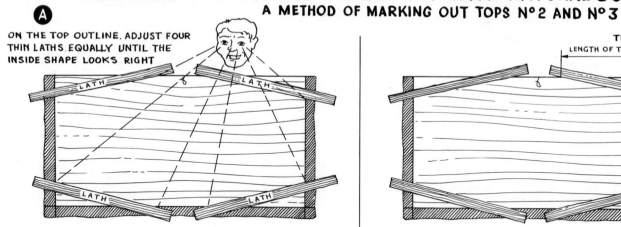

LATH

LATH

LATH

LATH

B THEN MEASURE

LENGTH OF TAPER

WIDTH OF TAPER

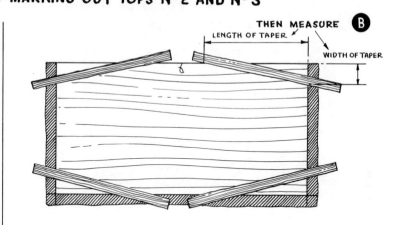

C MEASURE AND MARK POSITION OF TAPERS

LENGTH OF TAPER

LENGTH OF TAPER

WIDTH OF TAPER

WIDTH OF TAPER

WIDTH OF TAPER

WIDTH OF TAPER

LENGTH OF TAPER

LENGTH OF TAPER

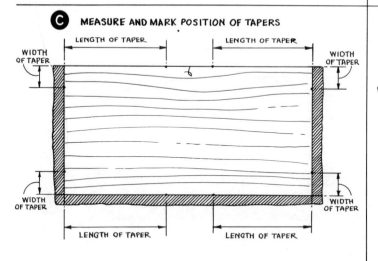

D MARK OUT THE TAPERS

STRAIGHT EDGE

TAPERS

E COLOUR IN THE WASTE

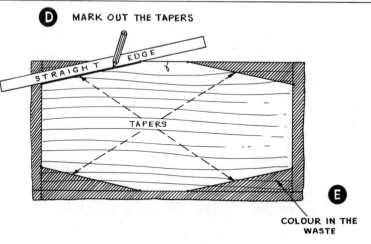

A METHOD FOR MAKING A TABLE TOP WITH NATURAL BOARDING

A METHOD OF MARKING OUT TOP Nº3

F AT ONE END GET SOMEONE TO BEND A THIN LATH UNTIL THE CURVE LOOKS RIGHT

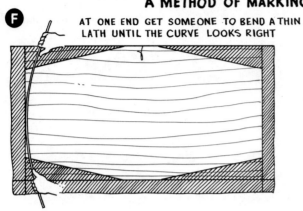

G MEASURE THE DISTANCE THE LATH IS BENT UP THE TAPER LINE

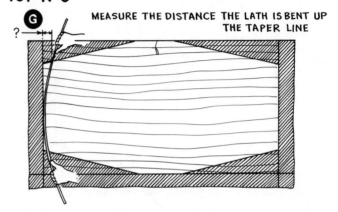

H MARK THAT DISTANCE AT EACH TAPER END

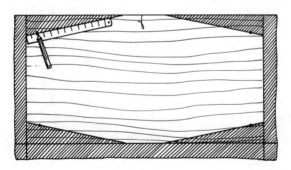

I DRAW ON THE CURVES

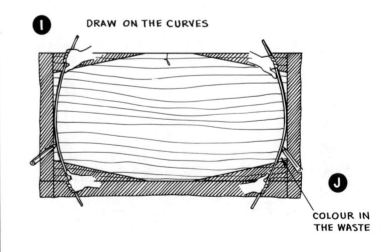

J COLOUR IN THE WASTE

A METHOD FOR MAKING A TABLE TOP WITH NATURAL BOARDING

A METHOD OF SHAPING TOP Nº3

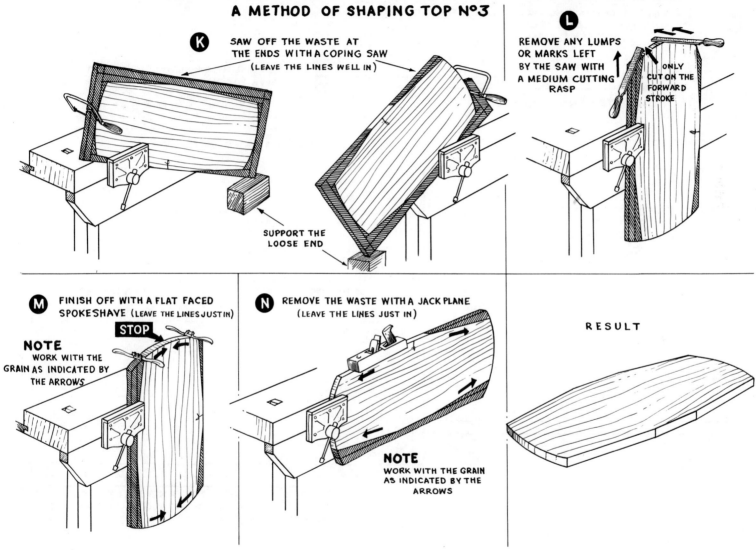

K SAW OFF THE WASTE AT THE ENDS WITH A COPING SAW (LEAVE THE LINES WELL IN)

SUPPORT THE LOOSE END

L REMOVE ANY LUMPS OR MARKS LEFT BY THE SAW WITH A MEDIUM CUTTING RASP

ONLY CUT ON THE FORWARD STROKE

M FINISH OFF WITH A FLAT FACED SPOKESHAVE (LEAVE THE LINES JUST IN)

STOP

NOTE WORK WITH THE GRAIN AS INDICATED BY THE ARROWS

N REMOVE THE WASTE WITH A JACK PLANE (LEAVE THE LINES JUST IN)

NOTE WORK WITH THE GRAIN AS INDICATED BY THE ARROWS

RESULT

A METHOD FOR MAKING A TABLE TOP WITH NATURAL BOARDING

 30 ON A SHEET OF DRAWING PAPER SKETCH FAINT OUTLINES
OF A NUMBER OF TABLE EDGES
(AN EXAMPLE BELOW)

TABLE TOP EDGE SHAPES

31 CONSIDER, THEN BUILD UP ON THE OUTLINES
SHAPES WHICH WILL BLEND WITH YOUR FRAMEWORK
AND TOP
(SOME EXAMPLES BELOW)

TABLE TOP EDGE SHAPES

① (FOR MARKING OUT AND SHAPING DETAILS SEE PAGES Nº257 & Nº258)

② (FOR MARKING OUT AND SHAPING DETAILS SEE PAGES Nº257 & Nº258)

? ③ ?

? ④ ?

NAME	?
FORM	?
DATE	?

 32 CONSIDER, MARK OUT AND SHAPE THE EDGE
WHICH WILL BE IN KEEPING WITH YOUR TOP
AND FRAMEWORK DESIGN

A METHOD FOR MAKING A TABLE TOP WITH NATURAL BOARDING

A METHOD OF MARKING OUT AND SHAPING EDGES Nº1 AND Nº2.
(FOR A TABLE TOP WITH CURVED ENDS)

A MARK OUT THE SHAPE OF THE EDGE

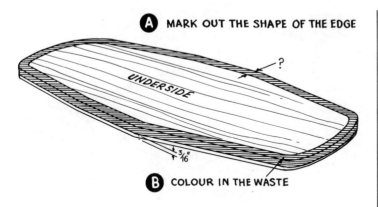

UNDERSIDE

?

3/16"

B COLOUR IN THE WASTE

C REMOVE THE END EDGE WASTE WITH A FLAT FACED SPOKESHAVE

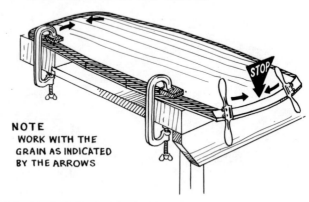
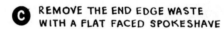

STOP

NOTE
WORK WITH THE
GRAIN AS INDICATED
BY THE ARROWS

D REMOVE THE SIDE EDGE WASTE WITH A JACK PLANE
(LEAVE THE LINES JUST IN)

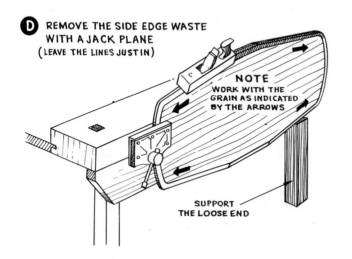

NOTE
WORK WITH THE
GRAIN AS INDICATED
BY THE ARROWS

SUPPORT
THE LOOSE END

E NOTE : WORK WITH THE GRAIN AS THE ARROWS INDICATE

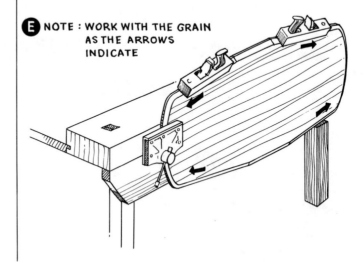

A METHOD FOR MAKING A TABLE TOP WITH NATURAL BOARDING

A METHOD FOR MARKING OUT AND SHAPING EDGES Nº1 AND Nº2
(FOR A TABLE TOP WITH STRAIGHT EDGES)

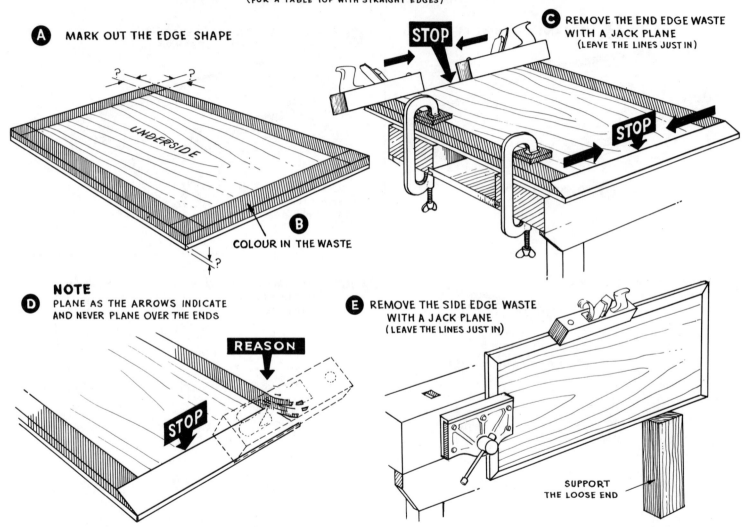

A MARK OUT THE EDGE SHAPE

UNDERSIDE

B COLOUR IN THE WASTE

C REMOVE THE END EDGE WASTE WITH A JACK PLANE (LEAVE THE LINES JUST IN)

STOP

D NOTE PLANE AS THE ARROWS INDICATE AND NEVER PLANE OVER THE ENDS

REASON

STOP

E REMOVE THE SIDE EDGE WASTE WITH A JACK PLANE (LEAVE THE LINES JUST IN)

SUPPORT THE LOOSE END

A METHOD FOR MAKING A TABLE TOP WITH NATURAL BOARDING

33 | **PREPARE THE TABLE TOP FOR RECEIVING A FINISH**
(A METHOD GIVEN BELOW FOR A CLEAR FINISH)

34 REMOVE ANY SERIOUS MARKS MADE WHILE SHAPING, WITH A SMOOTH PLANE

35

SCRAPE

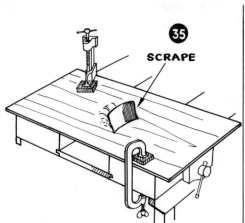

36 RUB DOWN
(GLASS PAPER GRADE Nº F 2
OR GARNET PAPER GRADE Nº 2/0)

37 THEN DUST

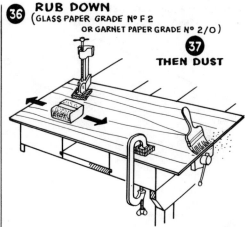

38 DAMP DOWN,
THEN LEAVE TO DRY

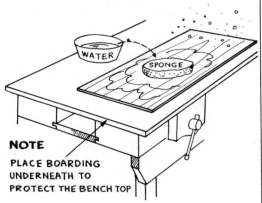

WATER

SPONGE

NOTE
PLACE BOARDING
UNDERNEATH TO
PROTECT THE BENCH TOP

39 RUB DOWN AGAIN
(GLASS PAPER GRADE Nº1
OR GARNET PAPER GRADE Nº4/0)

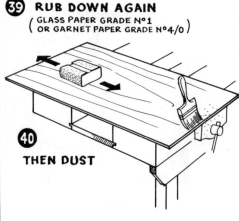

40 THEN DUST

41

APPLY THE FINISH

(FOR DETAILS SEE BOOK 1)

A METHOD FOR MAKING A TABLE TOP WITH A PLYWOOD BASE AND A FORMICA TOP

1 BUY A PIECE OF 15MM. PLYWOOD CUT TO THE REQUIRED SIZE **OR** FROM A LARGE SHEET OF 15MM. PLYWOOD AT SCHOOL PREPARE A PIECE TO REQUIRED SIZE
(FOR A PREPARATION GUIDE SEE PAGES N°30 & PAGE N°31)

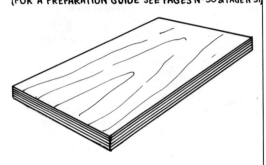

2 OBTAIN A PIECE OF FORMICA 1/8" LONGER AND 1/8" WIDER THAN THE PIECE OF PLYWOOD

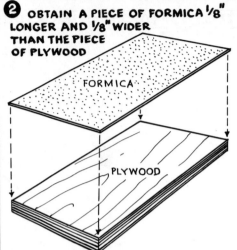

FORMICA

PLYWOOD

3 APPLY GLUE AND PLACE TOGETHER

BETTER FACE

4 TURN UPSIDE DOWN AND APPLY HEAVY WEIGHTS

5 FASTEN LOW DOWN IN THE VICE. USING A TRYING PLANE SHOOT THE FORMICA EDGES FLUSH TO THE PLYWOOD EDGES

STOP

SUPPORT THE LOOSE END

NOTE 6 PLANE AS THE ARROWS INDICATE AND NEVER PLANE OVER THE FAR ENDS

REASON

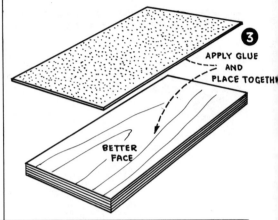

7 CONSIDER, MARK OUT AND SHAPE THE TOP
(SEE PAGES N°252 TO PAGE N°255)

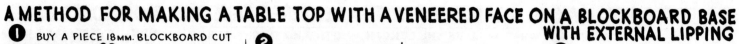

A METHOD FOR MAKING A TABLE TOP WITH A VENEERED FACE ON A BLOCKBOARD BASE WITH EXTERNAL LIPPING

① BUY A PIECE 18mm. BLOCKBOARD CUT TO REQUIRED SIZE **OR** FROM A LARGE SHEET OF 18mm. BLOCKBOARD AT SCHOOL PREPARE A PIECE TO THE REQUIRED SIZE.
(FOR A PREPARATION GUIDE SEE PAGES N°30 AND PAGE N°31)

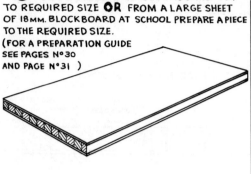

② ON THE BLOCKBOARD'S BETTER FACE APPLY THE VENEER AND LEAVE UNTIL THE GLUE HAS SET
(FOR DETAILS OF VENEERING SEE BOOK 1)

GLUE

③ TRIM OFF THE VENEER

STRAIGHT EDGE

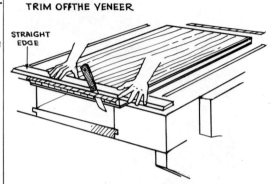

④ SMOOTH THE VENEER SQUARE AND STRAIGHT TO THE EDGES

NOTE
PLANE SLIGHTLY ACROSS THE VENEER TO PREVENT CHIPPING OFF

STOP

PLANE AS THE ARROWS INDICATE AND NEVER PLANE OVER THE FAR ENDS

STOP

SUPPORT THE LOOSE END

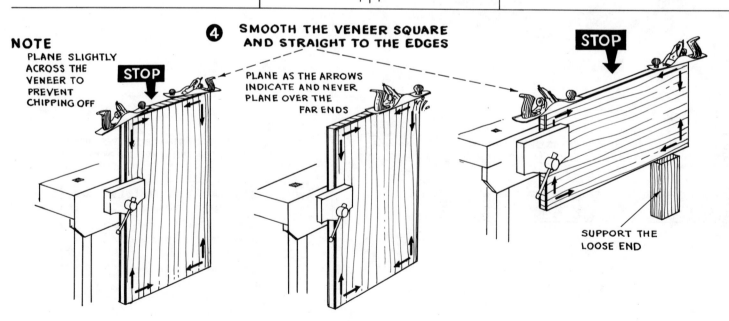

17*

A METHOD FOR MAKING A TABLE TOP WITH A VENEERED FACE ON A BLOCKBOARD BASE WITH EXTERNAL LIPPING

5 | WHAT WILL BE THE LENGTH, WIDTH AND THICKNESS OF YOUR LIPPING?

(GUIDE GIVEN BELOW)

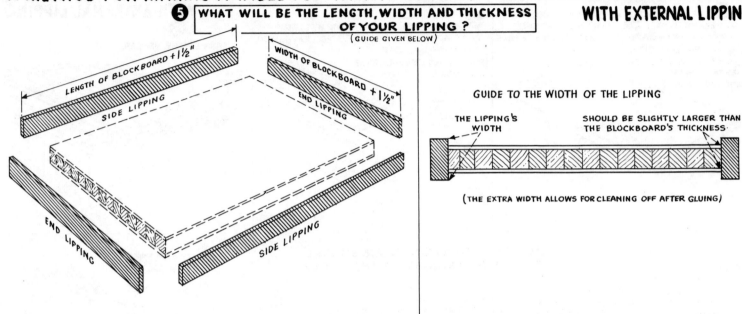

LENGTH OF BLOCKBOARD + 1½"

SIDE LIPPING

WIDTH OF BLOCKBOARD + 1½"

END LIPPING

END LIPPING

SIDE LIPPING

GUIDE TO THE WIDTH OF THE LIPPING

THE LIPPING'S WIDTH

SHOULD BE SLIGHTLY LARGER THAN THE BLOCKBOARD'S THICKNESS

(THE EXTRA WIDTH ALLOWS FOR CLEANING OFF AFTER GLUING)

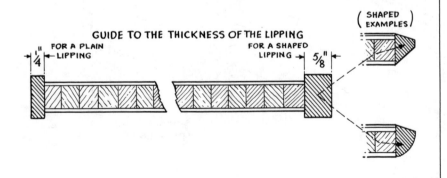

GUIDE TO THE THICKNESS OF THE LIPPING

FOR A PLAIN LIPPING — ¼"

FOR A SHAPED LIPPING — 5/8"

(SHAPED EXAMPLES)

NOTE

USE A VARIETY OF TIMBER FOR THE LIPPING THAT WILL MATCH THE VENEER YOU HAVE USED

6 | PREPARE THE TIMBER FOR THE LIPPING

PREPARE FROM MACHINE FACE-PLANED AND THICKNESSED NATURAL BOARDING

(FOR A PREPARATION GUIDE SEE PAGES N° 24 TO N° 27)

A METHOD FOR MAKING A TABLE TOP WITH A VENEERED FACE ON A BLOCKBOARD BASE WITH EXTERNAL LIPPING

7 APPLY GLUE TO THE END LIPPING AND BLOCKBOARD ENDS, THEN APPLY THE CRAMPS

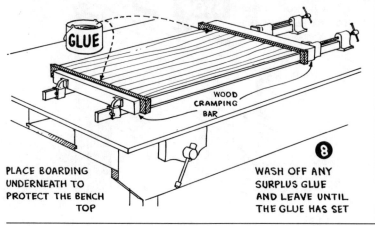

GLUE

WOOD CRAMPING BAR

PLACE BOARDING UNDERNEATH TO PROTECT THE BENCH TOP

8 WASH OFF ANY SURPLUS GLUE AND LEAVE UNTIL THE GLUE HAS SET

9 REMOVE THE CRAMPS, THEN SAW OFF THE LIPPING ENDS NEARLY LEVEL TO THE BLOCKBOARD WITH A TENON SAW

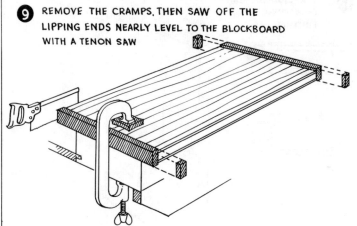

10 PLANE THE LIPPING EDGES FLUSH TO THE VENEER AND THE BLOCKBOARD WITH A SMOOTH PLANE

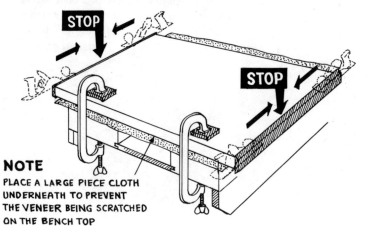

STOP

STOP

NOTE PLACE A LARGE PIECE CLOTH UNDERNEATH TO PREVENT THE VENEER BEING SCRATCHED ON THE BENCH TOP

NOTE PLANE THE LIPPING EDGES FLUSH AT A SLIGHT ANGLE **11**

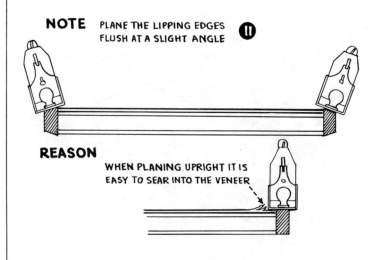

REASON

WHEN PLANING UPRIGHT IT IS EASY TO SEAR INTO THE VENEER

A METHOD FOR MAKING A TABLE TOP WITH A VENEERED FACE ON A BLOCKBOARD BASE WITH EXTERNAL LIPPINGS

12 IF REQUIRED, SHAPE THE LIPPINGS FURTHER

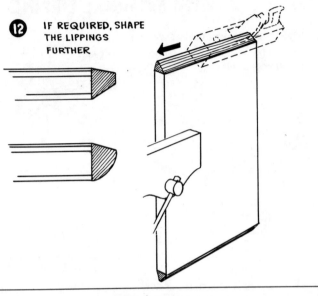

13 SHOOT THE SAWN LIPPING ENDS LEVEL TO THE BLOCKBOARD

STOP

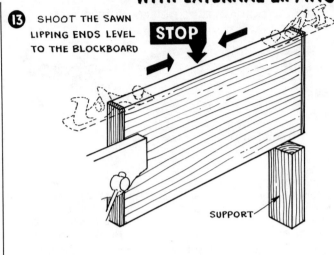

SUPPORT

14 APPLY GLUE TO THE SIDE LIPPINGS AND BLOCKBOARD SIDE EDGES, THEN APPLY THE CRAMPS

GLUE

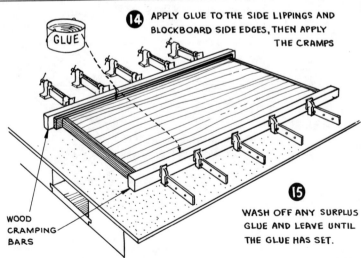

WOOD CRAMPING BARS

15 WASH OFF ANY SURPLUS GLUE AND LEAVE UNTIL THE GLUE HAS SET.

16 REMOVE THE CRAMPS THEN SAW OFF THE LIPPINGS ENDS NEARLY FLUSH TO THE END LIPPINGS WITH A TENON SAW

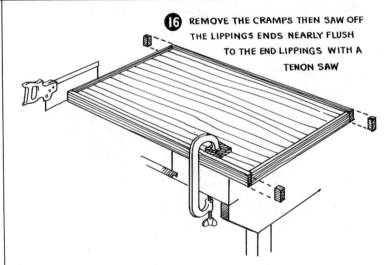

A METHOD FOR MAKING A TABLE TOP WITH A VENEERED FACE ON A BLOCKBOARD BASE WITH EXTERNAL LIPPING

17 AT A SLIGHT ANGLE PLANE THE SIDE LIPPING EDGES FLUSH TO THE UNDERSIDE OF THE BLOCKBOARD

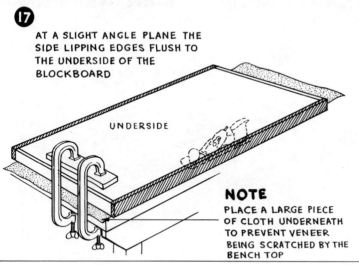

UNDERSIDE

NOTE

PLACE A LARGE PIECE OF CLOTH UNDERNEATH TO PREVENT VENEER BEING SCRATCHED BY THE BENCH TOP

18 AT A SLIGHT ANGLE PLANE THE SIDE LIPPING EDGES FLUSH TO THE VENEER

STOP

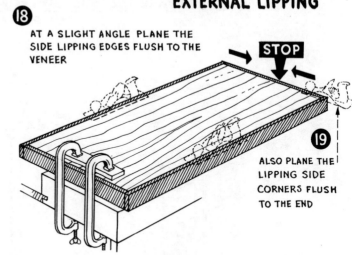

19 ALSO PLANE THE LIPPING SIDE CORNERS FLUSH TO THE END

20 IF REQUIRED, SHAPE THE SIDE LIPPING FURTHER

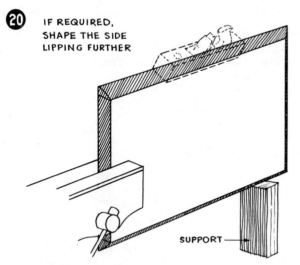

SUPPORT

21 PLANE THE SAWN ENDS FLUSH TO THE END LIPPINGS

STOP

A METHOD FOR MAKING A TABLE TOP WITH A VENEERED FACE ON A BLOCKBOARD BASE

WITH EXTERNAL LIPPING

22 PREPARE THE TABLE TOP FOR RECEIVING A FINISH

(A METHOD GIVEN BELOW)

23 SCRAPE

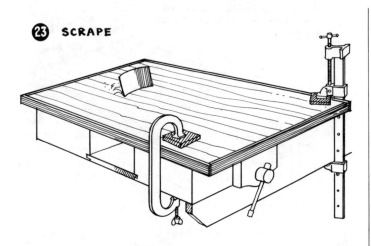

24 RUB DOWN

(GLASS PAPER GRADE N° F2)
(OR GARNET PAPER GRADE N° 2)

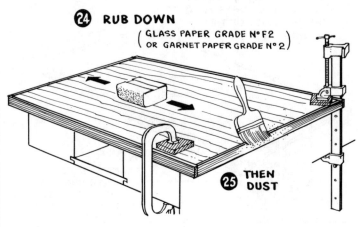

25 THEN DUST

26 DAMP DOWN

THEN LEAVE TO DRY

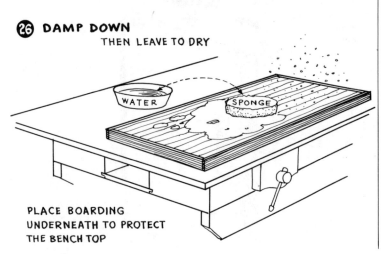

WATER

SPONGE

PLACE BOARDING
UNDERNEATH TO PROTECT
THE BENCH TOP

27 RUB DOWN

(GLASS PAPER GRADE N° 1)
(OR GARNET PAPER GRADE N° 4)

28 THEN DUST

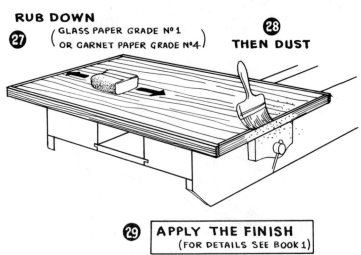

29 APPLY THE FINISH
(FOR DETAILS SEE BOOK 1)

DESIGN AND CONSTRUCTION GUIDE FOR MAKING A COFFEE TABLE

❶

SKETCH LARGE OUTLINES OF YOUR FRAMEWORK DETAILS ON A
PIECE OF DRAWING PAPER.   MAKE OUT A TIMBER LIST FOR
YOUR COFFEE TABLE FRAMEWORK THEN FOLLOW THE
INSTRUCTION AND ANSWER EACH OF THE QUESTIONS IN TURN.
AS YOU PROGRESS FILL IN THE NECESSARY INFORMATION ON
YOUR TIMBER LIST AND FRAMEWORK SKETCHES. EVENTUALLY
DEVELOP AN ORTHOGRAPHIC DRAWING OF YOUR COFFEE TABLE

❷

> WHAT TYPE OF FINISH WILL
> YOU USE ON YOUR FRAMEWORK'S
> SURFACE ?

(CONSIDER YOUR TABLE TOP MATERIAL
AND FINISH, AND CHOOSE A FINISH FOR
THE FRAMEWORK THAT IS IN KEEPING.)

❸

> WHAT VARIETY OR VARIETIES
> OF HARDWOOD
> OR SOFTWOOD
> WILL YOU USE FOR
> YOUR FRAMEWORK ?

(CONSIDER THE TYPE OF FINISH YOU
HAVE CHOSEN)

❹

> WHAT WILL BE THE HEIGHT OF YOUR
> COFFEE TABLE LEGS ?

(A METHOD FOR FINDING GIVEN BELOW)

CONSIDER THE PEOPLE WHO WILL USE
THE COFFEE TABLE.
THEN BY TRIAL AND ERROR
FIND THE MOST SUITABLE HEIGHT

(— THICKNESS
OF THE TOP)

?

DESIGN AND CONSTRUCTION GUIDE FOR MAKING A COFFEE TABLE

⑤

WHAT WILL BE THE WIDTH
AND THICKNESS OF YOUR
COFFEE TABLE LEGS ?

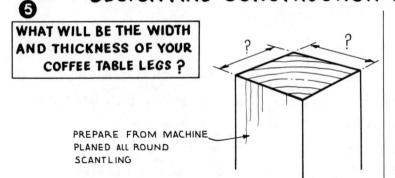

?   ?

PREPARE FROM MACHINE
PLANED ALL ROUND
SCANTLING

⑥

PREPARE THE TIMBER FOR THE LEGS
TO THEIR MARKING OUT SIZES

(FOR A PREPARATION GUIDE SEE PAGE Nº29)

---

❼ WHAT WILL BE THE LENGTH OF YOUR COFFEE TABLE RAILS?

(A METHOD OF FINDING GIVEN BELOW)

1

2

3

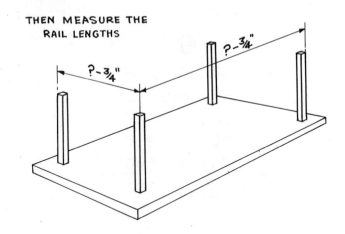

THEN MEASURE THE
RAIL LENGTHS

$? - \frac{3}{4}"$

$? - \frac{3}{4}"$

WHILE SOMEONE MOVES THE
LEGS EVENLY ON THE UNDER-
SIDE OF THE TOP, YOU OBSERVE
VARIOUS VIEWS FROM A DISTANCE
OF ABOUT 10 FT. UNTIL THE LEG
POSITIONS LOOK RIGHT

DESIGN AND CONSTRUCTION GUIDE FOR MAKING A COFFEE TABLE

8 WHAT WILL BE THE WIDTH AND THICKNESS OF YOUR TOP RAILS ?

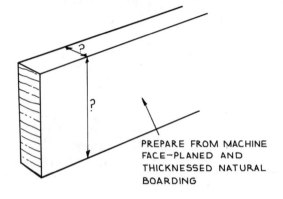

PREPARE FROM MACHINE FACE–PLANED AND THICKNESSED NATURAL BOARDING

9 WHAT WILL BE THE WIDTH AND THICKNESS OF YOUR BOTTOM RAILS ?
(IF ANY ARE INCLUDED)

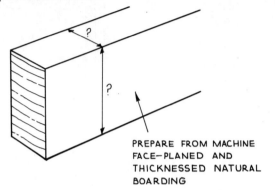

PREPARE FROM MACHINE FACE–PLANED AND THICKNESSED NATURAL BOARDING

10 WHAT WILL BE THE WIDTH AND THICKNESS OF YOUR FOOT RAILS ?
(IF ANY ARE INCLUDED)

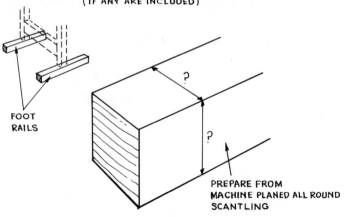

FOOT RAILS

PREPARE FROM MACHINE PLANED ALL ROUND SCANTLING

11 PREPARE THE TIMBER FOR THE RAILS TO THEIR MARKING OUT SIZES

(FOR PREPARATION GUIDE SEE PAGES Nº24 AND PAGE Nº29)

DESIGN AND CONSTRUCTION GUIDE FOR MAKING A COFFEE TABLE

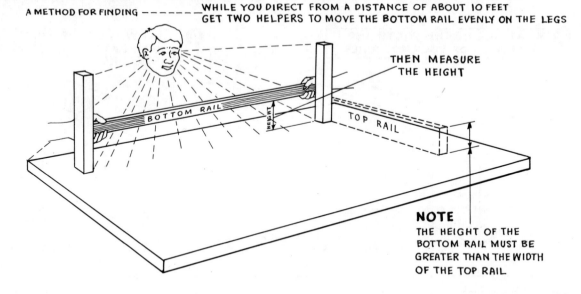

A METHOD FOR FINDING ----- WHILE YOU DIRECT FROM A DISTANCE OF ABOUT 10 FEET
GET TWO HELPERS TO MOVE THE BOTTOM RAIL EVENLY ON THE LEGS

⑫

WHAT WILL BE THE HEIGHT OF YOUR BOTTOM RAILS ?

(IF ANY BOTTOM RAILS ARE)
INCLUDED

THEN MEASURE THE HEIGHT

BOTTOM RAIL

TOP RAIL

HEIGHT

NOTE
THE HEIGHT OF THE BOTTOM RAIL MUST BE GREATER THAN THE WIDTH OF THE TOP RAIL

---

⑬

MARK OUT THE MORTICES AND HAUNCHES ON THE LEGS

(AND FOOT RAIL MORTICES IF ANY)

⑭

CHOP OUT THE MORTICES. THEN SAW AND CHOP OUT THE HAUNCHES

⑮

MARK OUT THE RAIL TENONS

(AND LEG TENON IF ANY)

DESIGN AND CONSTRUCTION GUIDE FOR MAKING A COFFEE TABLE

⑯

SAW THE
RAIL TENONS

⑰

MARK OUT THE
RAIL HAUNCHES

⑱

SAW THE
RAIL HAUNCHES

(MARK OUT AND REMOVE THE)
(RAIL'S MITRE WASTE IF ANY)

⑲

CONSIDER, MARK
OUT AND SHAPE
THE LEGS AND
RAILS

⑳

NUMBER OFF

THE JOINTS

㉑

FIT EACH JOINT
SEPARATELY,
THEN TRY
ALTOGETHER

㉒

GLUE AND
POSITION EACH
JOINT CAREFULLY

㉓

APPLY THE CRAMPS
AND CHECK FOR
SQUARENESS. THEN
LEAVE UNTIL THE
GLUE HAS SET

㉔

LEVEL THE TOP
OF THE FRAMEWORK
WHERE
NECESSARY

DESIGN AND CONSTRUCTION GUIDE FOR MAKING A COFFEE TABLE

25 CLEAN OFF THE
FRAMEWORK
FOR RECEIVING
A FINISH

26 APPLY THE FINISH
TO THE FRAMEWORK
(IN DETAIL SEE BOOK 1)

27 MAKE A SUITABLE NUMBER OF METAL
BRACKETS FOR FASTENING THE FRAMEWORK
TO THE TOP
(AN EXAMPLE BELOW)

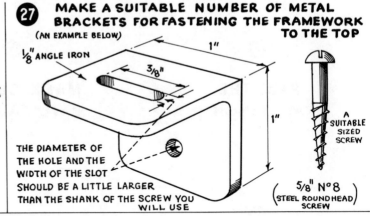

⅛" ANGLE IRON

1"

3/8"

1"

THE DIAMETER OF
THE HOLE AND THE
WIDTH OF THE SLOT
SHOULD BE A LITTLE LARGER
THAN THE SHANK OF THE SCREW YOU
WILL USE

A
SUITABLE
SIZED
SCREW

(5/8" N°8
STEEL ROUNDHEAD
SCREW)

28 POSITION AND SCREW
THE BRACKETS ONTO
THE FRAMEWORK

29 POSITION THE FRAMEWORK EVENLY
ON THE UNDERSIDE OF THE TABLE
TOP AND DRIVE HOME
THE SCREWS
(AN EXAMPLE BELOW)

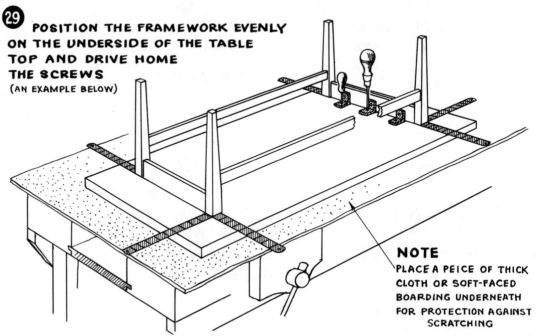

NOTE
PLACE A PEICE OF THICK
CLOTH OR SOFT-FACED
BOARDING UNDERNEATH
FOR PROTECTION AGAINST
SCRATCHING